INTERNATIONAL ENERGY

# Energy technologies for the 21st century

PARIS 1997

## INTERNATIONAL ENERGY AGENCY

9, RUE DE LA FÉDÉRATION, 75739 PARIS CEDEX 15, FRANCE

The International Energy Agency (IEA) is an autonomous body which was established in November 1974 within the framework of the Organisation for Economic Co-operation and Development (OECD) to implement an international energy programme.

It carries out a comprehensive programme of energy co-operation among twenty-four* of the OECD's twenty-nine Member countries. The basic aims of the IEA are:

- To maintain and improve systems for coping with oil supply disruptions;
- To promote rational energy policies in a global context through co-operative relations with non-Member countries, industry and international organisations;
- To operate a permanent information system on the international oil market;
- To improve the world's energy supply and demand structure by developing alternative energy sources and increasing the efficiency of energy use;
- To assist in the integration of environmental and energy policies.

**IEA Member countries: Australia, Austria, Belgium, Canada, Denmark, Finland, France, Germany, Greece, Hungary, Ireland, Italy, Japan, Luxembourg, the Netherlands, New Zealand, Norway, Portugal, Spain, Sweden, Switzerland, Turkey, the United Kingdom, the United States. The Commission of the European Communities also takes part in the work of the IEA.*

## ORGANISATION FOR ECONOMIC CO-OPERATION AND DEVELOPMENT

Pursuant to Article 1 of the Convention signed in Paris on 14th December 1960, and which came into force on 30th September 1961, the Organisation for Economic Co-operation and Development (OECD) shall promote policies designed:

- to achieve the highest sustainable economic growth and employment and a rising standard of living in Member countries, while maintaining financial stability, and thus to contribute to the development of the world economy;
- to contribute to sound economic expansion in Member as well as non-member countries in the process of economic development; and
- to contribute to the expansion of world trade on a multilateral, non-discriminatory basis in accordance with international obligations.

The original Member countries of the OECD are Austria, Belgium, Canada, Denmark, France, Germany, Greece, Iceland, Ireland, Italy, Luxembourg, the Netherlands, Norway, Portugal, Spain, Sweden, Switzerland, Turkey, the United Kingdom and the United States. The following countries became Members subsequently through accession at the dates indicated hereafter: Japan (28th April 1964), Finland (28th January 1969), Australia (7th June 1971), New Zealand (29th May 1973), Mexico (18th May 1994), the Czech Republic (21st December 1995), Hungary (7th May 1996), Poland (22nd November 1996) and the Republic of Korea (12th December 1996). The Commission of the European Communities takes part in the work of the OECD (Article 13 of the OECD Convention).

# FOREWORD

Against a background of changing energy issues and growing environmental concerns, it is important to reassess the potential for successful development and deployment of new and improved energy technologies and the benefits that could result. In addition, there is a need to identify the technology policies and collaborative framework necessary to realise this end in the international context. The present study reports the results of a wide-ranging analysis made with assistance from Member countries of the International Energy Agency (IEA). Its focus is on technology options and priorities, and on the goals and mechanisms for international co-operation in the long term. A 30-year horizon has been chosen to accommodate the long lead times associated with technology innovation and breakthroughs. *Energy Technologies for the 21st Century* outlines the technical, economic and market potential of new and improved energy technology concepts, both current and prospective.

The study focuses on:

1) progress in the clean use of coal;
2) increased availability of IEA hydrocarbon resources;
3) improved modes for transport of natural gas;
4) enhanced safety of nuclear fission technology and acceptable waste-management approaches;
5) demonstration of nuclear fusion energy technology;
6) extensive integration of renewable energy sources into the conventional energy system;
7) environmentally sound electricity production and distribution; and
8) efficient and flexible fuel use in transport and in technologies for energy end-use.

Countries differ in their resource endowments and in their technology strategies and research and development programmes. Where these are in consonance, however, there is evident value in sharing ideas, knowledge, resources and burdens.

*Energy Technologies for the 21st Century* concludes that IEA Member countries should maintain and enhance their efforts to collaborate on new and improved technologies that can produce substantial gains in all areas bearing upon energy security and environmental goals. The need to contain emissions of greenhouse gases in response to global climate change concerns may, in particular, be expected to influence technology priorities and necessitate new co-operation mechanisms. Another general finding is that in most sectors substantial non-technical barriers impede the commercial demonstration and market deployment of promising technologies, thus preventing the realisation of their potential. In addition, significant gains could be made through technology transfer to industrialising countries where the efficiency of energy conversion and use is much lower than that in most IEA countries.

The study is published under my responsibility as Executive Director of the IEA and does not necessarily reflect the views or policies of the IEA or governments of its Member countries.

**Robert Priddle**
Executive Director

## ACKNOWLEDGEMENTS

The IEA's Governing Board launched this study by pointing to the importance of investigating the impact of technology progress and international R&D collaboration from an energy policy perspective, against a backdrop of changing energy security concerns and new global environmental challenges. Like any multi-author work, this study reflects the efforts of many people over a long period. We are particularly indebted to the experts who worked on the various technology areas, contributed to the panels, produced early drafts, and accepted the time it has taken to bring the whole study together. The discussion of technology areas has also benefited from detailed comments and supervision provided by the IEA's Committee on Energy Research and Technology and its Working Parties. Thanks are due to them and to all those who contributed their time and efforts to the study.

The production of the study owes much to the efforts of the IEA Secretariat, which took the responsibility for directing and marshalling the very considerable volume of expertise, information and statistics which were shaped into the final work. From its inception, the work was co-ordinated and guided by Professor Sergio Garribba, former Director of the IEA Office of Energy Technology and R&D, and former Director of Energy of the National Agency for Energy, Environment and New Technology (ENEA) of Italy, who is now Commissioner, Regulatory Authority for Electricity and Natural Gas of Italy. In the IEA, Mr. Kenneth Friedman, Head of the Energy Technology Policy Division, had the main responsibility for this work and specific comments and questions should be sent to him (telephone: [33-1] 40 57 67 80; Fax: [33-1] 40 57 67 59; or E-mail: friedman@iea.org).

**Hans Jørgen Koch**
Director, Energy Efficiency,
Technology and R&D

## Table of Contents

## Chapter 3



## Chapter 4



## Chapter 5

## Chapter 6



## Chapter 7



## Chapter 8

Chapter 9



Chapter 10



Annex I

## LIST OF TABLES

## LIST OF FIGURES

# EXECUTIVE SUMMARY

## Overview

*Energy Technologies for the 21st Century* examines technology options, research and development needs and suggested mechanisms for international collaboration, with a view to helping IEA Member countries meet their broad shared objectives of long-term energy security, environmental protection and increased global partnership. It is hoped that its analysis will provide useful suggestions to guide Member countries' energy technology policy programmes over the coming decades.

It is important for IEA countries to focus their energy R&D efforts on the development of better technologies that can help them meet the important goal of secure, clean, affordable and reliable energy supply and use. Governments can influence the course of technology progress through institutional action and through economic, fiscal and regulatory policy measures designed to motivate the energy industry to devote a larger share of investment to technology development and deployment.

International co-operation can facilitate technology innovation, serving as a useful complement to technology assessment and R&D programmes in individual Member countries. Expansion of collaboration with non-Member countries adds a further important dimension to energy technology policy. IEA countries can assist non-Members in their approaches to energy, environmental and economic issues by offering access to more efficient technologies and practices.

## Global Interdependence

The increasing interdependence of energy markets means new approaches to energy technology policy are required. Global energy security concerns and environmental policy issues are assuming more important roles as driving forces in energy technology progress and encouraging greater international technology collaboration. The growth of energy consumption in non-IEA countries is of particular significance. The 1996 edition of the IEA's *World Energy Outlook* indicates that, moving towards 2010, primary energy demand in non-Member countries will be greater than in IEA countries. The expansion in demand is putting new pressures on the main energy markets and has profound consequences for the environment.

Energy security continues to concern governments of IEA countries; of particular significance are the growth of world oil demand, especially in the transport sector, and the concentration of most low-cost oil reserves in the Middle East and a few countries elsewhere. These considerations confirm the desirability of expanding IEA hydrocarbon production and of lowering the energy intensity and oil intensity of GNP through efficiency improvements and fuel switching. Governments are increasingly drawing back from direct participation in economies, relying more on competitive markets and the gradual elimination of energy and technology trade barriers. Such structural adjustment can generate considerable momentum for new energy investment and industry initiative.

Developments in energy markets have coincided with increasing awareness of the environmental impact of energy production and use. There is growing recognition of the inter-relationships among various forms of pollution, and of the consequent importance of an integrated approach to minimising total waste and pollution production. The environmental degradation caused by conventional atmospheric pollutants and by liquid and solid waste will continue to be tackled through technological means. The global climate change issue poses potentially the most profound environmental challenge.

The governments of IEA Member countries have ratified the United Nations Framework Convention on Climate Change, which came into force in March 1994. The Convention commits the contracting parties to reducing their greenhouse gas emissions. Since energy production, transformation and use account for over 90 per cent of reported emissions of carbon dioxide, a major greenhouse gas, action in relation to energy will be central to the realisation of the Convention's goals. IEA countries have pledged themselves to identifying the policies and measures necessary to respect their commitments, thus underlining the importance of technology progress as a means of meeting both energy security and environmental policy objectives. Governments can create the right conditions for technology to move forward, support technology advances and reduce barriers to market penetration.

Energy technology selection by IEA Member countries will be even more critical in coming decades. Along with the approach outlined in the *IEA/OECD Scoping Study: Energy and Environmental Technologies to Respond to Global Climate Change Concerns* (Paris, 1994), key elements of an energy technology strategy on the climate challenge are: reliance on demonstrated technologies for increased efficiency and productivity in all energy end-uses, improved fossil fuel conversion and electricity generation, expanded consumption of natural gas, greater exploitation of renewable forms of energy and safe use of nuclear energy technology. Pursuit of these options will, in effect, "buy time" for R&D to prepare further generations of highly efficient, low-carbon and carbon-free fuel cycles and technologies that could have a significant market impact in the longer term.

Given the scale and global nature of climate change concerns, international technology collaboration will be essential for mobilising the levels of investment and expertise needed to make the necessary breakthroughs. The increasing interdependence of national energy systems means that IEA interests will also be met by assisting non-Members to develop and adopt efficient and environmentally sound energy production, delivery and end-use technologies. For newly industrialising economies and the countries in transition towards a market economy, these issues are particularly relevant, and they call for joint effort and co-operation in the transfer of appropriate technologies. Energy technology assistance is likely to be made available at a number of levels and will involve a range of multilateral arrangements, including collaboration through the IEA's Implementing Agreement process.

## Energy Technology Progress

The factors that bring about energy technology innovation are numerous, and their interaction and dynamics are highly dependent on the context. Major generic factors include energy security requirements, environmental concerns, economic competitiveness, the availability of finance, and prevailing social values.

The engineering and organisational systems within which energy technologies develop are increasingly complex. In some energy technology systems, the degree of complexity can inhibit the incorporation of new elements and processes, and obscure the potential of new technological options. Conversely, existing systems can point the way towards fruitful directions for technical change. In addition, the capabilities of technologies now in common use can be substantially enlarged, and their cost reduced, through learning effects and economies of scale.

Another factor involves the absorptive capacity of firms and R&D organisations and the ability of the energy industry to incorporate technology developed elsewhere, in a process involving substantial investment. Formal and informal inter-corporate networks for the exchange of technology information can help address this issue.

Still another factor is that advanced energy technologies appear to have certain important features in common. Numerous technological innovations have broad applicability in a multitude of energy products and processes, as in the merging of microelectronics and information technology into energy systems. Innovations in other areas may be applicable in the energy sector, and vice versa. Sound energy R&D programmes thus must take advantage of technology development and breakthroughs in other fields.

In addition, energy technology advances, in both R&D and in application, are increasingly international in scope. Trade flows between industries are assuming greater importance, and new forms of energy technology innovation agreement are being developed.

## Key Findings

The environment in which public and private players interact is complex. Government energy and environmental policy-makers focusing on R&D decisions might usefully note that ultimate success depends largely on the institutional features of the national technology innovation system.

Each chapter on individual energy technologies uses a similar four-step approach: i) an outline of a conceptual framework to guide the analysis, followed by a set of technology-specific priorities; ii) a discussion of options that can contribute to these priorities, with assessment of technical and economic potential and the main R&D tasks involved; iii) a description of technology prospects and possible market trends; and iv) a review of the roles that governments and international co-operation can play. The courses of action proposed are not ranked against each other but are presented as a series of options from which policy-makers can choose according to their requirements. The technical, economic and market-deployment potential of each technology identified is examined. Each chapter concludes with a suggested technology strategy and R&D programme consisting of selected types of action and instruments as a basis for enhanced IEA Member country collaboration. The principles of reliance on free markets and the need for policy integration feature strongly in these suggestions.

Widespread commercialisation of promising energy technologies is being impeded by substantial non-technical barriers to their market deployment. Institutional and regulatory barriers are often entrenched, and may involve competing government objectives. Commitment among IEA Member countries to the removal of impediments to implementation of energy policies in their common interest is desirable.

The private sector in free market economies plays the leading role in advancing and commercialising energy technologies. Governments can leverage their energy R&D spending through cost-sharing with industry, thus increasing the market relevance of government R&D decision-making and accelerating energy R&D. There is a general trend towards closer co-operation between government and industry; improved partnerships to finance key next-generation technologies will enhance the effectiveness of energy R&D and increase the role of the private sector in commercialisation. Early involvement of industry in energy technology policy-making is a key factor in meeting environmental and energy-security goals.

Other common strategy themes to be found within the chapters include: supporting progress in safe and environmentally clean technologies; speeding up demonstration and testing of new and improved technologies; achieving transparency, harmonisation and flexibility in regulations and prices; increasing the use of life-cycle approaches; and supporting information exchange, collaboration and transfer of technology, particularly to developing countries and those in transition towards a market economy.

The key priorities and findings in each area are summarised below.

### *Clean Use of Coal*

With its abundance, widespread geographic distribution, relatively low cost and price stability and its ready availability in an established and competitive international market, coal is a key component of energy security in IEA Member countries and worldwide. Of all the fossil fuels, coal has the largest resource base by far and the highest reserves-to-consumption ratio. Technological challenges and priority goals for coal lie primarily in:

- improving the conversion efficiency, environmental acceptability and economics of coal use as a competitive energy source;
- diversifying clean uses of coal with a view to preserving flexibility and coping with changing energy needs in the long term.

Technology policy for the clean use of coal should aim to support R&D and the demonstration and testing of next-generation technologies – particularly ultra super-critical power plants, integrated coal gasification combined cycle and pressurised fluidised-bed combustion – to reconcile the energy and environmental dimensions of coal use while maintaining the fuel's economic competitiveness. New and improved technologies for controlling conventional pollutant emissions and consequences such as acid precipitation, and for reducing greenhouse gas emissions from coal combustion through improved efficiency, are available or in the advanced demonstration stage. Long-term programmes on coal gasification and conversion into liquid fuel will require government and industry support and co-operation.

There is considerable scope for direct government support and for government-industry technology collaboration to reduce uncertainty over performance characteristics, reduce cost and improve commercial operation and prospects of demonstrated and next-generation clean coal technology and power systems. Such collaboration could minimise the risks involved in large "first-time" projects and maintain adequate R&D on longer-term options, including synthetic fuels. In addition to other government approaches – including voluntary programmes, regulations standards and taxes – support to accelerate technology innovation will be required if greenhouse gas reduction is to receive high priority. Governments could do much to achieve this result by reducing market barriers to technology development and deployment by industry; for example by facilitating the work of international standard setting bodies. Governments can also play an important role by fostering transfer of "best practice" technologies to newly industrialising and transitional economies through national and international technology information centres. Several non-Member countries depend heavily on indigenous coal, often of low quality, and their coal use technologies are frequently inefficient and environmentally unfriendly.

### *Oil and Natural Gas Production*

Oil remains crucial for IEA countries, especially in transport, and demand for it continues to rise. Consumption of natural gas as a fuel is also growing because of its convenience, economics and what are perceived as comparative environmental benefits. From an energy security perspective, expected advances in exploration, drilling and production technologies will be important to facilitate expansion of indigenous IEA oil and gas resources. Most of these resources are relatively costly to produce and are in environmentally sensitive areas. If heavier or increasingly sour crudes are introduced into the market, substantial technology adjustment and innovation in refining will also be required.

In this context, the top technology priority goals for oil and natural gas production are:

- increasing access to economically exploitable oil and natural gas reserves;
- lowering the environmental effects and risks involved in hydrocarbon production.

Given the maturity of the industry, its worldwide scope and the demand for its products, the most significant government actions to facilitate progress would appear to be associated with promoting opportunities for high-risk, high-impact technology breakthroughs, enhancing safety and environmental protection, ensuring adequate scientific and engineering capability and promulgating market-based regulations and policies to enhance investment and promote risk-taking by the industry in responding to market needs. In particular, government support is needed in the search for technological breakthroughs to facilitate increased economic access to fragile frontier regions and difficult sources of new crudes, such as extra-heavy oils, oil shale and tar sands. Governments may also be able to aid in technology transfer to non-Member countries that have substantial oil and natural gas resources. Furthermore, governments have an important role in supporting the fundamental scientific R&D, education and training that underpin technology progress in areas such as geophysics and hydrocarbon geology advances, measurement while drilling, remote operation, multiphase flow, solvent extraction and microbiological recovery.

A continuing emphasis on environmental protection should be an integral part of technology development to enhance the international oil and natural gas supply. With increased oil consumption comes the possibility of increased pollution from oil exploration and production, its transport, refining, distribution and end-use systems. Other sources of environmental impact are associated with the more complex refining processes required for heavy oil, and the potential damage to marine environments from accidental oil spills, waste handling and disposal from offshore platforms and their associated sub-sea pipelines, loading terminals and shipping. With natural gas, safety problems and leakage during extraction and transport could partially offset its comparative environmental advantage.

### *Natural Gas and its Transport*

Natural gas demand and production will grow in coming decades, as will dependence among IEA countries on external gas supplies. Technology progress in natural gas transport has the potential to increase natural gas supply security by facilitating the exploitation of existing reserves, carried as natural gas or an intermediate energy form. It could also help to expand the diversity of available liquid fuels through chemical conversion of natural gas.

Technology priority goals for natural gas and its transport are:

- increasing market access for remote reserves through alternative energy carriers and lower transport costs;
- enhancing the diversity of liquid fuels;
- mitigating the environmental impact and risk to public health and safety of natural gas transport and delivery.

Technology progress in conventional gas transport and use (pipelines, liquefied natural gas transport, electricity generation and transmission, and existing chemical conversion technologies), as well as in natural gas storage, is likely to be significant but incremental. Industry will continue to be the main player in technology development in these areas, though indirect government involvement could facilitate advances. New and improved technologies will be needed to lower gas transport infrastructure costs, while helping extend gas applications into new market areas. The most appropriate area for government involvement and international co-operation is the basic chemistry of the direct conversion of methane to liquid fuels. A high-impact breakthrough in terms of plant scale and efficiency could result if the chemistry of direct conversion can be mastered, though this technology still requires substantial research.

### *Nuclear Fission Technologies*

Nuclear fission energy continues to make a substantial contribution to the diversification of IEA energy supplies. Uranium reserves, of which IEA Member countries have a major proportion, are abundant and widespread. The technology emits no sulphur dioxide, nitrogen oxides or greenhouse gases in power generation, thereby meeting a number of environmental requirements. But concerns about nuclear accidents, waste and proliferation may limit the full exploitation of nuclear fission energy advantages. These concerns need to be addressed if the nuclear option is to be preserved and its deployment prospects enhanced.

In this context, technology priority goals for nuclear fission energy are:

- developing and deploying economically competitive nuclear power generating technologies with standard or modular designs while maintaining and enhancing safety;
- developing and deploying acceptable nuclear waste management technologies and systems;
- widening the safeguarded applicability of nuclear fission energy and expanding its resource base.

Some countries intend to continue their nuclear construction programmes because they consider nuclear energy an important contributor to energy security that can play a significant role in reducing the growth of greenhouse gas emissions. Other countries are not developing nuclear power, either because they have ample supplies of other fuel, or because of what are perceived as potential adverse health and safety consequences. Furthermore, in some countries the economics of nuclear power have appeared less favourable than those for energy sources such as natural gas.

For nuclear fission R&D, the focus should be on: developing simpler standardised designs and paying constant attention to improving safety; ensuring that procedures for the safe disposal of radioactive wastes are not only technically feasible but also publicly acceptable; requiring adequately funded and publicly acceptable decommissioning of nuclear power plants; achieving uniform health and safety standards worldwide; increasing public participation in development of new electric generating capacity; and integrating energy security and environmental goals.

The future of nuclear power is heavily dependent on government action. These include activities to reduce the market risks of demonstrating new technologies, direct support for specific projects and indirect support through measures such as streamlining of regulatory principles and practices and their international harmonisation. Governments may wish to continue supporting basic research but leave commercial development to industry. IEA Member countries also have an interest in enhancing safety in nuclear fission technologies and safeguard practices in non-Member countries. But government policy and regulations alone are not enough to ensure the continued viability of nuclear power. Industry holds the responsibility for ensuring that nuclear plants are operated safely and economically and that the public has full access to information on this technology.

### *Nuclear Fusion*

Nuclear fusion, with its many potential advantages as an energy resource, is an important element of the long-term energy strategy of IEA Member countries. Successful application of practical fusion energy technologies at some point in the 21st century could help enhance IEA energy security, provide an environmentally acceptable alternative to fossil fuel combustion and contribute to continued economic growth through reliable electricity supply.

The technology priority goals for nuclear fusion are:

- continuing efforts geared towards demonstration of the technical feasibility of nuclear fusion power systems;
- assessing the potential impact of fusion power on future energy supply.

Nuclear fusion technology is still under development, at a rate governed by the building and operating in sequence of a number of devices, leading to a large-scale experimental reactor and then to a pilot-scale demonstration plant. The aim of current development is to demonstrate the feasibility of high magnetic fields (magnetic confinement) and very high plasma densities (inertial confinement).

Nuclear fusion, while not likely to be a widely available power source in the next 30 to 50 years, could prove to be an attractive solution for power generation in a longer time-frame. This makes it a fundamental component of any energy technology policy. Fusion R&D requires adequate, sustained government support because of the long time required for the various stages of development. International collaboration is a valuable element in the current programme strategy.

### *Renewable Energy*

Renewable energy technologies use resources generally not subject to depletion, such as heat and light from the sun, the force of winds, organic matter (biomass), falling water, ocean energy and geothermal heat. About 1000 times more energy reaches the earth's surface from the sun than is released by all the fossil fuels consumed. Though the resources exploited are often scattered, they can be converted in various ways to usable heat or power. New and improved technologies are being developed and tested with different technical and economic attributes, degrees of maturity, and potential in future energy systems. While not a major contributor to total primary energy supply in IEA countries, new renewable energy sources could increasingly become commercially competitive with conventional resources. During the last 15 years, intensive work by industry, national laboratories and R&D centres has steadily increased the performance of renewable energy systems, while dramatically lowering their costs.

To exploit their potential, two technology priority goals have been identified:

- improving the efficiency and economics of renewable energy systems;
- expanding their deployment and effective integration into existing or evolving energy systems, amid the widespread restructuring and privatisation affecting energy utilities.

While the technical potential of renewables is very large, they make a relatively small energy contribution, due to their present state of development, compounded by current energy economics, market factors and institutional constraints. They face significant barriers to market entry: lack of infrastructure, relative technical and economic immaturity, inadequately demonstrated reliability and maintainability, and a need for economies of scale in component manufacture and deployment techniques. But if national and social factors such as environmental and security concerns were internalised in energy system costs, the economic potential of renewables would improve and their contribution would grow significantly.

Government efforts should focus on selective and continuing R&D to reduce costs and improve the performance and efficiency of emerging renewable energy technologies and systems. Equally important is fundamental and applied research to foster progress in renewables technology and prepare further options for the longer term (hydrogen fuels, hot dry rocks, ocean energy and other emerging concepts).

### *Electricity Production and Distribution*

Throughout the world, demand for electricity is increasing, due to its versatility, ease of transport and control and to steady advances in generation and end-use technologies. Increasing fuel diversification will allow electricity to be produced from a variety of sources and help ensure greater energy security. Sustained increases in investments in new power generation capacity will be required to meet expected growth in electricity demand and to replace decommissioned plants. Given the demand growth forecast, efficiency gains alone will not be sufficient to cope with peak power requirements.

Over the next few decades, electric utilities throughout IEA countries and in the developing world will face heavy capital cost requirements, rising fuel prices and increasingly stringent environmental regulations. Addressing these challenges will require improved power system efficiency, increased unit modularity and standardisation, diversification of fuels, careful management of energy demand and better pollution control.

The technology priorities for electricity production and distribution are:

- reducing the environmental impact of power generation, including conventional emissions such as sulphur dioxide and nitrogen oxides as well as greenhouse gas emissions;
- encouraging greater energy source diversification and, where feasible, fuel flexibility;
- developing and applying advanced load and demand-side management techniques to increase the efficiency of the electricity supply system.

At its point of use, electricity is a clean, convenient and flexible energy source. At the point of production, however, electricity involves concentrated environmental impact, complex technology and high-cost investment in fixed facilities. Opportunities to mitigate the environmental consequences exist on the supply side, as well as through improved efficiency of fuel consumption, changes to the fuel mix and the introduction of strengthened demand-side management practices. Changing economic and environmental requirements necessitate greater emphasis on investment decisions for new technology and the upgrading of ageing power plants. Changing patterns of demand growth, however, combined with increased demand-side management, market deregulation and competition, could make load forecasting and the financing of large new units ever more difficult.

Meeting these challenges will require the development of a wide variety of technologies. No single technology will be the best choice for every situation; market forces will ultimately determine the most viable options for a given region or country. Only a broad technology base can give utilities the flexibility to respond cost-effectively to dynamic market conditions and to regulations. Governments and the electricity supply industry have a special role in ensuring that energy security, efficiency, power plant safety and pollution reduction are taken into account when new technologies are being assessed. IEA Member countries and their governments need to collaborate effectively during the move towards a new era of electricity technologies, so that both they and the newly industrialising and transitional economies may minimise pitfalls and maximise benefits.

***Transport Technology and Fuels***

Efficient transport of people and goods is central to IEA countries' concerns regarding energy security, environmental protection and economic growth. Oil remains the predominant transport fuel and its increasing use entails the creation of smog and acid precipitation, and growth in carbon dioxide emissions. The emphasis in transport technology is on the private car. While other modes are also important, cars are currently the primary factor in transport energy use and environmental impact.

The priority goals for road transport and fuel technology are:

- increasing the efficiency and flexibility of transport fuel use;
- continuing development of environmentally sustainable substitute fuels and facilitating their increased use.

The car is of special policy significance because of its overwhelming reliance on oil, its contribution to climate change concerns and the growing significance of the transport sector in industrialising countries. Great potential for technology improvement exists. Decisions need to be taken concerning R&D investments, environmental standards and fuel quality requirements, and the roles of public transport and the car manufacturing industry. For vehicles and fuels, the highest potential for energy efficiency and emission reductions lies in decreasing the basic energy intensity of vehicles through structural improvements and on-board generation of energy. Improvements in internal combustion engine technology and emission control can augment efficiency. Significant energy savings can also be achieved through technologies and policies relating to travel behaviour, urban planning and trip substitution.

Until alternative fuels and other options become economically practical on a large scale, reducing the specific fuel consumption of conventional vehicles is a key means of lowering carbon dioxide emissions from transport. Growth in vehicle numbers, however, means that programmes limited to reducing emissions per vehicle will eventually be unable to stabilise overall emissions. Among alternative fuels, alcohols have the advantage of being liquid and present the best potential for improved energy efficiency, but are highly dependent on feedstock source. Electric vehicles are the principal candidate to achieve energy savings and fuel substitution, but the net energy benefits also depend upon the primary energy sources. Natural gas has substantial potential to reduce specific emissions but, as for electric vehicles, infrastructure requirements can inhibit market penetration.

Hence, the most effective ways for governments to influence technology development will primarily involve indirect approaches that meet long-term performance goals and foster the penetration of substitute fuels and of advanced vehicle technologies, such as hybrid vehicles. The road vehicle manufacturing industry is global in scale, but individual operating entities are key components of local economies. Frequently, individual countries or blocks of countries develop policies and vehicle regulations that effectively become non-tariff barriers. Examples are new product standards (in particular, emission and safety regulations) and fuel pricing (as it affects efficiency), which can have significant consequences for trade and technology collaboration. Areas of direct government involvement include participation in long-range R&D on innovative concepts and enhancement of information-sharing, particularly in the field trial and demonstration phase. Proprietary interests may limit information-sharing to longer-term areas of interest, but regional market opportunities may induce closer inter-government and government-industry interaction and co-operation.

### *Industrial, Residential and Commercial Energy Use*

Improving energy efficiency or energy conservation is being seen increasingly as a promising strategy for attaining simultaneously the goals of energy security, environmental protection and economic growth. Widespread concern in IEA countries about the environmental impact of energy activities and, more recently, about global climate change has further underlined the importance of using energy more efficiently. Improvements in energy efficiency have played a significant part in limiting greenhouse gas emissions and reducing the carbon intensity of the energy sector of IEA countries. Though these results are encouraging, much more attention should be directed towards ways of increasing the use of efficient energy end-use technologies. While there is a vast potential, technically, for increased energy efficiency, significant barriers to its realisation exist. Bold and innovative approaches are required if the full technical and economic potential of increased energy efficiency is to be realised.

Analysis shows impressive technical opportunities to use energy more efficiently and effectively in the industrial, residential and commercial sectors. Technology priority goals are:

- enhancing the demonstration and market deployment of existing technologies to improve the efficiency, economics and flexibility of energy use;
- encouraging further development and application of next-generation technologies, with a view to maximising their potential environmental benefits, including reduction of greenhouse gas emissions.

All IEA countries appear committed to stimulating the development of a wide range of new, more energy-efficient technologies by setting long-term priorities and providing financial support for R&D and demonstration programmes. The expected achievements could make an important contribution to increasing the efficiency of energy use. In enhancing R&D and deployment of new and improved technologies, substantial government involvement, both direct and indirect and through international co-operation, is required to address market weaknesses (including the slow replacement rate for many types of energy-using equipment) in this highly disaggregated area.

Energy markets work best when they are competitive and when trade and investment distortions are limited. But there are many technical and institutional barriers, which may discourage R&D efforts and limit technological progress. Market forces alone are unlikely to bring about the level of efficiency improvement implicit in most environment-oriented energy policies seeking to stabilise and reduce greenhouse gas emissions.

Hence governments have a major role to play in removing barriers and bridging the gap between technical opportunities and decisions by individual consumers. In particular, government-industry projects focusing on the demonstration of innovative energy-efficient processes in energy-intensive industries need to be encouraged, especially for the aluminium, cement, chemical, food processing, glass and ceramics, iron and steel, and pulp and paper branches. Governments of IEA countries also have a major role in supporting the diffusion of efficient energy end-use technologies through the rest of the world. In general, access to technical and economic information and to capital are crucial in efforts to increase energy savings. Reliable information has to be made available on energy end-use, the cost of new technologies and the actual savings they offer. Such market information is a prerequisite for evaluating the effectiveness of efficiency programmes and for developing policies to accelerate the deployment of more efficient technologies and resulting improvement in the economy.

# Chapter 1

## INTRODUCTION

### Scope and Structure of the Study

As IEA Member countries look towards the 21st century, it is clear that dynamic energy markets and advanced energy technologies could in future offer yet greater potential to alleviate many of the economic, environmental and national energy security concerns that have driven energy policy in recent decades. Countries are unlikely to realise the full potential of this new era, however, unless international energy co-operation continually guides markets and technologies toward the goals of secure, clean, affordable and reliable energy supply and use. Technology policies that maximise energy productivity, minimise pollution and help shield IEA countries from global energy supply risks can improve the standard of living today and enhance the quality of life tomorrow. They can also help newly industrialising countries and those whose economies are in transition, which have limited investment funds and yet must make critical near-term decisions about the future of their energy systems and their strategies for economic growth.

Against this background, *Energy Technologies for the 21st Century* assesses the potential for successful development and deployment of new and improved energy technologies and the benefits that could result; and it identifies approaches that may be pursued to that end, both nationally and internationally, taking a 30-year time horizon.

A keystone of the approach in this study is the importance of a continuing policy of reliance on free markets. Whenever possible, markets should be allowed to determine technology choices and programmes, and their timing and scale. Where markets cannot – or do not – work efficiently, government intervention may be required. For example markets are unlikely to give adequate weight to the national energy security, foreign policy and social issues implied in IEA countries' goals of reducing dependence on uncertain energy supplies and fostering a healthy environment. So governments must act, alone or in co-operation with one another and the private sector, to incorporate these considerations. But direct government intervention and regulation can impose unforeseen costs by reducing the flexibility of the economy. Intervention in energy technology programmes must therefore be justified by rigorous cost-benefit analysis and incorporate economic incentives. Market players and national economies can thus attain the IEA countries' shared objectives of long-term energy security, environmental protection and increased global partnership, at the lowest possible cost.

Responding to the needs and challenges of the evolving energy situation necessitates new mechanisms and institutional arrangements. Many IEA countries are reviewing their energy technology programmes and priorities and some have made important adjustments. The changing circumstances also underline the importance of international collaboration.

It was with these points in mind that the IEA Secretariat evaluated the proposals submitted by IEA committees and by experts throughout IEA countries in preparing this report. These submissions were essential in building a study intended to present the energy technology panorama of the future and the opportunities it offers.

### *Background*

*Energy Technologies for the 21st Century* was initiated as a result of discussions at the IEA's Governing Board Ministerial meetings which took note of the continuing importance of energy technology as a policy instrument. The Governing Board requested the IEA Secretariat to conduct the study, and the IEA's Committee on Energy Research and Technology (CERT) subsequently decided that the result should be a reference work based on three sources of information and analysis: work carried out by an ad-hoc experts' group and by the CERT Working Parties at the CERT's request; the abundance of valuable information, evaluation and ideas arising from conferences on energy technology policy and issues held at OECD headquarters and in Member countries; and numerous related studies on energy policy and technology conducted by the Secretariat, notably the 1994 *IEA/OECD Scoping Study: Energy and Environmental Technologies to Respond to Global Climate Change Concerns.*

The CERT decided that to provide a structure, and to focus the assessment on critical energy topics, nine technology areas should be examined: clean use of coal; oil and natural gas production; natural gas and its transport; nuclear fission; nuclear fusion; renewable energy sources; electricity production and distribution; transport technology and fuels; and industrial, residential and commercial energy use. Accordingly, nine sets of technology-specific priority goals were defined, all linked to the objectives of secure, clean, affordable and reliable energy supply and use. Each technology area was represented in the ad-hoc experts' group by a specialist, supported in turn by a panel of experts. The initial technology area assessments conducted by these panels reflected the views of more than 80 experts drawn from most IEA Member countries. (Annex I shows the membership of the group of experts and its panels.) In addition, because of the importance of the global climate change issue, a special panel focusing on greenhouse gas technologies was established to provide other panels with better insight on how new environmental concerns may affect technology areas.

The choice of technology areas and technology-specific priorities shaped the structure of the study. A broad spectrum of energy technology issues is covered by addressing some of the key relationships between technology progress and diffusion, on the one hand, and institutional aspects, economic competitiveness and international partnership, on the other. Also examined are questions concerning energy technology and the environment, as well as opportunities for collaboration with developing countries and those in transition towards a market economy. The breadth of subject matter means the technology descriptions must be essentially overviews.

Although the study draws upon substantial technical information provided by international experts, not every technology option is discussed; nor is the level of treatment and analysis identical across all concepts. Nevertheless, the analysis in the study represents a substantial consensus of informed opinion and provides at least an indication of the relative attention and resources that should be committed to different energy R&D programmes and technologies.

The study describes a complex system in which numerous public and private players interact. The information that can be drawn from the study as a basis for action depends on a given player's situation and responsibilities. For energy R&D programme managers, attention focuses on priorities and on the innovation efforts and investments needed to create, disseminate and take advantage of technological change. R&D decisions involve multiple factors, and success depends on the institutional characteristics of national technology innovation systems, as well as on the broader network of international collaboration within which those systems operate. Ensuring energy technology progress and the availability of new and improved technologies may imply in some areas much more interdependence and collaboration among countries than in the past; in this, IEA countries may wish to take the lead. The study also suggests that much more attention should be paid to co-operative relationships among government, energy consumers and industry. In more open and competitive markets, greater reliance will be placed on all those who participate in the cycle of energy technology creation, absorption, deployment and application.

### *Framework for Analysis*

This chapter's subsequent sections will establish the policy context for the individual technology assessments contained in the body of the study. For example, the section headed Energy Technology Policy Background discusses perceptions relating to energy security, global environmental issues and the changing energy technology needs of non-Member countries, all of which involve significant new factors and concerns affecting the formulation of any energy technology strategy. Technology progress and current and historical trends in energy R&D investments by IEA countries' governments are then examined, as are the most significant determinants of the technology innovation process and the mechanisms used for IEA energy technology collaboration.

Chapters 2 to 10 that follow discuss the nine technology areas, using a five-step structure:

i) an outline of a conceptual framework to guide the analysis, followed by a set of technology-specific priority goals;

ii) a discussion of the most significant options that can contribute to these priority goals, with emphasis on their time horizon and current status, and an assessment of their technical and economic potential and the main R&D tasks and opportunities for future progress;

iii) a description of technology prospects and possible market trends, with a focus on the key technology players, their interaction, and the market barriers to energy technology deployment;

iv) a review of the role governments can play in technology advances, and of ways to facilitate technology progress through international co-operation;

v) in line with the policy objectives guiding the study and the technology-specific priorities they imply, proposals are put forward for technology R&D programmes, approaches and strategies consisting of selected measures that can form a basis for enhanced collaboration among IEA Member countries.

Each chapter is essentially self-contained, and develops a group of options from which policy-makers can choose according to their requirements. In general, these options are not ranked against each other, though priority goals within individual technology areas may be in competition with each other. For example, the development of certain alternative fuels may enhance energy security, but entail environmental concerns. Since decision-makers in government and industry, as well as the general public, are often not well informed about the role and importance of new and improved energy technologies, each option must be evaluated in a wider context, taking into account the entire fuel cycle and life cycle.

The technologies identified are assessed in terms of their interrelated technical, economic and market deployment potential. If the economics of an option are improved, markets for its application can expand and other deployment bottlenecks may be removed. If significant new technical capabilities are seen to be viable, the motivation to attack economic barriers and exploit technology spillovers may be reinforced. Nevertheless, given the slow historic rate of market penetration of new energy technologies, government support may still be necessary to increase the pace of development or penetration of a technology that would be particularly effective from the standpoint of strategic policy objectives.

Growing global interdependence is also taken into account. The communiqué of the 1996 OECD meeting at Ministerial level concluded: "The globalisation of the economy is the product of the interaction between trade and technological progress. It gives all countries the possibility of participating in world development and all consumers the assurance of benefiting from increasingly vigorous competition between producers. To take advantage of these prospects for improved living conditions and progress, individuals, enterprises and countries must show themselves capable of rapid adjustment and continuous innovation."

To ensure progress, a search for new and improved modes of collaboration must occur. Such innovation in collaboration could increase the vitality and effectiveness of international co-operative efforts. Joint action on difficult problems can bring not only new ways of defining the problems, and thus new types of solution, but also new ways of exchanging ideas, contributing experience, allocating resources and managing burdens.

Certain types of activity are more amenable to joint action than others. Energy technology collaboration becomes more difficult when proprietary interests and competitive trade issues are heavily involved. The prospects for co-operation are enhanced when global values are threatened and the course of events is unlikely to be altered easily by one nation acting independently. When needs and opportunities are similar, many may benefit from the advances that provide the answers. The motivation to solve problems is stronger where the solutions may be adopted simultaneously in a number of otherwise separate markets. A collaborative approach may also prove attractive where risks are high or the necessary time, capabilities and funding are substantial but the anticipated benefits of success are also high.

### *Definitions and Time Horizon*

To help ensure that the study treats the technologies uniformly, some general definitions have been adopted. "Technology R&D" signifies efforts ranging from investigation and fairly fundamental and applied research to exploratory development, including sophisticated hardware, programming and planning to establish the feasibility and practicability of proposed solutions to technological challenges; and on to advanced development, including integration of hardware for field experiments and tests, proof of technological feasibility and assessment of operability and producibility.

"Demonstration" refers to efforts that help expedite a technology's transition from the laboratory or pilot stage to operational use. This involves integrated technologies being evaluated and validated in a realistic operating environment to assess their performance or cost-reduction potential and make a first appraisal of the engineering and manufacturing needs.

"Technical potential" is defined as the capacity of a technology for achieving the priority goals in a given technology area, without reference to its economics. Due regard must also be paid to existing strategic policy objectives, such as security of energy supply and reduction of overall environmental impact.

"Economic potential" is the technology's potential cost-effectiveness. This is largely determined by its technical potential plus its capital and operating costs, compared with those of competing technologies, including the value of the product it delivers or the service it performs.

"Market deployment potential" is a measure of the relative ease or difficulty of disseminating cost-competitive technologies in the market place. It is determined by a range of factors that facilitate or constrain deployment and large-scale commercialisation, such as institutional and public support, or lack of support, and the effect of direct and indirect government measures such as pricing policies, taxation, incentives, standards and regulations, information and exhortation.

The study's policy focus is reflected in the time-frames used for the analysis. Within an overall time horizon the study employs three broad and somewhat overlapping categories: commercial technologies, next-generation technologies and technology options for the long term.

Commercial technologies are the available, demonstrated and tested technologies that in a significant number of IEA countries are being considered for market application and further diffusion in policy-making time-frames of up to five years. Their cost, operational characteristics, environmental impact and performance are well defined.

Next-generation technologies are those that might undergo large-scale dissemination within roughly 20 years. Some may still be in their pre-competitive R&D phase; others may have been tested and adopted on a near-commercial scale but not yet deployed commercially, though cost and performance estimates may be close to eventual net return. In general, it is assumed that large-scale dissemination could occur under existing market and policy conditions. Market and institutional barriers and other factors, however, mean dissemination might be partial and uneven among IEA countries and that only part of the economic potential (typically, 5-20 per cent, depending upon the technology and the general context) might be achieved within the time-frames.

The long-term technology category includes prospective technologies that R&D has shown to be feasible and applicable at the laboratory or pilot-scale stage. It is fairly certain that the adoption of these technologies on a commercial scale is technically possible, but estimates of cost and performance are very uncertain. Barriers include the lack of knowledge of the costs associated with industry's building and operating new commercial-size plants. In addition, key processes or components may not be fully understood. A 20 to 35-year horizon has been chosen as providing sufficient time to take into account the very long lead times associated with technology R&D and deployment, particularly for new energy technologies. While looking 30 or 35 years ahead and beyond is necessarily a speculative venture, it does allow the relevant merits of alternative technology development paths to be scrutinised and taken into account. This, in turn, allows shorter-term options to be evaluated with regard to their longer-term implications in comparison with alternative approaches.

There are also options for the very long term, whose time-span and ultimate significance may go beyond 2030. These emerging and conceivable energy technologies require further basic research or laboratory testing before their technical feasibility can be determined. Hence only very approximate and tentative estimates of economic cost, environmental consequences and performance can be made. Examples are nuclear fusion power generation, artificial photosynthetic energy conversion processes and carbon dioxide scrubbing.

### *Incorporating the IEA Shared Goals*

The decisive role of technology progress in addressing the strategic objectives of Member countries has been emphasised by the IEA Governing Board on several occasions. The communiqué following the meeting on 22 May 1995 reported: "Ministers identified specific means by which their countries could further their environmental, energy security and economic goals. They recognised the key role that cost-effective energy efficiency and conservation can play in increasing competitiveness, reducing pollution, enhancing energy security and promoting sustainable growth. The development of clean and efficient energy technologies has an important contribution to make and Ministers endorsed support for technological development and the removal of barriers to deployment in the marketplace." Intensified energy technology co-operation among IEA Member countries and with non-Member countries was highlighted as an indispensable means of accelerating technology advances and enhancing long-term energy security and environmental protection.

Six strategic technology policy principles have been identified and are defined below. International collaboration must help serve the broad shared objectives of energy security, environmental protection and increased global linkages, while focusing on these strategic principles and the technologies described in the study. The quotations are from the Shared Goals adopted by IEA Ministers at their June 1993 meeting (see Annex II).

- *Energy Diversification.* Fuel mixes and technologies should be diversified to increase flexibility in the overall energy system, from energy sources to end-use devices. "Diversity, efficiency and flexibility within the energy sector are basic conditions for longer-term energy security: the fuels used within and across sectors and the sources of those fuels should be as diverse as practicable." The many possible scenarios of changing energy security and environmental requirements over the 30-year time-frame of the study suggest that diversity and flexibility have a true economic and social value that needs to be captured in energy R&D programmes and in the design, production and deployment of new and improved energy technologies to ensure an expanded and diversified energy resource base.

- *Energy and Environmental Technology Policy Integration.* Energy technology policy must be integrated with the corresponding policies for environmental protection, economic competitiveness and development. "The environmentally sustainable provision and use of energy is central to the achievement of these shared goals. Decision-makers should seek to minimise the adverse environmental impacts of energy activities, just as environmental decisions should take account of the energy consequences. More environmentally acceptable energy sources need to be encouraged and developed. Clean and efficient use of fossil fuels is essential. The development of economic non-fossil sources is also a priority. A number of IEA Members wish to retain and improve the nuclear option for the future, at the highest available safety standards, because nuclear energy does not emit carbon dioxide. Renewable sources will also have an increasingly important contribution to make." The tenet is that energy technology progress cannot be pursued effectively as an end in itself but is substantially enhanced when it is compatible with and supportive of overall policies in closely related areas for application within a balanced market structure.

- *Energy System Efficiency.* Technological advances must be sought that increase the service quality and benefit provided per unit of energy employed. "Improved energy efficiency can promote both environmental protection and energy security in a cost-effective manner. There are significant opportunities for greater energy efficiency at all stages of the energy cycle from production to consumption. Strong efforts by Governments and all energy users are needed to realise these opportunities." This implies a continuing effort to increase the efficiency of overall energy systems (from fuel extraction, energy generation and conversion through to end-use) and thereby to increase the overall productivity of the economy. Cost-benefit criteria are needed to determine opportunities for trade-off among competing energy technology options. The market structure will facilitate technology advances of this type most effectively if environmental, social and other costs are internalised as completely as possible in the life-cycle cost of fuels, energy system components, end-use devices and services.

- *Pursuing Technological Breakthroughs.* "Continued research, development and market deployment of new and improved energy technologies make a critical contribution to achieving the objectives outlined above. Energy technology policies should complement broader energy policies. International co-operation in the development and dissemination of energy technologies, including industry participation and co-operation with non-Member countries, should be encouraged." Existing bases of knowledge generally are adequate to allow incremental technology improvements to be developed and applied. Energy technology policies and R&D programmes are required, however, to foster the more difficult and higher-benefit opportunities which are by definition long-term and most suitable for national and international attention and collaboration. Technology breakthroughs and high-value accomplishments should be pursued in key areas and sectors.

- *Improving Existing Energy Systems.* Existing energy systems should be improved and refurbished to allow for the long time lines required for new technologies to achieve maximum impact. Infrastructure requirements for new technologies may call for significant resource investments that can benefit from a suitable transition period for market introduction. Furthermore, decreasing government budgets increase the need for selectivity and resource optimisation when investing in new energy R&D programmes. "Co-operation among all energy market participants helps to improve information and understanding, and encourage the development of efficient, environmentally acceptable and flexible energy systems and markets worldwide. These are needed to help promote the investment, trade and confidence necessary to achieve global energy security and environmental objectives." Technologies that enhance and maintain existing energy systems can ease the difficulties inherent in transitions to new systems, and also offer the possibility that adaptation of improved technology additions or retrofits may make their use sustainable for longer in the future.

- *Emphasising Effective Operation of Free Markets.* Global energy and energy technology markets are less regulated and more open than they were some years ago and governments are continuing to reform their role. The precise effect of a particular market liberalisation measure on technology strategies will be highly dependent on the nature of the measure introduced, the organisation of the market subject to reform and prevailing economic circumstances. A competitive climate for new ideas expands the opportunities to find innovative technology solutions, diffuse them more rapidly and encourage diverse and flexible technology responses to energy challenges. "Undistorted energy prices enable markets to work efficiently. Energy prices should not be held artificially below the costs of supply to promote social or industrial goals. To the extent necessary and practicable, the environmental costs of energy production and use should be reflected in prices. Free and open trade and a secure framework for investment contribute to efficient markets and energy security. Distortions to energy trade and investment should be avoided."

## Energy Technology Policy Background

With differing circumstances and needs, countries have differing energy technology preferences and likely strategies. Time and the ability to prepare and deploy new technology are prerequisites for expanding the response options. Even then, the consequences of technology policy choices may remain unclear and involve risks. Hence it is clearly useful for countries (and the energy industry) to co-operate by sharing ideas, knowledge, resources and burdens. This can help increase the likelihood of success, for example by expanding the information base, exploring a larger variety of options in greater depth, enhancing market pull, accelerating time lines and augmenting the resources to meet common needs.

Co-operative action presumes a common understanding of current energy problems, of the status of present options to address them and of trends that may prove particularly important for implementing solutions in the future.

### *The IEA's* World Energy Outlook

Energy scenarios and projections can anticipate problems, indicate the likely limits of future energy changes and help focus attention on the technology options and strategies that have the greatest potential for meeting objectives, in particular those relating to energy security concerns. An understanding of long-term energy perspectives is essential to guide near-term programmes and policies concerning technology R&D and institutional frameworks. In the IEA's *World Energy Outlook* (Paris, 1996), supply and demand are forecast to 2010 by major primary energy source and end-use sector. Other projections, such as those by the World Energy Council, go beyond this time-frame; see, for example, *Global Transport Sector Energy Demand Towards 2020* (1995) or *Energy for Tomorrow's World* (1993). The European Commission report *European Energy to 2020: A Scenario Approach* (1996) uses four different scenarios to discuss a range of situations and to "reflect the uncertainty and sense of transition that pervades the energy sector today" in the European Union.

Three major conclusions can be drawn from the IEA's projections of world energy demand:

- world primary energy demand is expected to continue to grow steadily, as it has over the past two decades;
- fossil fuels will account for almost 90 per cent of world primary energy demand in 2010;
- a structural shift in the shares of different regions in world energy demand is likely to occur, and the OECD share of demand will fall.

Individual chapters in this study will highlight selected projections from the *World Energy Outlook*. The following points present the context within which energy technology R&D will progress.

- World energy demand is projected to increase by between 34 per cent and 46 per cent from 1993 to 2010. This increase will be met primarily by fossil fuels. Energy consumption outside the OECD, central and eastern Europe and the former Soviet Union could more than double by 2010. OECD energy consumption could represent less than half of world consumption in 2010.
- World oil demand is projected to rise from 70 million barrels per day now to between 92 and 97 million in 2010.
- OECD oil import dependence is set to rise. In 2010, around 60 per cent of OECD oil consumption may be met by imports, compared with 50 per cent now. The importance of the Organization of Petroleum Exporting Countries in world oil supply is likely to increase.
- Rising fossil fuel consumption implies increasing greenhouse gas emissions. By 2010, world carbon dioxide emissions could be 36 to 49 per cent above their 1990 level. The majority of this increase will come from non-OECD countries. The increase in China alone could be of an order similar to that in the OECD as a whole.

### *Environmental Concerns*

While the overriding energy policy goal of IEA countries remains security of energy supplies, attention has focused increasingly on environmental objectives. Over the past two decades, environmental challenges have simultaneously assumed a broader dimension and greater acuteness for the public and for policy-makers. A first issue concerns the quantity of pollution, which has risen dramatically with the explosive growth in economic and energy activity and human population in the 20th century.

A second major issue is the broadening range of environmental threats. There is a new awareness of the impact of pollutants such as volatile organic compounds and toxic heavy metal emissions. Meanwhile, the focus has gradually moved from air and water pollution near points of energy production and use, and from resource degradation at local and national levels, to issues of a regional and transboundary nature, such as control of acid precipitation and safeguarding water resources. IEA countries have developed technologies to tackle this range of environmental consequences of energy use with considerable success, but further problem areas are emerging.

A third critical issue, since the mid-1980s, has been global environmental problems such as the prospect of climate change and the threat to the stratospheric ozone layer, which have not only heightened concern regarding the energy future but also raised complex new questions relating to energy technology policy and R&D. Part of the background to the focus on environmental issues has been the international debate on the links between energy activity, economic growth and the environment, as well as the notion of sustainable economic development. The concept of sustainable development, elaborated by the World Commission on Environment and Development, is rooted in the premise that economic and ecological systems are completely interlinked. From this premise stems a major redefinition of international energy technology collaboration. The essence of the idea of sustainable development is that economic and energy development should meet the needs of the present generation without compromising the ability of future generations to meet their own needs. It also embodies the view that the natural environment – air, water, land and ecosystems – are resources that can be depleted, to the detriment of the quality of life on the planet.

For the world energy industry, these ideas have carried the message that new technologies and energy supply entailing an acceptable level of environmental impact should be made available at prices moderate enough to ensure continuing economic growth. Environmental factors have become important determinants of IEA energy technology programmes and the development of sustainable energy policies.

Technological advance is critical for the long-term conservation of any kind of natural resource and protection of the environment, particularly for the prevention of most forms of energy-related pollution and the economic recycling of waste products. Yet, one element in the argument presented in this assessment is that while new opportunities, and indeed whole new technological trajectories, can be opened up by R&D progress, technology deployment will be shaped by market dynamics that determine future costs of energy production and patterns of energy end-use. To the extent that environmental concerns take a central place in policy-making, environmentally driven technologies (affecting energy technology innovation, diffusion and technological strategies) may shift market structures and competitive advantages in the energy area, both nationally and internationally.

Two of the key environmental policy concerns affecting energy R&D priorities are conventional pollutants and the climate change issue. As regards the former, trends likely to shape energy R&D programmes include: working "upstream" to change the energy components, processes and systems that generate waste and pollution; increasing emphasis on integrated pollution prevention and control relying on market-based economic incentives; and re-examining the interaction between technology development and regulatory regimes.

As to concerns about climate change, currently available energy and environmental technologies can be expected to provide only a partial solution. The development and deployment of new and improved technologies will be essential if atmospheric concentrations of greenhouse gases are to be reduced significantly. Thus energy technology policy is a key instrument in attaining greenhouse gas containment objectives. More cross-sectoral, multidisciplinary approaches are called for. The *IEA/OECD Scoping Study: Energy and Environmental Technologies to Respond to Global Climate Change Concerns* identifies energy and environmental technology options and areas where international co-operation can enhance technology progress. In terms of greenhouse gas reduction potential, energy technology options can be grouped into three categories:

- increased energy efficiency (including savings and structural changes that reduce energy consumed per unit of real GDP);
- fuel substitution (with shifts to lower-emission products within a fuel group or among different fuels, or to carbon-free sources of energy);
- emission abatement (including process changes that reduce emissions, and add-on emission controls).

These categories can serve as the starting point for identifying responses that limit greenhouse gas emissions in each sector of energy use. The more that can be accomplished in the near term, the less massive the responses that may be needed later. Employing measures to accelerate the introduction of useful technologies that are already economic (the "no regrets" principle) can be considered an insurance policy, a prudent investment now against a potentially adverse outcome. Meanwhile, further R&D and demonstration could continue to provide new economic technologies over the time horizon of this study. In such a "phased" approach (which can be proposed although the need is recognised for simultaneous work on a broad range of technologies), energy R&D programmes seek to advance each promising technology option according to its current status. As the status of each technology will change over time, with some proving to be technically feasible and others becoming cost-competitive, the focus of efforts should also change, in a phased fashion.

A phased approach would be flexible and cost-effective. Scarce funds would not be wasted on commercialising technologies that are not yet economic, or on developing technologies for which no firm conceptual basis yet exists. R&D programmes could be modified as more information on the linkage between greenhouse gas emissions and global climate change became available, without significant economic losses.

Having identified increased efficiency, cleaner fuels and emission abatement as the principal selection criteria for technologies to receive marketing priority in a "first wave", IEA country governments would need to select policy instruments to stimulate the level of technology penetration and other responses considered possible and cost-effective, while overcoming any barriers that might hinder achievement of the desired outcomes. Differences in each country's energy system, including demand-supply structures, possibilities for fuel substitution and varying regulatory and taxation regimes, should be taken into account.

In deciding which new and improved technologies should receive priority for marketing efforts, information can be developed on the environmental emissions that result from various energy technologies and systems. In deciding which future technologies should receive priority for cost-reduction efforts, information can be developed on current and prospective costs under a variety of assumptions regarding technical progress. These technologies may include a number of so-called next-generation energy technologies for the long term and very long term, for which progress and breakthroughs are difficult to anticipate, even though R&D priorities can be reasonably set and periodically revised on the basis of the latest scientific knowledge.

The choice of energy technology response to greenhouse gas emissions has many additional implications, but two are of particular relevance:

- the extent to which response to global climate change will affect levels and patterns of energy consumption, and the impact of this on global energy security;
- the consequences for international co-operation, notably between IEA countries and the rest of the world.

Regarding future levels and patterns of energy demand, an energy technology response that can balance and integrate objectives such as improving energy security and economic well-being with that of limiting greenhouse gas emissions should be identified and adopted. Energy technology programmes must be tailored to help ensure benefits in light of the costs and macro- and microeconomic effects of measures to contain greenhouse gas accumulation. Over time, the relative costs and benefits can be reviewed, and adjusted where necessary, as understanding advances regarding the complex global situation, the technology options and the economic evaluations. In this vein, voluntary agreements have attracted policy-makers' attention. Such agreements range from relatively informal arrangements to agreements involving a high degree of co-operation that are combined with incentives such as technical assistance to identify energy savings or technology R&D priorities.

In terms of international co-operation, governments of IEA countries can create the right conditions for energy technology to move forward. In particular they can help to support technology development and reduce barriers to market deployment. Although there has long been international co-operation in addressing energy-related environmental concerns such as hazardous waste and transboundary air pollution, the climate change issue requires global co-operation. Given this dimension, international energy technology collaboration will be fundamental in mobilising the levels of investment and expertise needed to make the necessary breakthroughs. Consistent long-term policies are needed on funding R&D in technologies to improve energy systems' performance and the quality of the environment, and collaborative technology dissemination and transfer should be promoted.

Efforts undertaken co-operatively between countries, or entities within them, to reduce net greenhouse gas emissions – that is activities implemented jointly – hold significant potential both for combatting the threat of global warming and for promoting sustainable energy technology development. Energy projects implemented jointly can achieve greater, more cost-effective emission reductions than individual domestic action in each country. Joint implementation may thus spur technology co-operation, increasing developing countries' access to energy-efficiency and renewable-energy technologies while stimulating export markets for industrialised countries.

"Activities implemented jointly", or AIJ, is recognised under the UN Framework Convention on Climate Change and is open to all parties to the Convention. At the same time, significant questions arise about what kinds of technology advance might take place under the AIJ rubric. Would they produce real greenhouse gas reductions? Would they be "new and additional" developments, beyond ongoing technology development assistance or private business transactions? How would net emission reductions be measured and tracked? Can it be ensured that net reductions in one place do not give rise to increases in another, or that net reductions are not lost or reversed over time?

### *Responding to Technology Needs of Non-Member Countries*

A major conclusion of the IEA's 1996 *World Energy Outlook* about future global energy consumption is that energy resource requirements will increase. Growing pressure and competition for energy supplies will affect all regions and both net exporters and importers of energy. While IEA countries have developed technologies and mechanisms to deal with the issue of energy supply security, most non-IEA countries have yet to address the issue comprehensively. This is all the more important since, according to the *World Energy Outlook,* non-IEA countries can be expected to account for by far the larger proportion of incremental energy demand in coming years. Furthermore, their environmental priorities are likely to be different from those of IEA countries, as they are now facing the environmental problems that the industrialised world started to address more than twenty years ago.

If open energy markets and fair economic competitiveness are taken as a basic tenet, it can be argued that liberalised trade and investment will produce financial resources that developing countries could use for energy technology improvements. This presupposes, however, that a country practices effective energy policy management; in addition, active citizen involvement in a receptive political system can be crucial for effective environmental policies, and this is lacking in many developing countries.

The transition of centrally planned economies towards market orientation also calls for reforms in energy technology programmes and R&D priorities, including the adoption of new technologies and practices, creation of new legal and institutional frameworks for technology R&D development and deployment, improvement of energy efficiency in most sectors and rehabilitation of inefficient and environmentally unsafe energy facilities. Such reforms cannot be achieved quickly. Major problems exist, involving inefficient energy transformation, transport losses and end-use inefficiency in all sectors, but particularly in industrial activities and space heating. Economic change is likely to bring increasing burdens for the energy system and the environment from domestic electricity use and the transport sector. Long lead times and significant financial resources are needed to restructure activities. Nevertheless, such countries now have an exceptional opportunity to move to more sustainable energy development patterns.

The increasing interdependence in the global energy system can ensure that assistance to non-Member countries to develop and adopt more efficient and environmentally sound energy production, delivery and end-use technologies will also help meet IEA interests. Because it addresses these areas of self-interest, energy technology assistance may be made available at a number of levels through a range of multilateral and bilateral arrangements.

Much of the work on improving energy technologies, particularly in the area of R&D, is undertaken in the industrialised countries of the IEA. The near absence of R&D in many developing countries is usually the result of a lack of technical skills and, often, the necessary investment climate. These countries also lack the institutional structures and human capital that would allow them, with the assistance of market forces, to absorb, reproduce, adapt and improve imported energy technologies. Constraints on the transfer of energy-efficient and environmentally sound technologies to developing countries stem from the complexity of the learning process as well as from institutional weakness.

On the question of technology adaptability, it is often found that the application of new technologies in developing countries can only be achieved after a considerable amount of adjustment and modification to respond to local conditions. As noted in the United Nations' *Agenda 21,* technology co-operation should entail "an interactive process involving government, the private sector, and research and development facilities" and "continuing systematic training and capacity-building at all levels over an extended period of time". Many proven energy technologies are not widely used outside IEA countries and the potential gains from technology progress are not being achieved.

Three principal groups of barriers may limit technology access and transfer. The first barrier is a lack of information-transfer mechanisms such as training programmes; the establishment of such programmes is an important means of developing capacity for technology assessments and demonstrations. As societal goals and trade-offs in developing countries are likely to differ from those in the industrialised world, such countries should build their own technology evaluation capabilities. A second barrier is that information on energy technologies can be difficult to identify and disseminate. In developing countries, institutions that would enable R&D to make a contribution may be ineffective or not yet created. Efforts could be devoted to initiating or strengthening technology centres in developing countries, as such centres are a promising instrument to facilitate transfer, adaptation and development of appropriate technologies, including those from domestic sources. Third, non-Member countries do not necessarily have an efficiently functioning system of patents and intellectual property rights. Many suppliers of energy technologies in industrialised countries have been reluctant to provide technology to countries without the protection provided by such a system.

Until some of these barriers are overcome, the potential contribution of new technologies to energy efficiency and fuel diversification in non-Member countries will remain substantially unexploited. Reasons for this situation are given below.

*Improving Energy Efficiency*

The frequent underpricing of energy, especially electricity, in non-Member countries, as well as a range of other economic distortions can bias decision-making away from investments in improving energy efficiency towards investment in new energy supply capacity and technology. It also distorts individual consumer decisions. Another structural factor that is particularly significant in many countries is scarcity or high cost of capital for investment in energy-saving equipment and processes. Lack of information about available energy technologies and about the success of conservation programmes in other countries also constitutes a barrier, as does lack of information regarding energy consumption patterns (and hence the potential for efficiency gains). In the lower-income developing countries, the skills necessary to implement effective energy efficiency programmes are often unavailable.

Barriers to international trade can create substantial bottlenecks for efficiency improvements. Organisational structures can also be problematic: IEA experience indicates that the successful implementation of efficiency measures and improved technologies is enhanced where authority for energy conservation is visible and has adequate resources to pursue its objectives.

New and improved energy technology can be used to ameliorate the industrialising world's energy security and address its environmental problems in two ways: by applying new technologies that have proved viable in the IEA countries (notably those aimed at pollution control and remediation) and by transforming basic fuels and employing energy processes in a way that takes the local context into account. Some trade conflicts reflect sharp differences between developed and developing countries over responsibility for the environment. While there are a growing number of exceptions, many non-Member countries see environmental protection as a barrier to their energy plans. Conversely, countries with strong environmental standards sometimes view the absence of comparable regulations in other countries as a *de facto* subsidy.

*Fuel Diversification and Switching*

The second major mechanism by which global energy security might be enhanced is through strategies to diversify sources of supply of any particular fuel, but particularly of oil. While in IEA countries the share of oil in the fuel structure has fallen considerably since the first price shock of 1973/74, the trend has been less pronounced elsewhere. Oil represents about 35 per cent of non-Member countries' total primary energy supply (compared with 40 to 43 per cent in Member countries) and is likely to remain at this level through 2010.

The energy security implications of heavy dependence on oil can be modified by technologies developing a range of alternative oil supply sources. This approach raises questions for both IEA and non-Member countries, including: the appropriate level of energy and hydrocarbon exploration efforts, the role of foreign investment in facilitating technology transfer and institutional impediments (notably price factors) to foreign participation in many resource-rich but capital-poor countries. Governments need to create framework conditions so that private investors, operating in open and transparent markets, can deliver what is expected of them.

Governments in IEA countries are focusing increasing attention on renewable energy technologies, recognising the sizeable contribution they can make in the longer term to furthering energy security and environmental protection. Increased use of renewable energy sources in non-IEA countries could play a substantial role as well, but a major impediment is lack of access to appropriate technologies at competitive prices. A similar pattern applies to the use of clean coal technologies and natural gas, because of a lack of capital and infrastructure, while technical and political constraints stand in the way of the development of nuclear fission power.

In countries in transition towards a market economy, rehabilitation and completion of existing energy facilities should take precedence over support for new capacity. Where there are distortions in energy prices and production costs, market forces cannot always be relied upon to provide the right signals to decision-makers and investors. Long-term planning is essential, particularly in the hydrocarbon and electricity industries, to ensure that technology needs are met at the lowest feasible cost. Joint ventures, for instance, can provide innovative technologies and management expertise in efforts to diversify energy supply and increase production in existing hydrocarbon installations and low-rank coal power plants.

## Factors Influencing Technology Progress

Energy R&D and the necessary testing and demonstration generally take a long time. Technologies are conceived, developed and diffused via long and costly investment efforts, in response to both individual commercial demands and collective needs, and under multiple economic constraints. Energy technology commercialisation on a scale sufficient to make a significant contribution is in itself often time-consuming and may involve substantial investments. Broadly speaking, investments are of two types: the traditional or tangible R&D expenditures; and such "intangibles" as outlays on human resources, training and regulatory and infrastructural activities.

The concept of energy R&D has changed dramatically as the focus has shifted from the quest for innovation to the complex economic mechanisms underpinning new energy production and end-use technologies. Implicit in this shift is acknowledgement of a dual role for R&D: in addition to preparing new energy processes, components and systems and helping firms maintain market position, R&D develops capacity to anticipate needs and remain in pace with progress. The two aspects go hand in hand: adoption of new technology presupposes the capacity for absorption; the latter depends in large measure on the capacity for innovation.

Most IEA countries recognise that a successful energy technology policy should include programmes to promote the market deployment of new and advanced technology products. Such measures should include comprehensive energy technology information efforts, training programmes in energy industry sectors and financial instruments such as tax incentives, subsidies and third-party financing. In some IEA countries, regulations are being used to push new and improved energy technology into the marketplace.

Integration of energy technology priorities and R&D programmes into comprehensive economic and environmental policies is also essential. The integrated character of the innovation process calls for organisational structures and mechanisms to ensure interaction and feedback within and between government and industry, as well as among the various institutions involved. Expanded co-operation on technology dissemination and deployment between Member and non-Member countries, including industry participation, may offer substantial mutual benefits.

### *Trends in Government Energy R&D Investments in IEA Countries*

An accurate assessment of national R&D efforts focusing on energy technology innovation is difficult to obtain because of a lack of data and differences in the way support is measured from one country to another. Such information would help Member countries target their energy R&D and technology investments and programmes. The current situation can be attributed largely to three partly interdependent reasons:

- Member countries' statistics are incomplete: changes in the rates of deployment of new technology, for example, are the subject of very rough and unsystematic estimates, or do not appear to be measured at all.
- Practices differ by country regarding the integration and co-ordination of energy- and environment-related activities, and notably R&D. None of the approaches adopted allows for environment-related R&D effort to be consistently visible and therefore its capture in statistical enquiries is at best unsystematic.
- The definition of energy R&D would seem due for a rethink: the definition and approach adopted in the standard classification limits our understanding of R&D funding trends, but changes would require additional effort and cost.

Tables 1.1 and 1.2 show that government-sponsored energy technology R&D and demonstration spending is declining in many IEA countries, and that efforts are increasingly oriented to shorter-term objectives and non-nuclear energy sources. Concerning energy R&D investment priorities, *Energy Policies of IEA Countries: 1995 Review* and Member country submissions indicate a wide variety of approaches. Roughly half of the different governments do not invest in nuclear fusion technology, while a few continue to support nuclear breeder reactors.

Several general features seem to characterise public funding on energy R&D across IEA countries and may also affect future technology programmes and priorities:

- Governments increasingly concentrate on selected areas of energy technology. Budget restrictions have meant that even the larger countries, which in the past have tended to cover a broad range of technologies, are becoming more and more selective. Furthermore, energy policy and technology priorities are not always clearly reflected in the funding portfolio mix.
- From an institutional viewpoint, there is a marked tendency to establish mechanisms for rationalising and co-ordinating R&D efforts hitherto dispersed among different organisations or under different interdepartmental committees or programmes, and so to address more collectively specific issues of national or global interest.
- Environmental factors appear to influence budget allocations: priority is given to cleaner energy production, improved energy efficiency and the use of alternative energy sources, including alternative transport fuels.

*Table 1.1*

**IEA Governments' Energy R&D Budgets, 1985-1995**

(US$ Million at 1995 Prices and Exchange Rates)

| | 1985 | 1990 | 1991 | 1992 | 1993 | 1994 | 1995 |
|---|---|---|---|---|---|---|---|
| Australia | 77 | - | - | - | 85 | - | - |
| Austria | 61 | 16 | 28 | 23 | 30 | 27 | - |
| Belgium | 168 | - | - | - | 18 | 46 | - |
| Canada | 469 | 297 | 277 | 277 | 236 | 239 | 239 |
| Denmark | 17 | 42 | 50 | 58 | 56 | 47 | 47 |
| Finland | - | 44 | 53 | 49 | 50 | - | - |
| France | - | 714 | 645 | 638 | 620 | 637 | 673 |
| Germany | 1589 | 711 | 690 | 538 | 523 | 419 | 406 |
| Greece | 22 | 12 | 11 | 7 | 6 | - | - |
| Ireland | 4 | 1 | - | - | - | - | - |
| Italy | 1137 | 626 | 575 | - | 297 | 282 | 290 |
| Japan | 4355 | 4047 | 4134 | 4179 | 4270 | 4570 | 4714 |
| Netherlands | 275 | 211 | 206 | 198 | 220 | 197 | 184 |
| New Zealand | 20 | 1 | 1 | - | 3 | 3 | 3 |
| Norway | 39 | 55 | 61 | 65 | 60 | 58 | 48 |
| Portugal | 17 | 15 | 9 | 7 | 5 | 4 | 4 |
| Spain | 99 | 56 | 126 | 100 | 84 | 85 | 142 |
| Sweden | 156 | 99 | 88 | 110 | 83 | 87 | 64 |
| Switzerland | 138 | 180 | 182 | 196 | 195 | 190 | 182 |
| Turkey | 4 | 2 | 2 | 3 | 4 | 2 | 3 |
| United Kingdom | 708 | 314 | 253 | 226 | 162 | 82 | 83 |
| United States | 3214 | 2828 | 2833 | 2398 | 2350 | 2953 | 2915 |

Notes: Data do not include the new Länder of Germany for 1985.
Luxembourg has no energy R&D programme.
Belgian figures for 1993 refer to Wallonia only.

Source: country submissions.

*Table 1.2*

**Aggregate IEA Government Budget Spending in Key Energy R&D Areas, 1983-1995**

(US$ Million at 1995 Prices and Exchange Rates)

| Energy Area | US $ | % of Total |
|---|---|---|
| Conservation | 941.62 | 10.80 |
| Fossil Fuels | 984.07 | 11.29 |
| Renewable Energy Sources | 703.01 | 8.06 |
| Nuclear Power | 4786.50 | 54.89 |
| Power and Storage | 240.74 | 2.76 |
| Other Technology/Research | 1064.21 | 12.20 |
| Total Energy R&D | 8720.00 | 100.00 |

Notes: Data do not include European Commission figures.
No 1995 data were provided by Belgium, Finland, Greece, Ireland, Luxembourg or New Zealand.
Source: *Energy Policies of IEA Countries. 1996 Review* (Paris: OECD, 1996)

- The focus of R&D programmes has gradually evolved from large experimental facilities and pilot projects to understanding the inner mechanisms of environmental phenomena and industrial processes involving energy. This shift spans R&D activity from its basic to its pre-competitive stage, most of it conducted in national institutions.
- Overall budgets relating to nuclear technology (especially breeder reactors) and fossil energy (in particular coal-related research) have declined significantly in some countries, while support for developing renewable energy sources (especially photovoltaics and biomass energy conversion) and efficient energy end-use technology has been on the rise.
- Privatisation of public energy utilities and expanding independent power production are increasingly focusing the attention of players in this sector on short-term priorities and shorter paybacks on R&D investments.
- International co-operation is expanding, which reflects heightening concern with transnational energy and environment issues. Available financial data seem to suggest growth in the share of government funding allocated to international programmes, and a number of international collaborative energy R&D activities have been set up in recent years. Some are intergovernmental and others have no direct formal government support. It is being recognised that better energy technologies for developing countries can yield numerous benefits. Steps are being taken to increase the involvement of industry in international collaborative R&D.

Support for long-term energy R&D does not necessarily imply equal support for all technologies. Periodic assessments of resource allocation and the effectiveness of R&D strategies are required. Many countries regard such assessments as an important component of their energy policy. Policies for resource allocation should give priority to interdisciplinary research and to technologies that play a natural interface role, such as the engineering and other transfer sciences, as well as cross-cutting technologies.

All IEA Member countries are encouraging energy R&D support from private industry. Governments could perform a valuable service by evaluating programmes in areas such as waste reduction and energy conservation, which can provide economic as well as environmental benefits, and they might usefully publish information on those benefits. This could be particularly relevant at a time when widespread cutbacks in government energy R&D expenditure and foreshortening of time horizons by both governments and industry could threaten the timely development of future technology options, since energy technology progress is of growing importance for meeting the new global challenges. Energy technology programmes that do not promise satisfactory capital return or business expansion in the near term may still have to be supported by governments.

Private industry prefers to invest in energy technology that is either near commercialisation or required by environmental or other regulations and standards. In several IEA countries, as has been noted, corporate R&D expenditures are being reoriented towards shorter-term, quicker-payback projects, in reaction to corporate restructuring and competitive pressures. Longer-term, higher-risk and more uncertain projects are thus less likely to be undertaken in the private sector. Considerable technological effort is needed to stay abreast of and deploy new technology and to respond to changing user demands. In energy industries where technology is advancing rapidly, firms often invest considerable resources in monitoring the innovations introduced by their competitors and advances in basic and applied scientific and technical knowledge. Government cost-sharing with industry can leverage government energy R&D spending, introduce market relevance into government R&D decision-making, and accelerate the energy R&D process and transfer of results into the economy and the marketplace. In general, there is a tendency towards closer co-operation between government and industry. The effectiveness of energy R&D activity will be improved by government-industry partnership to finance key next-generation technologies, such as those for advanced clean coal use, energy conversion of biomass or large-scale deployment of photovoltaic systems. Further advances in nuclear power technology are likely to depend similarly upon government-industry partnership if nuclear power is to make a contribution to longer-term energy requirements.

Public energy R&D efforts cannot act as a substitute for corporate efforts, so government action can be only limited. However, environments conducive to innovation can be created and governments have at their disposal a battery of instruments. They can encourage the diffusion of generic technologies and support strategic technologies. They can encourage firms and public laboratories to interact and create networks. They can encourage long-term R&D by large firms, develop contract R&D firms and technical centres, and promote the industrial development of high-technology industries through international collaborative agreements between companies.

### *The Changing Technology Innovation and Diffusion Process*

The present and projected trends in energy technology seem to be diverging from those seen in the past. Energy technologies are in a continuous state of evolution, and on a timescale of decades there have been fundamental technical changes that have radically altered the ways energy is produced and used. Energy forecasts have frequently proved badly wrong because they have overlooked or seriously misjudged the impact and directions of technological change.

Support for energy technologies appears often to have reflected a belief that success is primarily a function of the scale of R&D expenditure, whereas general energy policy in many IEA countries is now increasingly guided by the idea that liberalised energy markets will encourage increased innovation and select the optimum energy technologies. The determinants of energy technology innovation, however, are numerous and their inter-relationships complex. And the process of technological change varies across IEA countries, as do the factors influencing the adoption and penetration of competing energy technologies and the possible implications of new and improved technologies for future energy policy and markets. Among these determinants, not only R&D activities themselves but also diffusion of technology, financing, government economic and environmental regulation, energy security requirements and the general economic situation are playing a role. Further determinants are related to changes in the energy technology innovation and diffusion process. For these reasons this study attaches great importance to the forces and constraints described below.

*Increasing Complexity of Energy Systems*

Individual energy technology components and processes are combined and used in increasingly complex engineering and organisational systems; thus, each should be evaluated according to the function it fulfills in a wider context. Some existing energy technology systems, because of their complexity, may preclude the introduction of new technological components and processes. For instance, integrating new renewable energy sources and technologies into the existing electric grid involves severe technical, institutional, regulatory and infrastructural difficulties. Engineers and organisations often tend to focus on established directions and ignore other technological options. The innovation process is a matter of very long-run planning, which can make innovative answers seem less attractive than waiting for changes in the energy technology market.

Conversely, existing systems may open the way to synergy and help indicate which directions of technical change should be pursued. Learning effects and economies of scale can reduce the cost and significantly extend the capabilities of technologies now in common use. For example, a new oil rig that would permit faster, cheaper drilling of deep-water wells would eventually, for a given exploration investment, substantially increase the volume of new additions to oil and natural gas reserves.

*Technology Supplier-User Interaction*

Energy industries must not only satisfy consumers' preferences, which are increasingly sophisticated and personalised, but also meet society's collective needs, expressed through a wide range of professional and users' associations. Hence the rapid development of new forms of interaction between energy technology designers, producers and suppliers, on one hand, and those who are applying, adapting and using the technology, on the other.

New energy products and processes tend to be more complicated than existing ones and demand a considerable learning effort; users may prefer to follow more familiar paths.

Informing and training both the public at large and specialised users in the characteristics of new energy technologies will lead to more informed decision-making and more effective participation in the selection of technology options.

Interaction with demanding and informed consumers is an essential factor in encouraging energy market penetration and helping improve industrial competitiveness. Several examples of technology diffusion, including utility demand-side management programmes with more active customer participation, strongly indicate that substantial increases in energy end-use efficiency will be possible with the adoption of new approaches to consumer demand.

A related dimension of energy technology diffusion involves the capacity of firms and R&D organisations to absorb innovations. Absorptive capacity consists in the ability of firms to become familiar with and use technology developed elsewhere through a learning process that involves substantial investment. In this respect, energy R&D has a dual role: in addition to developing new products, it must help enhance the capability of firms to learn, anticipate and keep pace with technology progress. This again implies the creation of networks of industries and firms, within which participants are at once helping to supply and to acquire new and improved technology.

A capacity to absorb new energy technologies is the *sine qua non* for taking full advantage of the range of benefits that they may offer. Government support is important for contract R&D organisations, even those that depend on commercial contracts. It helps them renew their stock of knowledge, stay on the cutting edge of technological development and fully play their role in the wide diffusion of the most advanced technologies. Governments use many mechanisms or approaches to support R&D organisations, including making support proportional to the level of contracts won or to participation in large technological programmes.

### *Role of Cross-Cutting Technologies*

Numerous technological innovations have broad application and find use in a multitude of energy products and processes. This category of cross-cutting, generic and highly diffusible technologies includes information technology, electronic controls and local area networks, robotics, measurement systems, biotechnology and certain types of new materials and chemical processes. Their main characteristic is wide applicability in almost all industries and can transform the R&D and economic environment. The merging of microelectronics and information technology with energy systems illustrates this tendency.

Cross-cutting technologies underlie innovation and production in the same sense that basic knowledge does. However, while in energy R&D programmes the body of knowledge concerned is specific to the energy technology area, generic technologies underlie innovation and production in industries that rely on a variety of technologies. Generic R&D also requires major investment from firms to adapt it to their own use. Since generic technologies are developed in certain industries and then diffused widely, these investments may not build on users' own accumulated technological capital.

Since technology advances in other areas may find application in the energy sector, and vice versa, energy R&D programmes should not be conceived in isolation; the external context may significantly influence the quality of results, the research spillovers and the timing of new technological progress. Research spillovers are defined as any valuable technological know-how generated in the R&D process, whether it is knowledge fully capable of generating an innovation, or knowledge of a more intermediate sort. The existence of research spillovers suggests that technology innovation issuing from a particular energy R&D programme or industry depends not only on the R&D effort and resources but also on outside efforts and the pool of technological know-how that the energy R&D programme or industry can draw upon.

*Technology Training and Standard-Setting*

A number of IEA countries place emphasis on the strengthening of institutional mechanisms to help ensure that new energy technology is adopted. These mechanisms include national education and training systems, local training centres and university programmes. Large public support programmes can thus help develop capabilities for market dissemination (for example, information technology-related public training programmes are available in many countries). The creation of networks for energy R&D co-operation between firms and professional associations is also promoted. Whether through industry-university links, or through industry-wide co-operative R&D laboratories, the aim of such diffusion policy is to increase technology transfer and help firms share their perceptions both of future threats posed by technology and of opportunities the market is likely to offer.

The role of standard-setting and labelling programmes is also important, in particular for increasing energy efficiency in the end-use sectors. Standards have a significant bearing on the development, marketing and purchase of new and more efficient technologies, products, processes and appliances. In their absence, high costs often delay adoption until an industry standard emerges, either through market domination or through administrative guidelines or legal rulings. On the other hand, efficient diffusion of new technology can be hampered if markets are required to "lock-on" (i.e. make a commitment) to a specific technology or technological trajectory that later might be regarded as wrong. The role of policy in this respect is to encourage multiple technology options and discourage premature standardisation. Sharing of experience can lead to more appropriate voluntary approaches to standard-setting on the part of the energy industry, thus increasing the effectiveness and economic efficiency of technical standards and making for better harmonisation of countries' policies.

*Globalisation of Technologies and Markets*

Progress in energy technology has become increasingly international, both in R&D and in application. Basic science has always involved the international research community, but international co-operation and competition have now spread to applied R&D. Two main driving forces are accelerating changes in patterns of internationalisation and leading to the globalisation of energy technology markets. The first is market deregulation and free trade. The second is the role played by the new energy technologies and by other technologies, which are acting both as an enabling factor and a spur towards still further globalisation.

Inter-industry and inter-firm technology trade flows are gaining ever increasing importance. They tend to reinforce the cumulative nature of innovation-based competitive advantages for large multinational firms, though they may weaken the resource base and organisational cohesion of domestic systems of innovation. New forms of inter-firm agreement bearing on energy technology innovation have developed alongside the traditional channels for international technology transfer – licensing and trade in patents – and they have often become the most important way for firms and national authorities to gain access to new knowledge and key energy technologies.

Energy technology assumes an international scale in this fashion because business must be globally competitive and draw on worldwide know-how to achieve technological innovation. For example, no international oil company wishing to remain competitive can afford to draw only on its national sources of expertise to improve its technology. The competitiveness of large firms will be increasingly governed by their ability to make the best use of R&D and human capital resources located in more than one country.

### *International Energy Technology Collaboration*

To face new and evolving challenges, IEA Member countries need to reinforce their technology co-operation structures, establish collaborative agreements on critical energy technologies and prepare more flexible, effective mechanisms for joint international R&D activity. An important component in technology collaboration will continue to be mechanisms and facilities to identify, compile and disseminate technical, environmental and economic information on energy technology options. International organisations can play a vital role as information clearinghouses, diffusing information about the effects of national policies on the development and use of more environmentally sound energy technology.

Intensified international collaboration can provide a means to accelerate progress and develop new and improved energy technologies by sharing limited financial and human resources and broadening the prospects of market deployment in all countries. The view is dwindling that national energy R&D is the only way to develop better technology, as programme costs grow and as business activities and technological innovation become increasingly worldwide in scope.

In creating the IEA, the aim of Member country governments was to enable industrialised nations to work together to implement an international energy programme. The IEA's work in fostering international energy technology co-operation includes annual reviews of Member countries' national energy policies and R&D programmes, as well as sponsorship of reviews and conferences on promising technologies. Recognition of the systemic aspects of the relationships among technology, competitiveness and growth, as well as the importance of economic, institutional and social factors in a country's or region's ability to profit from technological change, is a catalyst for innovative approaches to international efforts.

A key aspect of technology co-operation among IEA countries is the IEA Implementing Agreement, which provides a legal framework for collaboration on a given project for energy technology R&D and demonstration, or on information exchange. The collaboration programme offers the capacity to target simultaneously the technical goals of a project and the broader general objectives of participating governments. Implementing Agreements can relate to all phases of the energy technology cycle: R&D, demonstration and testing of technical, environmental and economic performance, market deployment (through joint performance evaluation and standard-setting, for instance) and information exchange. They constitute one of the key mechanisms to address emerging international technology co-operation needs as the next century approaches.

Each Implementing Agreement specifies the commitments of the contracting parties and creates a management structure, headed by an executive committee of signatories' representatives. The agreement also broadly defines the operating conditions for the project, provides for intellectual property rights and arrangements for commercial energy technology exploitation and benefit-sharing, and is financed on terms mutually agreed among its signatories. Since they have themselves chosen the area of work, the participants are countries with a particular interest in that area of technology and with capabilities to contribute.

The increasing interdependence in the global energy system suggests that IEA Member countries' interests can be served through improved contact and co-operation with selected non-Member countries to help the latter develop efficient, environmentally sound energy supply and end-use systems. Given the combined effects of globalisation of energy markets and technologies, developing countries and those in transition towards a market economy are particularly likely to benefit from international co-operation. A growing number of non-Member countries are reaching a stage of transition or development that encourages greater collaboration with IEA countries. If this trend is to be reinforced, special attention must be paid not only to facilitating their access to new energy technologies, but also to helping them establish the physical, educational and managerial structures that will enable them to assimilate and harness technological change. Member countries' policy advice may provide users in non-Member countries with a better understanding of the potential benefits of the available energy technology options, as well as information on possible investment regimes and institutions that can encourage and manage structural adjustment, thus facilitating energy technology adoption and absorption.

Brazil, China, Israel, Korea, Mexico, Russia and Venezuela are among the non-Member country participants in the IEA's collaborative R&D programme. Many IEA collaborative projects are of interest to both IEA Member and non-Member countries. There are 41 active Implementing Agreements. Experience has shown the instrumental role they can play in speeding progress of energy technology. Scarce resources are shared, and prospects are enhanced for the deployment of new, higher-performance energy technologies into the market-place.

In recognition of the importance of international collaboration in preparing technology responses to global environmental concerns, the governments of IEA and OECD Member countries are supporting the IEA/OECD Climate Change Technology Initiative. Its purpose is to enhance the cost-effectiveness of efforts to meet the objectives of the Framework Convention on Climate Change by accelerating the development and deployment of more climate-friendly technologies. It may also help establish and optimise practical international co-operation, with projects involving government and industry players from both Member countries of IEA and OECD and non-Members, and thus contribute substantially to the consolidation of an energy technology co-operative structure that can help mitigate emissions of greenhouse gases and constitute a support network for the world programme, appropriate to the needs of all countries.

# Chapter 2

## CLEAN USE OF COAL

### Goals and Rationale

Coal is a key component in the range of energy sources that underpin energy security in IEA Member countries and on a global basis. The reasons are its abundance, its widespread geographic distribution, low cost and price stability in comparison with other fuels, also its ready availability in an established and competitive international coal market. It has by far the largest resource base of all the fossil fuels and its reserves-to-consumption ratio is the highest. Coal is a complex and varied mixture of solid organic compounds, and its quality varies greatly, from pure hard metallurgical coals to dirty brown mixtures. Deposits vary from seams many metres thick near the surface, which can be stripped out in huge volumes at minimal cost, to complex, narrow seams at great depth, which may be difficult and expensive to exploit.

The energy role of coal has increased steadily since the early 1970s and solid fuels presently provide approximately one-third of global primary energy supply, and 45 per cent of the energy requirements for the world's electric power generation. Over the period since 1973, coal has also increased its share of total IEA primary energy supply from 22 per cent to 25 per cent, mainly due to the substitution of steam coal for fuel oil in electricity production. Because of its particular advantages and the very large established coal-related infrastructure, most energy projections show that the role of coal in the global energy mix will continue to increase well into the twenty-first century, particularly in the expanding electricity generation sector.

According to the IEA's *World Energy Outlook* (1996 edition) to the year 2010, world solid fuel consumption is projected to increase at an annual average rate of up to 2 per cent over the outlook period. Solid fuel consumption is expected to rise from less than 2 300 million tonnes of oil equivalent (Mtoe) in 1993 to over 3 000 Mtoe in 2010. The contribution of coal to world energy supply would remain substantial and relatively stable in relation to the current 29 per cent level. OECD-region total solid fuel consumption is also projected to increase by up to 0.9 per cent per annum to 2010. Growth in the rest of the world (excluding the OECD, central and eastern Europe and countries of the Former Soviet Union) is projected to increase consumption by up to 3.8 per cent per annum to 2010. Coal plays an important role in the development strategies of many newly industrialising countries and countries in transition towards a market economy because of the balance-of-payments and security benefits of using an indigenous and widely traded fuel. In the non-IEA region, final energy demand for coal is projected to increase by over 3.2 per cent per annum to the year 2010, leading to a doubling of coal consumption by the end of the period.

This chapter assesses the technology strategy and R&D programmes which could make the most significant contributions towards the following priority goals:

- improving the conversion efficiency, the environmental acceptability and the economics of coal use as a competitive energy source; and
- diversifying clean uses of coal with a view to preserving flexibility and coping with changing energy needs in the long-term.

Coal is a major contributor to both total energy requirements and local, regional and global environmental problems, and this combination gives a particular importance to energy technology policy in this area. Technology policy for the clean use of coal should aim to reconcile the competing energy and environmental dimensions of coal use, while simultaneously maintaining coal's economic competitiveness. Given coal's energy-security role, continuing efforts should be made to extend coal use beyond the power sector. These goals are relevant in both the industrialised and the developing worlds.

Though coal is generally seen as the major long-term fossil energy resource, it presents significantly greater environmental challenges than do the other fossil fuels. It contains or produces significant levels of conventional pollutants (sulphur and nitrogen oxides, also particulates) and unconventional pollutants such as heavy metals. (As a sedimentary rock, like any other mineral material, coal contains a hundred or so natural trace elements for which there is no evidence of pollution effects). Technologies to contain these emissions to acceptable levels are now commercially available, though the additional costs are significant and they are not as yet completely deployed. The deployment is most incomplete in the developing countries and, as a consequence, coal use there tends to be more inefficient, with greater environmental impacts.

Coal produces significant greenhouse gas emissions. On a full fuel-cycle basis, coal has relatively higher levels of carbon dioxide emissions than natural gas, due to the higher carbon content per calorific value of coal and the lower efficiency with which coal is converted to useful energy. For power and heat generation, efforts are under way to improve the thermal and mechanical efficiency with which coal is used. In the context of the global climate change issue, coal efficiency and carbon dioxide emissions have received considerable policy attention, in part because of the critical contribution of coal to world energy supplies throughout the time-frame of this study.

The scope of this chapter covers technologies for the use of coal in power and heat generation and the production of synthetic fuels. The selection of technologies is restricted to those which are judged to have the greatest potential for contributing to the goals set for this technology area. Although best practicable techniques must be considered over the whole coal market to ensure the cost-effectiveness of approaches and ensure future industry competitiveness, a number of areas are excluded from this study, including coal mining technologies and technologies that apply specifically to the many non-power uses of coal in the developing world.

## Technology Description and Assessment

The coal-use technologies assessed are grouped according to their level of development, and to the anticipated time-frame of their market availability. The time-frame issue is of particular significance for coal use technologies because of their large scale and capital intensity, their long life cycle and slow turn-over time. Power-generation equipment, for example, typically has a lifetime of more than 30 years, so that technology installed today will remain in use throughout this study's time-frame.

The technologies can also be categorised according to their function. The term "clean coal technology" entered the energy vocabulary in the 1980s. It describes a new generation of advanced coal technologies, environmentally cleaner and in many cases more efficient and less costly than conventional coal-burning processes. These new power-generating and pollution-control concepts are the products of years of R&D in many government and private laboratories throughout the world.

Clean coal technologies can be installed at any of the three functional stages in the coal chain, or in a fourth manner that departs from the traditional method of coal burning, as listed below.

- Coal cleaning: sulphur and other impurities in coal are removed before it reaches the boiler or any conversion process into other fuels or products.
- Combustion: pollutants inside the combustor or boiler are removed while coal burns.
- Post combustion: flue gases released from coal boilers are cleaned in the ductwork leading to the smokestack or in advanced scrubbers.
- Conversion: the combustion process is bypassed altogether; coal is changed into a gas or liquid that can be cleaned and used as a fuel.

All of the technologies described in this chapter fall into these categories or are some combination of them. The more advanced power-generation technologies possess two major advantages in comparison with current conventional technology (i.e. pulverised coal-fired combustion). They increase thermal efficiency and thereby reduce fuel consumption and carbon dioxide emissions; and they combine combustion, conversion and emissions-reduction functions, thereby simplifying pollution control and increasing thermal efficiency. Efficiency is increased by replacing part or all of the relatively inefficient steam cycle by higher-temperature, higher-efficiency gas or electro-chemical cycles. Co-generation with the combined production of heat and power can increase the overall efficiency of energy used in all power-generation technologies (including those still being developed which are discussed in following sections) through recovery of what would otherwise be waste heat. Depending on ambient temperatures, a district heating plant can convert up to 85 per cent of the heating value of coal into useful energy. These technical advantages increase the economic potential of the advanced technologies to well beyond that of current technology.

Summary data on the technical and economic potential of key technologies is presented in Tables 2.1, 2.2 and 2.3. Information is given on the status of development, thermal efficiency (which is also a measure of $CO_2$ reduction), capital cost and potential reductions of $SO_X$ and $NO_X$. Data on outstanding R&D needs of the major technologies is provided in Table 2.4.

*Table 2.1*

**Technical and Economic Status of Advanced Coal Combustion and Conversion Technologies**

| Technology | Status | Conversion Efficiency % | Capital Cost (US$/kWe) | Emissions Reductions (%) | |
|---|---|---|---|---|---|
| | | | | $SO_x$ | $NO_x$ |
| Pulverised Coal-fired Combustion (PCFC) - sub- and super-critical steam | Commercial | 38-47 | 1300-1500 | | |
| Atmospheric Fluidised Bed Combustion (FBC) | Commercial/ Demonstrated | 34-37 | 1450-1700 | 90-95 | 60 |
| Circulating FBC (sub- and super-critical steam) | Commercial/ Demonstrated | 37-39 | 1450-1700 | 90-95 | 60 |
| Pressurised FBC (sub- and super-critical steam) | Demonstrated | 42-45 | 1450-1700 | 90-95 | 70 |
| Integrated Gasification (IG) Combined Cycle (cold gas and hot gas cleaning) | Demonstrated | 45-48 | 1450-1700 | 98-99 | 98-99 |
| IG Fuel Cell | R&D | 40-60 | 1700-1900 | 92-99 | 92 |
| Direct Coal-fired Combustion (DCC) Turbine | R&D | 35-45 | 1200 | 85-95 | 70-80 |
| Direct Coal-fired Combustion (DCC) Diesel | R&D | 35-40 | 500-1000 | 80 | 50 |

Note: Net plant thermal-electric conversion efficiencies based upon the lower heating value of the fuel. Emissions reduction range depends upon which emissions control technology is adopted (See Table 2.3).

*Table 2.2*

**Technical and Economic Status of Air Emission Control Technologies for Pulverised Coal-Fired Power Plants**

| Technology | Status | Conversion Efficiency % | Capital Cost (US$/kWe) | Emissions Reductions (%) | |
|---|---|---|---|---|---|
| | | | | $SO_x$ | $NO_x$ |
| Advanced Flue Gas Desulphurisation (FGD) | Commercial/ Demonstrated | 37-39 | 200-350 | 90-97 | |
| Sorbent Injection | Commercial/ Demonstrated | 37-39 | 88-100 | 55-75 | |
| Spray Drying | Commercial/ Demonstrated | 37-39 | 120-380 | 70-90 | |
| Combined $SO_x$/$NO_x$ | Demonstrated/ R&D | 37-39 | 280-360 | 70-95 | 70-90 |
| Reburning | Demonstrated | 38-40 | 15-50 | 0-20 | 60 |
| Low $NO_x$ Combustion | Commercial/ Demonstrated | 38-40 | 10-30 | | 45-60 |
| Post-combustion $NO_x$ | Commercial/ Demonstrated | 37-38 | 100-130 | | 40-90 |

Note: Net plant thermal-electric conversion efficiencies based upon the lower heating value of the fuel and sub-critical steam cycle. Capital costs add to power plant investment.

*Table 2.3*

**Technical and Economic Status of Coal Upgrading Technologies**

| Technology | Status | Conversion Efficiency % | Operating Cost (US$/ tonne coal) | Emissions Reductions (%) | |
|---|---|---|---|---|---|
| | | | | $SO_x$ | $NO_x$ |
| Physical Cleaning | Commercial/ Demonstrated | 90 | 1-3 | 30 | n.a. |
| Chem/Bio Cleaning | R&D | 85-90 | 5-10 | 90-95 | n.a. |
| Low Rank Upgrading | R&D | 80 | 1-5 | 30-95 | n.a. |
| Coal/water Mixtures | Demonstrated | n.a. | n.a. | 50-75 | n.a. |
| Gasification | Commercial/ Demonstrated | 75-80 | n.a. | 90-99 | n.a. |
| Indirect Liquefaction | R&D | 60 | n.a. | 95 | 70 |
| Direct Liquefaction | R&D | 55-60 | n.a. | 99 | 97 |

Note: Conversion efficiencies measure the ratio between heating value of the fuel in process output and input stream.
n.a. signifies not available.

*Table 2.4*

**Clean Coal Technologies: R&D Needs and Opportunities**

| Technology | R & D Requirements |
|---|---|
| Pulverised Combustion | • Optimised combustion parameters, theoretical and experimental research to reduce $NO_x$ formation<br>• Improved construction techniques and application of high temperature materials |
| Flue Gas Cleaning | • Improved catalysts with lower costs and longer lifetimes<br>• Non-catalytic reduction of $NO_x$<br>• Dry sorbent for $SO_2$ removal<br>• Utilisation of solid products |
| Fluidised Bed | • Improved long-term behaviour of Fluidised Bed Combustion components<br>• Disposal of FBC ashes<br>• Demonstration of Pressurised Fluidised Bed Combustion |
| Gas Turbine | • Higher inlet temperatures and development of blade cooling and ceramic materials<br>• Low $NO_x$-burners at high temperatures - 1100°-1300°C for low calorific gas<br>• Resistance to corrosion from coal gas (PFBC and IGCC) |

*Table 2.4 (continued)*
**Clean Coal Technologies: R&D Needs and Opportunities**

| Technology | R & D Requirements |
|---|---|
| Combined Cycle | • Hot gas cleaning<br>• Integration of PFBC and coal gasification into power plant<br>• Part-load operation of different components<br>• Pressurised pulverised coal combustion<br>• Liquid-metal components for binary Rankine cycle |
| Coal Gasification | • Demonstration of reliable operation |
| Coal Hydrogenation | • Improvement of hydrogenation process, including refining |
| General Environmental Impact | • Increased process efficiency (methanol production, combined products, fossil and non-fossil energy systems)<br>• $CO_2$ removal and disposal |

***Description of Significant Technologies***

Several new and improved coal-combustion and emissions-control technologies have been technically and economically demonstrated, are commercially available and could make a market contribution during the next decade. The most significant options are described below.

a) *Coal Cleaning*

Coal-cleaning technologies are used to remove substantial fractions of ash and sulphur from coal prior to its combustion or process use, thus reducing the production of ash and $SO_X$ in the combustion stage. Coal cleaning is standard practice in industrialised countries, but in only a few developing countries. Further market deployment in the latter could make a major contribution towards improving the environmental and economic performance of coal use in these countries. Coal cleaning can be useful not only to clean thermal coal for power plants, but also to prepare high-quality graded solid fuels for industrial applications; for example, by using conventional moving grates.

Research to improve pre-combustion cleaning has concentrated on two major categories of cleaning technology: physical cleaning and chemical cleaning. A new category, biological cleaning, has recently attracted interest as advances have been made in microbial and enzymatic techniques for removing sulphur from coal. Physical cleaning commercially in use today can remove 30 per cent to 50 per cent of the inorganic sulphur (or 10 per cent to 30 per cent of total sulphur) in coal and about 60 per cent of ash-forming minerals. Typical physical methods include froth flotation, heavy liquid cycloning, selective agglomeration and electrostatic or magnetic separation. Physical cleaning can access inorganic sulphur bound in the coal mineral matter, but not the organic which is chemically combined with the coal. Nor can it remove nitrogen from coal, another source of pollution.

b) *Pulverised Coal-Fired Combustion*

In today's pulverised coal-fired combustion (PCFC) units, coal is burnt as finely pulverised particles. The most modern technologies achieve burnouts of 99 per cent of the carbon. Heat losses via ash and stack gas, or in the boiler, reduce primary or gross conversion efficiency by some 8 per cent for hard coal and some 12 per cent for soft brown coal, while further efficiency losses occur in the conversion of heat into useful work.

Conventional sub-critical and super-critical steam cycle power plants have net thermal to electric energy conversion efficiencies in the approximate range of between 38 per cent and 43 per cent, depending on the technology, coal quality, and steam parameters. This compares with average efficiencies in the market of about 35 per cent based upon the lower heating value (lhv) of the fuel. Producing steam at super-critical pressure enables power stations to achieve net conversion efficiency of around 43 per cent. This may be possible through modified designs, new construction techniques and application of new and advanced high alloy materials. Super-critical power plants have been in service in Europe, Japan, the United States and Russia for about 25 years. Some achieve additional efficiency gains through dual steam reheating. However, the benefit of increased fuel savings comes at the expense of the more costly high-temperature materials required and the loss in plant availability inherent in higher-temperature operation. The development of ultra-super-critical pulverised combustion power plants may go beyond 50 per cent efficiency as a result of further improvement of steam parameters to beyond the range of between 700°C and 720°C.

c) *Fluidised Bed Combustion*

Atmospheric fluidised bed combustion (AFBC) technology allows in-furnace removal of sulphur and, because of lower combustion temperatures, reduced production of $NO_X$. It therefore avoids the penalties involved in post-combustion control of $SO_X$ and $NO_X$ emissions. It also permits the burning of a wider variety of coals, including lower-grade fuels, than is possible in pulverised coal combustion technology. The technology suspends a bed of fine coal and limestone particles in a "fluidised" state in a stream of upward-moving air in order to increase effective surface contact and combustion rate and ensure rapid and efficient heat removal from the combustion process. The limestone (or dolomite) reacts with sulphur from the coal and flue gas during the combustion process and is discharged as bottom ash from the base of the bed. Heat is removed both in the flue gas and through heat exchange tubes in the bed or water-wall enclosures in the reaction chamber. The technology is differentiated according to the type of circulation flow: "bubbling" fluidised beds employ relatively low air velocities, while "circulating" fluidised beds employ high air velocities and fine particle recirculation. Fluidised bed combustion is presently the only technique capable of burning specific difficult solid fuels and fuel oil residues to meet current environmental laws in the United States.

AFBC technology contributes to attaining both leading goals for coal technology innovation because it has applications in both the power and the non-power sectors. Its significant technical and economic potential arises from its being the first commercialised technology which can simultaneously remove sulphur and control $NO_X$ formation in-furnace. Thermal efficiency of bubbling atmospheric fluidised bed is no greater than that for pulverised coal-fired technology. 250 MWe units have been developed and larger units to 600 MWe are in the development phase. Because the technology can combust waste and low-quality coals with low emissions, it has considerable potential for waste incineration and for both industrial heat and power generation in developing countries. The main development need is for further operational experience to confirm the long-term behaviour of AFBC components.

The relative merits of circulating fluidised bed combustion (CFBC), in comparison with bubbling AFBC technology, is a subject of long-standing debate. Recirculation of finely ground fuel and limestone ensures good gas/solid contact to achieve high carbon burn-out and efficient sulphur capture with high calcium utilisation. Another reported advantage of this system is that staged input of combustion air can be arranged more easily than in other systems. Primary air is supplied through a suitable distributor at the bottom of the chamber and additional air is introduced through the sidewalls at various levels higher up the chamber. Air staging minimises the excess of oxygen available at any point in the combustion process, which helps to control local temperatures and limits the formation of unwanted oxides of nitrogen.

d) *Atmospheric Emissions Control*

Because of the ash and impurities contained in coal, pulverised coal fired plants require special emission control technologies to meet environmental standards. Contaminants include sulphur, nitrogen, halogens, alkali metals and heavy metals, and the technologies to remove them include those described below.

Particulate removal technologies from flue gas (cyclones, baghouse fabric filters and electrostatic precipitators) have reached a high state of development. Most solid-fuel plants in IEA countries have some form of equipment capturing most particulates before they can be released from the stack. The simplest devices, which attain removal efficiencies of up to 90 per cent by weight, are cyclone separators that remove the heaviest particles from the air stream through gravity and inertia. Because regulatory requirements now usually demand higher removal rates, especially for small particles, such mechanical collectors are no longer used except as pre-collectors in combination with more advanced devices. Much more effective are electrostatic precipitators and fabric filters, or "baghouses". The former work by applying an electrical charge to the particles, which makes them adhere to one another and fall out of the flue gas stream. Fabric filters simply trap particles in inverted fabric cones. Precipitators can remove up to 99.75 per cent of particles by weight, and future designs can attain even higher efficiency, while adding approximately 5 per cent to capital cost of the power station.

Flue gas desulphurisation (FGD) can achieve very high levels of removal of sulphur oxides ($SO_X$), though at the cost of a loss of thermal efficiency of approximately one to two percentage points and the production of significant volumes of solid waste. Plant investment costs are increased by approximately 15 per cent for new plant and up to 30 per cent for retrofitting. The technology is now widely deployed in the United States, Europe and Japan. Technology development is directed towards reducing stack gas scrubber costs and improving handling and disposed of the sludge waste product, either by minimising volume, upgrading its physical and chemical characteristics or producing marketable by-products. A large number of process configurations are available.

In sorbent injection, dry $SO_x$ sorbent is injected into the combustion chamber or downstream as an alternative to flue gas scrubbing. Owing to the simplicity of the approach, efficiency loss is low (about 1.5 per cent), but FGD's high levels of $SO_x$ removal cannot be attained.

With regard to reduction of nitrogen oxides ($NO_x$) emissions, post-combustion $NO_x$ control processes use urea or ammonia to reconvert $NO_x$ in flue gas to nitrogen and oxygen. The most advanced version of this process is termed Selective Catalytic Reduction (SCR) and routinely achieves 65 per cent to 80 per cent $NO_x$ reduction. The technology has now been widely demonstrated and increases in investment costs for new plant are in the range of 7 per cent to 15 per cent. Other versions of the technology are in varying stages of demonstration and application. Staged combustion in successive combustion zones controls combustion temperature and, thereby, $NO_x$ formation (which is temperature-dependent). Natural gas and pulverised coal are both suitable reburning agents. If incorporated in new plant design, investment costs are increased by only about one to 2 per cent.

Post-combustion emissions control, though effective, is expensive and reduces efficiency. Treating the high-volume flue gas stream requires large-scale equipment, the conditions are corrosive and erosive, significant levels of chemicals are required and substantial levels of waste are produced. The market deployment of best practice pulverised coal-fired technology with advanced emission controls can contribute immediately towards meeting the goals for this technology area. The most significant options for further technology advancement are efficiency improvements through upgraded steam conditions, further cost reductions through improved economies of scale and increased modularity in unit design, further optimisation of combustion parameters, and theoretical and experimental research to reduce $NO_x$ formation. The economic potential for achieving the first two of these R&D objectives is constrained by the cost of the equipment required for the high temperatures involved in ultra-super-critical steam cycle operation, and the tendency towards lower reliability with larger sized units.

### *Assessment of Technical and Economic Potential*

Several attractive coal technologies are still being demonstrated but are not expected to become available for large-scale commercial application until towards the end of the next decade or later. Some of these next-generation technologies may therefore have achieved a significant level of market penetration by the end of the time-frame of this study. In addition, there are other coal technologies that will require considerable further technical development before they can become commercially available. These technology options for the long term would not enter the market to a significant extent within the time horizon of the study, and some, in fact, may never become commercially competitive.

a) *Advanced Coal Cleaning*

Advanced coal cleaning technologies are based on deep physical, chemical and biological processes. Technologies falling within the former two categories are technically proven, while biological cleaning is in an early stage of development. In most cases, the new physical cleaning technologies achieve their increased effectiveness by first grinding the coal much more finely than is done commercially today. In its finer state, coal takes the consistency of talcum powder and more impurities can be freed from the coal. Once the coal is finely ground, a host of new processes specifically designed to work with ultra-fine particles can be used. These new processes can remove more than 90 per cent of the inorganics, sulphur and other undesirable minerals. Removing organic sulphur that is chemically bound to the coal is a far greater challenge for pre-combustion coal cleaning. One chemical technology that has shown promise is molten-caustic leaching. In this technique, coal is exposed to a hot, sodium-or potassium-based chemical. The chemical leaches sulphur and mineral matter from the coal.

Advanced coal cleaning can achieve very high levels of de-sulphurisation, de-mineralisation and removal of trace elements, though at a significant cost. For example, conventional cleaning methods are estimated to cost about US$ 0.3/GJ, whereas deep physical and chemical cleaning methods cost, respectively, around US$ 2.0/GJ and US$ 2.5-3.5/GJ. The net benefits of the current state-of-the-art coal cleaning in conventional pulverised coal-fired combustion do not appear to justify this additional expenditure, in large part because the new technology would not remove the necessity for flue gas cleaning equipment under modern environmental requirements. Economics may be improved if advanced coal cleaning is incorporated into an integrated approach to coal/water mixture technology. Clean coal is not warranted in fluidised bed technologies, but the low ash may be attractive for low waste gasification. Finally, "ultra-clean" coal could be justified in direct coal-fired engines if the latter were proved technically and economically viable (see section below).

b) *Coal/Liquid Mixtures*

Coal/liquid mixtures are stable oil-like blends (from 50 per cent to 75 per cent coal by weight) which can be stored, pumped and combusted in a manner analogous to oil. Initial development was based on coal/oil mixtures, but current programmes focus primarily on coal/water mixtures. Earlier R&D efforts were devoted to developing a direct substitute for fuel oil in terms of both transport and firing. This option remains promising despite the fact that it would be uneconomic at current oil price levels. But the technology has more recently gained additional ground in the context of advanced clean coal utilisation and fuel switching. Coal/water mixtures have been developed which can be used in conjunction with intensive liquid-phase cleaning and as a substitute fuel for pulverised coal in both conventional and advanced coal technologies. Moreover, the technology can be adapted to integrate the cleaning, transportation, storage and utilisation of coal, though economic competitiveness is highly dependent upon the specific site location.

c) *Ultra-Super-Critical Power Plant*

Ultra-super-critical plants are a further development of PCFC with a steam cycle. They operate at higher pressures (250-300 bar) and temperatures (around 600°C) than does the super-critical technology reviewed in the preceding section. An ultra-super-critical pulverised coal-fired plant has the technical potential (with higher temperatures and pressures) to increase net thermal efficiency in power production to over 50 per cent. Such improvements would bring PCFC units up to the efficiency levels expected from more sophisticated technology. But, as peak temperatures are increased, problems of materials strength, oxidation and corrosion rapidly become more serious, dictating shifts to more costly high-strength, oxidation- and corrosion-resistant alloys for the large steam-tubing heat exchangers that transfer heat from the combustor to steam at high temperature and pressure. The ultra-supercritical power plant remains essentially at the demonstration stage because, at present fuel prices, the operating cost savings resulting from improved efficiency are offset by the higher investment costs. Further R&D to reduce component costs could bring forward the market penetration of the technology.

d) *Pressurised Fluidised Bed Combustion (PFBC)*

With the advanced power generation technologies discussed below, the steam cycle is replaced, either partly or completely, by a gas cycle. If finally proved viable, these technologies may provide significant efficiency improvements over conventional steam-cycle power generation. Pressurised fluidised bed combustion (PFBC) technology is a development of the atmospheric fluidised bed technology described above and it exhibits AFBC's particular advantages such as *in situ* removal of sulphur and ability to handle a wide variety of coal or waste types and qualities. It operates at pressures ten times or more above atmospheric, and this allows the introduction of a gas cycle and an increase in unit power output. It also allows substantial reductions in plant size for a given output, and thus makes possible cost reductions through modular factory production. A second-generation PFBC design employs a pyroliser step to provide low BTU gas as a fuel source to raise turbine inlet temperature and, as a result, increase system efficiency. PFBC has the technical potential to achieve net thermal efficiencies some two to three percentage points higher than those of advanced PCFC and AFBC technology, as well as very low emissions of $SO_x$ and $NO_x$. Because of PFBC's higher unit output and its modular design, its economic potential in the power sector in the medium term may be significantly higher than that of AFBC's. One demonstration plant has successfully completed its performance tests and several demonstration units are currently operating. Though a number of technical issues have yet to be resolved before the technology will be widely deployed commercially, it is one of the most promising medium-term coal utilisation technologies. Some experts believe that the technology will have fewer technical problems to overcome than will the other next-generation technologies and that it will be commercially available and competitive before the end of the1990s. R&D needs include demonstration of effective and reliable clean-up of intermediate particulate-laden gas streams. This would significantly improve overall thermal efficiency.

e) *Integrated Coal-Gasification Combined Cycle (IGCC)*

In the case of combined gas and steam cycles, high-pressure fuel gas (natural gas, biomass gas, coal gas) is combusted in the gas turbine to generate electricity. The exhaust gas from the gas turbine is used to generate steam, which is converted into additional electricity by a steam turbine bottoming cycle. Integrated coal-gasification combined cycle (IGCC) uses synthesis natural gas (SNG) obtained from a coal gasifier to drive the gas turbines. Systems range in size from less than 100 MWe to more than 200 MWe. Different configurations of gasifiers ("fixed", "entrained" and "fluidised bed") and heat cycles are available. As with PFBC, IGCC can also use lower quality fuels as feedstocks and, in fact, the efficiency gains with lignites compared with conventional combustion are larger than for high-quality coals. Sulphur control is achieved both *in situ* in the gasifier and externally via hot or cold chemical gas clean-up systems using both sorbents (such as zinc ferrite) and reagents. Because of the reducing atmosphere, the fuel-bound sulphur and nitrogen are not oxidised. Sulphur removal is chemically simpler than that involving flue gases and, because of the much lower gas volume of fuel gas relative to flue gas, it is also technologically simpler. Particulates, also, are removed from the fuel rather than the flue gas. Solid waste volumes are lower than with fluidised bed technologies because limestone is not required for sulphur removal. Moreover, in most versions of the technology, the solid waste is in the form of a glassy slag, which is more convenient to handle and much less leachable than is ash waste, and which can produce marketable by-products.

The technology has the potential for thermal efficiencies even greater than those attained by PFBC, with 98 per cent removal of sulphur and $NO_X$. There is technical scope for further efficiency improvements as more advanced gas turbine technology (which would allow higher turbine inlet temperatures) is developed and higher levels of process integration are achieved. The United States goal for this technology is US$ 1 200/kw and 45 per cent efficiency by 2000, and US$ 1 050/kw and 52 per cent efficiency by 2010, with extremely low $SO_2$ and $NO_X$. The technology also has a longer-term strategic significance in that it is the first electric power technology to use gasified coal. It could therefore act as a bridge to the more advanced coal gas-based cycles, as well as to concepts such as integrated "coal refinery" and power station complexes. Another potential advantage is that carbon dioxide removal from IGCC is substantially less expensive than its removal using conventional power plant technology.

A number of important technical bottlenecks remain. The most important of these relate to the combination of the coal gas pollutants and the high gas temperature. The hot gas contains impurities including melted ash, acid gases and vaporised alkali metals which are highly corrosive and erosive, particularly to turbine blades. The technology has been technically demonstrated on a commercial scale but has not yet been widely deployed. Considerable development work is required to filter out particulates in hot gas streams (as for PFBC) and to remove alkali metals without unacceptable losses in efficiency. Integration of the gasifier and combustion elements of the plant also requires further development. There is a large potential market for IGCC technology, though commercially demonstrated high-efficiency units are unlikely to be available until after 2005.

f) *Integrated Coal-Gasification Fuel Cell (IGFC)*

The integrated coal-gasification fuel cell (IGFC) introduces an electro-chemical cycle. Fuel cells are devices that convert chemical energy directly into electric energy. They use a coal gasifier and gas cleanup system to supply a methane-rich gas to the fuel cell stack. The direct current output can be converted through solid state electronics (a power conditioner or invertor) to alternating current of high quality. A waste heat recovery bottoming cycle (either steam cycle or combined gas and steam cycle) can be incorporated to generate additional electricity from the high-temperature fuel cell stack exhaust. Waste heat can also be used for heat production.

IGFC has the technical potential to achieve very low emissions of sulphur and nitrogen oxides, and efficiencies as high as 60 per cent. The latter would result in substantial fuel savings and reductions in carbon dioxide emissions of up to 40 per cent compared with current best practice.

Other advantages are the ability to operate in both base load and partial load with little loss in efficiency, insensitivity to changes in ambient temperatures and the possibility of being used in both central power station and decentralised modes. However, major technology development remains to be completed before this technology can be commercialised. Technology bottlenecks include corrosion of materials by electrolytes, difficulties in protection sealing, and loss of cathode metals. Development of heat-proof and anti-corrosive materials is required. Natural gas-fired fuel cells will be commercialised well before IGFC.

g) *Coal Liquefaction*

Technologies for coal liquefaction to produce hydrocarbon fuels constitute the major potential option for diversifying coal use beyond the power sector in industrialised countries. They are of policy significance because of the transport sector's continuing heavy reliance on oil-based fuels and the relative abundance of coal. Several of these technologies have already demonstrated their technical potential, but all would require a substantially different energy price regime from today's if they are to become economic. Substantial advances have been made in the areas of process integration, liquid product quality improvement, and the refining and end-use of coal liquids. The United States Department of Energy views coal liquids as a viable future option to supplement decreasing petroleum supply, and considers that continued R&D could make coal liquids a commercial reality after 2010. In the interim, further technology progress could improve performance and reduce costs.

Coal liquefaction technologies are categorised as processes of either direct hydrogenation or indirect gasification. The direct hydrogenation processes react a coal slurry, a solvent and hydrogen at high temperature and high pressure to produce hydrocarbons of a type suitable for liquid transport fuels. Coal hydrogenation processes have the advantage of higher thermal efficiency, lower cost and more suitable product spectrums. The indirect processes chemically convert a coal-derived synthesis gas into mixed hydrocarbons or into methanol. Substantial progress has been made with indirect coal liquefaction, particularly in relation to methanol production. The methanol option is becoming commercially more interesting because methanol is gaining importance as a transport fuel, as a constituent in motor fuel blends, as a feedstock for the production of octane enhancers and as a potential fuel for direct firing of combustion turbines for peak electric power generation. It can also be catalytically converted to high- octane gasoline. The most notable application of indirect coal liquefaction is the South African Coal, Oil and Gas Corporation (SASOL) three-plant complex which was initiated in 1955. An additional advantage of the indirect route is that it provides the option of co-producing multiple product streams such as gasoline/synthetic natural gas and methanol/coal gas for electric power production (Table 2.5).

Variations of synthetic fuel technologies could offer better economics. Rather than liquefying only coal in a complex and expensive process, coal-oil co-processing mixes coal with the heavy residual oil that is the waste product of refineries. The slurry is then processed in an advanced refining concept called a cracking unit. The residual oil provides all or most of the hydrogen needed for the coal conversion into hydrocarbons. This eliminates or reduces the need for hydrogen production, a step that adds considerably to the cost of other synthetic fuel processes. Once produced by the co-processing plant, the coal-based liquid can be cleaned of its sulphur and ash before being used.

*Table 2.5*

**Efficiencies for Conversion of Coal and Other Fossil Feedstock to Liquid and Gaseous Fuels**

| Feedstock | Process | Product | Thermal Efficiency % |
|---|---|---|---|
| Hard Coal | Gasification/Fischer Tropsch Synthesis | Motor Fuels | 40-41 |
| | Gasification/Fischer Tropsch Synthesis | Motor Fuels & SNG | 56-58 |
| | Gasification/Methanol Synthesis | Methanol | 48-50 |
| | Gasification/Methanol Synthesis | Methanol & SNG | 61-63 |
| | Gasification/Methanol Synthesis/MTG | Gasoline | 45-47 |
| | Gasification/Methanol Synthesis/MTG | Gasoline & SNG | 60-62 |
| | Gasification/Methanation | SNG (25 bar) | 62-64 |
| | Gasification/Hydrogen | Hydrogen (98%, 25 bar) | 60-62 |
| | Coal Hydrogenation | Motor Fuels | 50-55 |
| Natural Gas | Gasification/Fischer-Tropsch Synthesis | Motor Fuels | 54-59 |
| | Gasification/Methanol Synthesis | Methanol | 63-68 |
| | Gasification/Methanol Synthesis/MTG | Gasoline | 60-64 |
| Heavy Oil | Gasification/Methanol Synthesis | Methanol | 52-54 |
| Crude Oil | Refinery with Atmospheric and Vacuum Distillation and Hydrocracker | Motor Fuels | 88-90 |

Notes: MTG is methanol to gasoline conversion.
SNG is synthetic natural gas.
Thermal efficiency is defined as the lower heat value of the products divided by the lower heat value of the feed coal, including the coal necessary for the generation of the utilities.
The figures have been calculated for a bituminous coal with high reactivity and low ash and moisture content. When processing lignite, the thermal efficiencies will be slightly lower due to the need for drying the coal.
Ranges indicated for the different efficiencies in the table take into account the influence of different plant locations, processes used, individual process layouts and flexible product distributions.

A major environmental issue for coal liquefaction is its substantially higher level of $CO_2$ emissions when compared with petroleum- and natural gas-based methods of producing liquid fuels. For example, the thermal conversion efficiency of producing automotive fuels from an average crude oil refinery (distillation plus hydrocracking) is approximately 88 per cent to 90 per cent, while natural gas-based systems have efficiencies of up to 68 per cent. Coal liquefaction technology efficiencies range from 40 per cent to 47 per cent for indirect liquefaction, but could be improved to 50 per cent with more advanced technology, and from between 50 per cent and 55 per cent for direct liquefaction to up to 60 per cent with advanced two-stage technology currently under development. The comparison is even more disadvantageous on a comparative full fuel-cycle basis. However, the comparison of thermal efficiencies should be made with caution, since estimates are often based on conceptual plant designs that may be 15 to 20 years away from large-scale implementation. The crude refining thermal efficiency by then could be lower than the 88 per cent cited above because of mandated requirements for cleaner fuels and a gradual shift to heavier crude feedstocks.

As can be seen from Figure 2.1, the coal-based cycles are estimated to be less efficient than the crude-oil and natural gas-based cycles. Carbon dioxide emissions associated with the (crude oil) Diesel cycles follow a similar trend. These disadvantages are reduced in the case of indirect liquefaction when multiple product streams are produced. For example, co-production of gasoline and synthetic natural gas from coal gasification has an overall process thermal efficiency of 60 per cent to 62 per cent.

The data points to the following conclusions, which may serve as guidelines for the future application of coal conversion processes.

(i) For the production of motor fuels, the thermal efficiency of coal hydrogenation (direct liquefaction) is generally higher than coal gasification (indirect liquefaction). The qualities of automotive products from gasification are superior to coal hydrogenation products, especially for the diesel oil fraction, although there may be exceptions.

(ii) Coal gasification is particularly attractive for the production of methanol: efficiency increases to 50 per cent. In addition, methanol has a superior efficiency in Otto and Diesel engines and can be readily stored for combustion-turbine peak electric power generation.

(iii) Coal gasification plants can be designed to co-produce a combination of two or more end-products, raising efficiency to more than 60 per cent.

h) *Integrated Coal Refinery/Power Plant*

The integrated coal refinery/power plant concept attempts to capture economic and thermal efficiency benefits from a more systematic approach to co-production. For example, at a relatively low level of integration, a plant could produce base-load electricity for, say, 65 per cent of the time and methanol for 25 per cent of the time. The methanol could be used in chemicals production, as transport fuel or as a peaking load fuel in the power station. A further level of integration would be achieved through utilisation of the low-level heat for industrial or process heat. Technically, this level of integration could increase the overall efficiency of coal conversion to somewhere near 90 per cent. The carbon dioxide reductions inherent in this high level of thermal efficiency would need to be assessed against less $CO_2$-intensive chemicals production from natural gas or refinery naphtha. The economic potential for integration will depend upon a wide range of factors, including costs arising from possible reduced process flexibility, comparative product demand and prices, and cost effects of environmental legislation and of siting in relation to other industrial activities. Lower levels of integration are economic now, while other levels are likely to become competitive at various stages in the future. Integration would contribute towards both of the leading goals of this technology area.

*Figure 2.1*
**Fuel Cycle Efficiencies and Carbon Dioxide Emission in Converting Coal, Natural Gas and Oil to Hydrocarbon Fuels for Transportation**

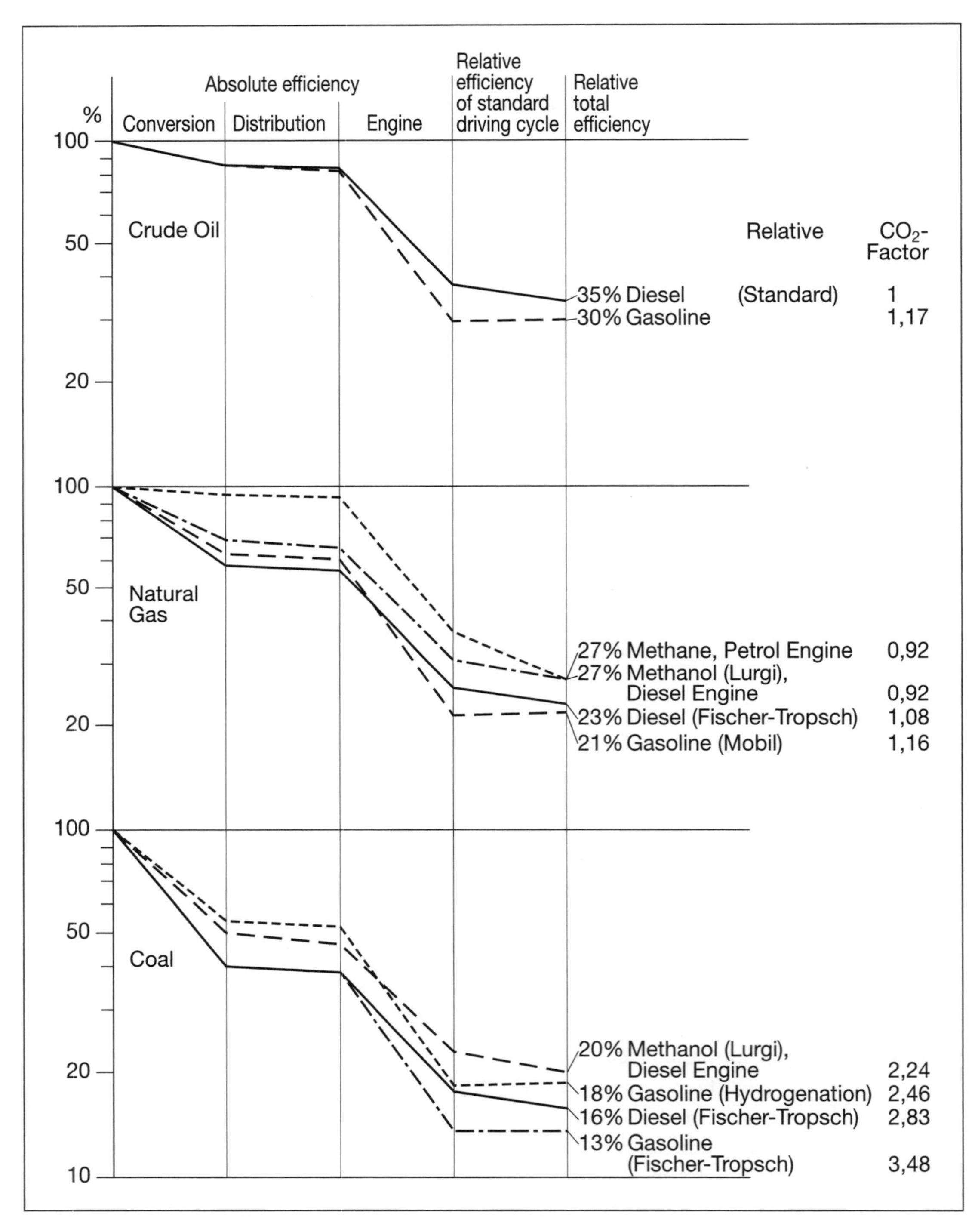

i) *Industrial Clean Coal Technology*

Coal is used by factories and industrial facilities to produce heat or steam for a variety of manufacturing and production processes. Typically, coal is used to produce steel and cement, and it can be a valuable raw material for the chemical industry. Clean coal technologies are being developed for these applications. In some cases (industrial steam production, for example), scaled-down versions of electric utility clean coal systems, such as fluidised bed combustors, offer attractive options. Industrial-size fluidised bed combustors can be found today in paper mills, food processing plants, tyre manufacturing factories, hospitals, and district heating systems. R&D is under way to improve these systems further, making them more practical and economical for smaller businesses, and perhaps someday even for apartment buildings and homes.

In steelmaking, coal produces coke which is used in smelting iron ore to make steel. Coke is made by a process called "carbonisation" in which a blend of two or more bituminous coals is baked in the absence of air. The coke is then combined with iron ore and limestone in a blast furnace. The resulting carbon monoxide and heat reduce the ore to produce molten pig iron, essential to steel production.

Cement is made by heating a mixture of limestone, clay, sand and other minerals in a kiln until they fuse. One innovative clean coal technology uses the waste products from a cement kiln to reduce air pollutants. When the minerals in a cement kiln are heated, they release vapours containing sodium and potassium salts. These vapours later condense as a fine dust. Usually the dust should be disposed of, but the clean technology can use it to absorb sulphur from the kiln's exhaust gases. Sulphur-laden kiln gases are bubbled through a slurry made of the dust and water. Additional process steps recover solid calcium products that can be re-used in the kiln. The result is a cement kiln that emits virtually no waste products other than clean water.

j) *Long-term Options: MHD and DCCD*

In magnetohydrodynamics (MHD), a high-temperature combustion gas stream, seeded to increase electrical conductivity, is passed through a strong magnetic field to generate electricity. Either natural gas or coal-derived gases can be used, but coal is a more problematic fuel because of its higher level of impurities. While the fundamental scientific principles have been demonstrated on a small scale for short periods, the remaining technical and engineering requirements for high-temperature materials, heat and seed regeneration and power extraction are extensive. MHD is of interest because of its potential use in a topping cycle for very high thermal conversion efficiency (more than 50 per cent) and low pollutant emissions. However, because of the lengthy development lead times and technical uncertainties, MHD is unlikely to be deployed within the time- frame of this assessment. Its relative technical advantage will also be reduced to the extent that the expected developments in competitor technologies such as IGCC and IGFC are achieved.

Direct coal-fired combustion devices (DCCD) include direct coal-fired diesel engines and gas turbines. They have been proved technically feasible for feeds of either coal/liquid mixtures or beneficiated dry coals. Protection of turbine blades against erosion and corrosion is the essential development target, and advanced coal cleaning can make a significant contribution in this regard. Diesel design must allow for a longer combustion residence time for each engine power stroke because coal does not ignite as readily as diesel oil. Diesel engines may also be fuelled with the liquid products of coal liquefaction or mild coal gasification. Successful commercialisation of DCCDs would make a significant contribution towards diversifying coal use into the industrial sector and, possibly, into transportation.

k) *Post-Combustion Carbon Dioxide Abatement*

Among the fossil fuels, the coal category has the widest variations in $CO_2$ emission factors. Under the heading of "coal" fall several types or grades of coal, ranging from anthracite, to bituminous coal, and to brown coal or lignite, with heating values ranging from more than 32 GJ/kg to less than 10 GJ/kg. Depending upon the type of coal being combusted, rates of $CO_2$ emissions can vary. Average values in the IEA region are 25 kgC/GJ for bituminous coal to 30 kgC/GJ for brown coal with a weighted value of 26 kgC/GJ (against 13.8 kgC/GJ for natural gas).

For carbon dioxide removal, natural photosynthesis by plants and aquatic vegetation or, in the very long term, artificial photosynthesis may be viable technologies for absorbing carbon dioxide from the atmosphere. In view of the large areas involved, massive afforestation may not be an economically feasible solution for capturing the large amounts of $CO_2$ emitted. Offsetting the emissions of a single 500 MWe coal-fired power plant operating at 35 per cent efficiency would require planting a high-growth forest of about 2 000 to 2 500 square kilometres. Alternatively, $CO_2$ could be recovered directly from the emissions of large point sources, such as power plants, and sequestered.

## Technology Prospects and Markets

### *Market Trends*

The preceding analysis evaluated the technical and economic potential of key candidate clean coal technologies as well as their R&D requirements. The factors should now be examined that influence market penetration and deployment of promising options and the strategic options which governments could adopt to facilitate the realisation of energy policy objectives.

The market penetration of new coal technologies depends not only on market conditions and structures, on the technology's cost and performance characteristics and energy price levels, but also on political aspects and public policy. A few of the likely market outcomes are easy to project, though most are difficult, and some evade all but the boldest speculation. Capital investment for environmentally acceptable coal-burning equipment is generally higher than for less complex fuels such as natural gas and oil. Economic competitiveness depends on total cost; the additional capital cost has to be compensated for by savings in the fuel cost. A number of secondary factors affect the result, such as interest rates, amortisation times or capacity utilisation. The economic framework is set partly by international economic conditions and partly by national government decisions. The price level of competing fuels, particularly the oil price, is an important element.

The largest market for new coal technologies will be the power sector. At present, annual world electricity generation has exceeded the 12 000 TWh level, with solid fuels contributing some 40 per cent. The total installed capacity in coal-fired plants is of the order of one million MWe and growing. The fossil-fuelled generating capacity is expanding at about 50 000 MWe per annum. Assuming a 30-year lifetime for existing units, the electricity industry needs to replace 50 000 MWe of thermal power plants per year. The potential market for new and improved coal-burning technologies is therefore around 100 000 MWe per year.

The main competitor for new coal-fired equipment is the natural gas-fired combined cycle plant, at present mostly in countries with indigenous resources. The capital investment for natural gas-fired combined cycle plants is roughly one half of that for a standard pulverised coal-fired plant with flue gas cleaning equipment. Coal is a competitive fuel in electricity generation even with oil prices in the region of US$ 15 to US$ 18 per barrel. The estimated capital costs of new coal-burning technologies are comparable to, or slightly higher than, conventional technology and are compensated for by fuel savings.

In the electricity sector the largest near-term market changes will be driven by more stringent environmental regulations. These have already accelerated the market entry of emission control equipment for coal-fired power plants. Flue gas desulphurisation has reached commercial status in many industrialised countries and, along with other $SO_x$/$NO_x$ control technologies, is likely to become mandatory in most of the IEA region. It is also expected that the developing nations and countries in transition towards market economies will follow a similar path, though with significant time lags.

In many countries, new in-furnace removal of $SO_x$ and reduction of $NO_x$ may meet emission standards without post-combustion controls and, being more economical, this technology will penetrate the market without further support. This seems to be the case for atmospheric fluidised bed combustion in smaller to medium-size units of up to 250 MWe. Reduction of $NO_x$ in the flue gas is not as widely practised as $SO_x$ control but should follow the same general trend. With cleaner burning coal and flue gas treatment, the conventional coal-steam generating plants have become environmentally acceptable. Coal-based combined cycles are also likely to enter the market in the next decade. Given positive operating experience, both pressurised fluidised bed combustion and integrated coal gasification could become viable alternatives. Despite uncertainties affecting their technical and economic promise, the demonstration process for these technologies has been very extensive.

Due to the comparatively low thermal efficiency of coal-conversion processes and the high capital investment, substitute energy carriers from coal conversion need high product prices to be a viable market proposition on purely economic grounds. The investment cost for a coal upgrading plant producing substitute oil is in a range higher than for a comparable crude oil refinery. Under the most favourable local conditions with cheap coal, an oil price in the order of US$ 20 to US$ 30 per barrel may suffice, but many experts regard prices in excess of US$ 40 as the threshold with advanced technologies in their current state of development and cost. The quantification of particular price assumptions depends strongly on the type of product and on the economic and political environment. Project designs that integrate electricity production, co-generated thermal energy service and co-produced product streams (e.g. SNG and methanol) may be the first to overcome the cost barrier. Two additional barriers, noted below, may affect the commercialisation time-frame of coal conversion technologies.

- The high specific $CO_2$ emission in coal conversion could possibly serve as a barrier to further development.
- In the absence of technical breakthroughs in coal liquefaction technologies, upgrading of heavy oils, bitumen and the richer oil shales is likely to be less expensive and to precede coal utilisation.

In comparing the competitive advantage of different coal upgrading technologies, the market penetration of coal gasification appears more likely than does coal hydrogenation. First, there already exist considerable capacities and operating experience; and secondly, there are parallel efforts and joint interests involved in utilising coal gas for other applications such as combined cycle power plants. Coal hydrogenation technology also requires further R&D to reach the commercial threshold.

In newly industrialising countries, economic development and the expansion of energy supply are the priority goals. The availability of domestic energy resources, together with capital requirements and imported equipment, will be major factors influencing the choice of technologies. To the extent that environmentally improved coal utilisation technology is more expensive than the technologies currently being used (but cost-effective), there is a perceived conflict between environmental goals and economic development and energy supply expansion objectives. This is the major barrier to the market deployment of new technologies. On the other hand, the use of best available technologies, which are improved versions of technologies currently in use, could be adopted as more affordable approaches in developing countries and in economies in transition. Other important barriers are created by the absence of the information, infrastructure and training which are necessary to technology transfer and the adoption of new and/or improved technologies.

### *Key Players*

The key non-government players influencing technology innovation in coal use sectors are in general large, well established, and often international, companies. The main players are the coal industry, the engineering and equipment supply industries, the electric power utilities, the non-power industrial users of coal, such as the steel and chemicals industries, and the financing organisations. In the case of developing countries, national and international aid and development agencies are also significant players.

The coal mining industry is becoming an increasingly active player in the refining and marketing of the product and, as a result, has become more actively engaged with clean and efficient coal-use technologies. A trend towards vertical integration is being seen, partly as a result of coal-user investment in coal mining. This trend has a parallel in the downstream activities of the oil industry. Such increased downstream involvement in coal as an energy service rather than a commodity may be essential for the long-term viability of the coal supply industry.

The engineering and power equipment supply industry, and especially the power plant manufacturers, continuously improve their products, bringing in both new technologies and upgraded versions of existing technologies. For example, the equipment supply industry has played the major role in developing the fluidised bed and IGCC technology and the FGD, also Selective Catalytic Reduction (SCR) equipment. It is now pushing back the technical limits for new gas turbines and is engaged in demonstrating advanced coal gasification. An important characteristic of the equipment supply industry is that it is becoming more and more concentrated within companies of an increasingly global character which could help speed up the deployment of new technologies.

In a conventional regulatory context, the electric utilities, the largest users of coal, tend to buy the technology which will enable them to meet projected future energy needs at minimum cost and with minimum risk. Surveys conducted by the Coal Industry Advisory Board to the IEA suggest that a major barrier to the adoption of new coal-fired technologies is the unwillingness of electric utilities to adopt any technology which has not been satisfactorily and comprehensively demonstrated on a commercial scale. This inevitably leads to a time lag between the point at which a process is ready for use and its widespread adoption. Risk avoidance is of particular importance for industries in which the major investments will have life-times of more than 30 years and for which regulatory regimes often fail to reward successful innovation. Within the more competitive market contexts which some national regulatory regimes are beginning to impose on the electric utilities, the utilities are more likely to make only those risk-weighted technology choices which promise the highest return on investment. In some national environments this has led utilities to switch from coal to natural gas. But in others it has led to more innovative choices in coal technology and has encouraged new forms of inter-utility co-operation. Possible changes in utility ownership may also support this trend. For example, chemical companies involved in coal gasification may participate more directly in the electricity supply industry if favourable market environments exist. Such owners may also be more likely to engage in integrated co-production of various product streams. The oil and natural gas industries would become more active players, either competing with coal interests or collaborating with them, if coal-derived gas and liquids entered the market.

The role of financing institutions is of particular importance in such a capital-intensive industry. Among other things, the financing institutions have a major influence on technology choice and, in particular, on the level of innovation in such choices. As for the utilities, this influence will tend to be conservative rather than innovative, to the extent that successful implementation of new technologies cannot be rewarded by higher returns. Environmental regulators and the general public also play a major role in defining the direction of technological progress. The siting and licensing of coal facilities very often encounter problems with public acceptability. This is partly a legacy of coal's past and partly a disenchantment with large-scale technologies involving any fuel type. It is therefore essential that technology development programmes incorporate strong elements of dialogue and information-sharing with the concerned parties.

### *Market Barriers*

If coal is to remain acceptable as a major energy source, it must be produced, transported and used in ways that fully protect the environment. At the same time, the cost of complying with environmental and health requirements must not increase the overall cost of using coal to the point that coal becomes uncompetitive in the market place.

Where available and demonstrated technologies are concerned, the option offering the largest technical and economic potential for the power sector is best-practice pulverised coal-fired combustion, with advanced emissions controls, atmospheric fluidised bed combustion and, where it is economical, combined heat and power. Atmospheric fluidised bed combustion and combined heat and power can contribute towards the diversification goal, the former through domestic and commercial heating, and the latter through clean industrial coal combustion. The potential of these technologies can be realised through both the construction of new plants and the retrofitting and repowering of existing power stations.

Available and demonstrated coal technologies are those which are most likely to contribute towards meeting the needs of newly industrialising countries and countries in transition towards a market economy. Technologies especially suitable for low-rank coal combustion will be of particular relevance to many of these countries. Opportunities for establishing integrated coal-using facilities, including combined heat and power, may sometimes be greater in industrialised than in developing countries because of the greater infrastructure flexibility in the former. Many of these technologies are commercial in IEA countries. Concerted bilateral and multilateral action to promote technology transfer and co-operation would greatly assist market deployment of these technologies in the rest of the world, with results of environmental benefit to the IEA region.

A number of next-generation coal power technologies in demonstration show great technical and economic potential. The power-generation options which are closest to commercial availability are pressurised fluidised bed combustion and the integrated coal gasification combined cycle. Considerable further demonstration is required to reduce costs and to ensure reliability before these technologies will become commercially available. Integrated gasification fuel cells present great potential in the longer term, though the path to commercialisation of this technology is less sure than for the other two.

In addition to ensuring appropriate environmental regulatory frameworks, providing support for demonstration and R&D programmes could significantly assist the market introduction or further development of these technologies. Obviously, regulation or legislation favouring one particularly advanced technology should be avoided. Developing countries' needs for these more advanced technologies will not be as great as for the available technologies, but selective participation by developing countries in R&D and demonstration programmes would facilitate subsequent technology transfer.

From a long-term perspective, the diversification goal could be served through further integration of the production of power, chemicals and other products. If the potential for fully integrated power/ chemicals/heat production, based on coal gasification, is realised as a viable option, it could make a major contribution towards simultaneously meeting both of the leading goals for this technology area.

Because of the relevance of the global climate change issue, government involvement in R&D programmes is called for, to ensure timely preparation of technology response strategies. From a policy perspective, the most significant long-term option is $CO_2$ removal and disposal. It is important to establish authoritatively whether this response is required and whether it is technically, economically and environmentally feasible, then to proceed with the R&D necessary for the identification and definition of the most promising options.

## Technology Policy Issues

### *Role of Governments*

As in other energy technology areas, a government's overall role is to supplement and encourage technology innovation in the market, in alignment with the government's policy objectives. The desired direction and level of technology innovation must be established, as well as the extent to which the market is achieving these and the most appropriate mode and level of government intervention to achieve its objectives. Thus the analysis should take into account the nature of the market and its players, also the relative effectiveness of direct and indirect forms of government action.

The markets influencing coal utilisation technology have a long history. They are dynamic markets, to a large extent international, and operated by large-scale players, so that the appropriate role for government will be limited and largely indirect. However, the level of recent market activity that will affect future technology options can be judged to be insufficient from the perspective of energy and environmental policy objectives. For example, the commercial demonstration process has been slow for the next generation of electric power technologies such as PFBC and IGCC. The result is a delayed realisation of the market benefits of new technologies, and also reduced incentives to develop the more advanced longer-term technologies. Moreover, given the significance of coal's role in energy security and environmental considerations, particularly in the global climate change context, government has a particular responsibility in relation to R&D for the long-term technology progress that is beyond the normal planning horizons of the private sector and individual companies. This applies to technology progress that is required to meet this chapter's priority goals.

In the critically important electricity sector, probably the most significant ways in which governments can contribute to technology innovation are to create more competitive market conditions and establishing stable and transparent environmental regulatory regimes. Increased market competition will encourage more innovative technology decision-making by utilities, attract more readily available bank finance for investments and, probably, lead to more diversified patterns of utility ownership. This will result in the closure of inefficient and uneconomic plants, encourage new and improved technologies with improved efficiency and lower capital investment requirements.

Government support, financial and otherwise, for the demonstration of key coal technologies for power generation can be beneficial, particularly to the extent that early market penetration may have to overcome non-commercial barriers. Early large-scale demonstration of PFBC and IGCC, for instance, would have strategic significance for other clean coal technologies and would free government R&D resources for longer-term breakthroughs that may follow. Governments also have an important role in monitoring, and supplementing, the R&D effort with indirect policy measures. R&D issues which require priority attention were identified earlier. They span the full range of coal use technology areas: improved environmental performance in relation to both conventional and other pollutants, with particular emphasis on technologies which reduce or remove carbon dioxide and other greenhouse gases; enhanced performance of coal-use technologies in sectors other than electricity generation; and, in all areas, reduction of technology costs so as to facilitate market deployment.

Given the widespread perception of coal as a "dirty" fuel, IEA governments can also play an important leadership role in areas such as outreach programmes to provide the public with accurate information about the environmental performance of new and improved coal-use technologies. IEA governments can play an equally important role in facilitating technology transfer of appropriate technologies to transitional economies and newly industrialising countries.

### *Role of International Co-operation*

Markets for coal utilisation technology are on an international scale and characterised by considerable bilateral and multilateral commercial co-operation. While this activity does involve governments, the main agents of international technology transfer are industrial entities. This being the case, international co-operation is based more on market opportunities and international work-sharing between companies than on a framework of international legal agreements.

There are important areas where governments can foster beneficial international co-operation and thereby help reduce the level of resource allocation required from individual budgets. Most of the outstanding technical issues relating to the technologies being assessed in this chapter are potential areas for beneficial co-operation. There are more opportunities for international co-operation at the R&D stage than at later stages of technology development because of the reduced level of commercial sensitivity. This is common to all energy technologies. IEA Member countries collaborate in the IEA Greenhouse Gas R&D Programme to conduct technical and economic evaluations of the various aspects of carbon dioxide removal, disposal and fixation, as a basis for identifying future R&D priorities in the area. The IEA has facilitated numerous collaborative efforts focused on reducing air-borne emissions. Solid waste treatment and disposal is of growing importance and presents a further opportunity for international R&D co-operation. Longer-term work on total waste minimisation could also be a promising area for activity. Problems arise in all countries with ash from the various combustors and with solid and liquid wastes from de-$SO_x$ and de-$NO_x$ treatment of flue gas. This is a problem requiring environmentally acceptable disposal or re-use, but addressing it today has limited commercial appeal.

IEA Coal Research, which functions within the framework of an IEA Implementing Agreement, is perhaps the most extensive international collaborative activity existing for the exchange of technical, economic and environmental information about the coal industry and related industries. Review and assessment reports are prepared and specialised data bases, which are unique in their detail and breadth of coverage, are created and maintained. The IEA Coal Research Centre was established in 1975 and is supported by the governments of twelve IEA Member countries, by the European Commission, and by one non-IEA Member country. The participation of non-IEA major coal-using and producing countries is encouraged.

International co-operation can play a valuable role, even in activities which are close to the market and subject to strong market interests. Because of the scale of the resources required and the risk involved in the demonstration phase, international government co-operation can accelerate developments by reducing the exposure of individual participants. One example of such a mutually fruitful activity was the IEA-sponsored collaborative demonstration project, during the 1980s, on PFBC technology. Another IEA project has acted as an information-sharing mechanism for technology suppliers and R&D organisations involved in demonstrating the AFBC technology. Co-operation can be beneficial on specific technical bottlenecks impeding the commercialisation of a newly developed technology. One such case is an IEA collaborative project to run a test facility and programme on filters to clean hot gas streams in PFBC and IGCC. Successful hot gas filtering would constitute a breakthrough in the demonstration of high-efficiency systems, and coal technology suppliers share an interest in its early demonstration. The IEA collaboration involves major coal technology suppliers, engineers and users.

In principle, there is significantly greater technical and economic potential for improving the efficiency, economics and environmental acceptability of coal use than for diversifying the use of coal beyond the power sector.

Analysis in this chapter shows that, in some cases, technology options contribute simultaneously to the achievement of both of the stated goals. Coal gasification is a course that offers promising long-term strategic potential for the clean use of coal. Gasification-based technologies provide scope for addressing multiple objectives in several time-frames. The suggested approach is the introduction of IGCC and related technologies, followed by coal gas-fired fuel cells. Coal gas-based integrated production of two or more products (such as electricity, chemicals, transport fuels and process heat) opens further opportunities for international co-operation and major gains in the overall efficiency of coal utilisation processes.

The field of environmental protection is clearly of broad interest, since pollution is a trans-boundary problem. Broader agreement on international standards for environmental emissions from electric generating plants would speed the diffusion of innovative technologies by reducing barriers that create otherwise unnecessary technology product differentiation. So R&D efforts on the mitigation and management of emissions call for direct governmental support. Technology progress and capital stock turnover lead times are very long. Near-term action would therefore appear to be warranted to keep future options open, particularly on a global collaborative basis.

To establish large-scale upgrading of coal as an option, international co-operation will be necessary, not only in demonstration of commercial-scale conversion technology, but also in utilisation of the new energy carriers such as methanol, or other alcohol fuels. The development of appropriate end-use technologies, the creation of the infrastructure and the introduction of suitable standards could be facilitated by widespread international programme co-ordination and collaboration. Commercial interests can be expected to fill market niches for new fuels, but a broader strategy for large-scale substitution seems beyond the scope of unconcerted corporate action. IEA-sponsored international co-operation could contribute usefully in these areas as well.

Non-Member countries have a special interest in coal as it is frequently a domestic energy resource and requires less technically demanding technology. Currently, coal is often the cheapest fuel in these countries, and it is easy to transport and store. International co-operation can be particularly productive in facilitating technology transfer of best-practice technologies to developing countries and countries in transition towards a market economy. Obsolete coal technologies in electricity generation, industrial energy production and district heating in a number of newly industrialising nations impose substantial environmental burdens, not only locally but also regionally and, in the case of greenhouse gas emissions, globally. The existence of such highly polluting technologies also contributes to negative public perceptions of the status of modern coal utilisation technology. Rapid deployment of best-practice technology, particularly in plants using low-rank coals, could lead to major reductions in current levels of emission of particulates and sulphur and nitrogen oxides. Repowering and retrofitting of older electric generating plants with modern high-efficiency technology can substantially increase efficiency and reduce the level of greenhouse gas emissions per unit of energy produced. Technology transfer and technical assistance can ensure access to best available practice on a world scale for the upgrading of current systems and the selection of future systems.

Industrialised countries should encourage these countries to participate in coal R&D related to their problems and in the training and exchange of technical personnel. Financing is a severe constraint for such technology-importing countries. The adoption of best-practice technology may carry additional costs and, in general, have a low priority for scarce capital. In contrast, encouragement to adopt best available technology entailing competitive costs may help to disseminate affordable techniques to these countries.

In order to enable early introduction of clean coal technologies, concerted action involving major international finance institutions may be required. In the countries that import technology and in those that export it, industry should play a substantial role, so that commercial interests will ensure effective construction and operation. Transfer of know-how at an early stage is advantageous, and commercial joint ventures have proved successful vehicles for this purpose.

### Approach

With a view to meeting the technology priority goals identified in this chapter, and to enabling IEA Member countries to benefit in the future from availability of enormous coal reserves, they may wish to consider contributing to and co-operating in a technology strategy and collaborative R&D programme aimed at the measures listed below.

- Supporting progress in environmentally clean coal technologies based upon advanced coal beneficiation, coal-liquid mixtures, new and improved combustion processes and atmospheric emissions control.

- Speeding up the demonstration and testing of next-generation technologies, particularly ultra super-critical power plants, integrated coal-gasification combined cycle, pressurised fluidised-bed combustion and new industrial clean coal technology, in order to ensure that coal will continue to compete with other fuels in the marketplace, and to maintain and increase the diversity of sources and technologies for energy and power production.

- Setting up R&D projects and defining means and technologies for the long term to reduce carbon dioxide and other greenhouse gas and air emissions associated with the use of coal and its entire fuel cycle (in other chapters this is discussed in the context of other fossil fuels where improved energy efficiency remains an important goal).

- Achieving transparency and stability of environmental standards and regulations which enable the coal industry sufficient flexibility in the development of technology options for addressing changing environmental concerns.

- Favouring inter-industry and inter-utility technology collaboration to reduce uncertainty over the performance characteristics and to reduce cost and improve commercial operation and prospects of demonstrated and next-generation clean coal technology and power systems.

- Promoting special long-term technology programmes for coal gasification and conversion into liquid hydrocarbon fuels.

- Supporting information exchange and assisting with initiatives for the adoption of best-practice coal technology in the developing countries and countries in transition towards a market economy to increase efficiency and support environmental improvements.

# Chapter 3

## OIL AND NATURAL GAS PRODUCTION

### Goals and Rationale

Oil is of primary importance in energy supply and economic development in IEA countries, particularly in transport, where demand has proved extremely resilient, despite rapid increases in petroleum prices since 1974. Projections to the year 2010 in the IEA *World Energy Outlook* (1996 edition) show that world oil demand is expected to grow from around 70 million barrels per day (mbd) in 1995 to between 92 mbd and 97 mbd in 2010 in the two cases studied, with demand in non-OECD nations growing much more rapidly than demand in the OECD countries. The OECD nations will consume around one half of total world oil consumption in 2010, down from almost 60 per cent today. In the industrialising countries, strong economic growth, a dramatic population shift to urban centres, and the rapidly increasing demand for transportation all contribute significantly to the projected growth in oil demand. In the OECD, transportation energy demand is expected to account for virtually all the increase in oil demand over the outlook period. Oil demand is expected to grow somewhat faster in the future than over the past two decades, primarily because of the continuing growth in OECD transport demand, the lack of remaining substitution possibilities in other sectors and fast economic growth in the rest of the world.

World demand for natural gas is projected to increase rapidly to 2010, this being the fastest growing fossil fuel, with an average annual growth rate of between 1.6 per cent and 2.9 per cent over the outlook period. In absolute terms, world gas consumption will rise from just over 1 700 Mtoe in 1993 to as much as 2 795 Mtoe by 2010 and increase its fuel share in total primary energy demand from 22 per cent to as much as 24 per cent over the same period. This could amount to over 50 per cent growth over the period 1993 to 2010, although in a second case that emphasises energy efficiency the share of gas remains fairly constant.

In the OECD, the share of gas in the primary energy mix in one of the cases studied is projected to rise from its 1993 share of under 21 per cent to nearly 25 per cent in 2010. Close to 60 per cent of the increase in annual gas demand in the OECD is accounted for by the power generation sector. In the recent past, technological improvements in the design, efficiency and operation of combined cycle gas turbines have moved the economics of power generation in favour of natural gas.

From an energy security perspective, the most significant advances will come in exploration, drilling and production technologies, facilitating the expansion of indigenous IEA oil and gas resources. Most of these resources are more costly to produce than previously tapped resources and are in environmentally sensitive areas. The introduction of heavier or increasingly sour crudes into the market will also require substantial technology adjustment and innovation in oil refining. Leading technology priority goals for the oil and natural gas production area are:

- increased access to economically exploitable oil and natural gas reserves, and
- lowering the environmental impacts and risks involved in hydrocarbon production processes.

A continuing emphasis on environmental protection should be an integral part of technology advances to enhance the international oil and natural gas supply. With increased consumption of oil comes the possibility of increased pollution from oil exploration and production, transport, refining, distribution and end-use systems. Other sources of environmental impact are associated with the more complex refining processes required for heavy oil, and the potential damage to marine environments from accidental oil spills, waste handling and disposal from offshore platforms and their sub-sea pipelines, also from loading terminals and shipping. With natural gas, on the other hand, safety problems and leakage during extraction and transport could partially offset its comparative environmental advantage. Methane ($CH_4$), which is the main constituent of natural gas, is a greenhouse gas and a more efficient absorber of infrared radiation than is $CO_2$, although its remains in the atmosphere for a much shorter time.

Energy policy implications are generally seen to be more significant for oil production than for natural gas. Natural gas is an increasingly important energy source that is often a co-product of oil production. However, in some countries, including the United States and Russia a large proportion of gas production results from gas production that is not related to oil production. From a technological perspective, the issues regarding natural gas production are very similar to those affecting oil. The priority technological needs associated with natural gas supply relate to gas transport and are addressed in Chapter 4, but other upstream natural gas supply technological challenges are also important.

Where oil production is concerned, the need for government to play a significant role in technology progress may be less acute than in other energy areas. The oil industry has established R&D organisations both within the international operating companies and in the equipment manufacturing companies which supply them. Moreover, the associated technology is sufficiently mature, and innovation is likely to be incremental rather than revolutionary. Still, the shared energy security concern among IEA countries' governments is to manage and reduce their vulnerability to disruptions in the oil market and to chart a course toward increased and diversified worldwide sources of oil; this includes support for new oil and natural gas production technology.

## Technology Description and Analysis

Oil and natural gas technologies have been examined carefully and extensively in a 1995 report from the United States' National Petroleum Council (NPC), *Research Development and Demonstration Needs of the Oil and Gas Industry*. The study was undertaken at the request of the United States Energy Secretary to assess RD&D needs of the nation's oil and gas industry. Its conclusions and recommendations, however, are broadly applicable worldwide and seek to establish priorities for RD&D needs. This step goes beyond the objectives of this IEA study but represents an industry viewpoint. Since the NPC study represents a considerable milestone in identifying and prioritising industry RD&D needs to the year 2010, its key findings are summarised below.

The study clearly identifies the importance of technology to the future of the oil and natural gas industry and to meeting the challenges of "effectively and efficiently finding, producing and processing new reserves of oil and gas, and converting these reserves into products while complying with regulations at acceptable costs".

"In our vision of the future," the study notes, "the competitive edge of the industry will increasingly depend on the ability to manage and apply technology effectively and rapidly. This will include leadership in technology for environmentally sound operations and environmentally acceptable hydrocarbon fuels".

The Gas Research Institute in the United States, it is observed (cited in the NPC study pp.14-15), has estimated that advanced technology could increase United States' domestic gas supplies in the year 2010 by about one-third over current levels, and nearly double supplies compared to those projected, based on existing technology.

The NPC's survey was used to identify desired technology advances, their impact, and their likelihood of commercial availability both in the short term (by 1999) and the long term (between 1999 and 2010). Responses received from some 89 companies identified some 250 technologies in eleven technology areas: Exploration; Development; Drilling and Completion; Production; Deepwater Offshore; Arctic Region Activities; Oil Processing and Refining; Gas Processing; Gas Gathering; Gas Storage; and Environment Regulation. A total of 105 long-term technologies (to 2010) were identified that could have moderate to high impacts. Of these, eight, could have a high impact. Important long-term RD&D priorities were identified in five of the eleven technology areas. Findings for high priority technologies are summarised in Figure 3.1. A full listing of the identified technologies with moderate to high potential impacts is presented in the Appendix to this chapter.

The NPC suggests that a "new paradigm" for oil and gas RD&D is evolving because "intense competition that contributes to low oil and gas prices, and the need to reallocate scarce funds for large investments related to environmental compliance, have forced the industry to re-evaluate every aspects of its business, including their RD&D investments." In general, the study finds that "This re-evaluation brought better efficiency and cost-effectiveness to private sector RD&D activities. In many companies, in-house programs have moved toward projects that are likely to provide a competitive advantage and a nearer term payout." Such a new paradigm for oil and gas RD&D may also suggest significant opportunities for greater international collaboration among IEA Member countries and the oil and natural gas industry.

The new paradigm is shown in Figure 3.2 and would focus on increasingly user-driven collaborative RD&D (including government-industry collaboration) to compensate for smaller in-house industry programmes.

*Figure 3.1*

**High Priority Technologies from the NPC's 1995 Survey of Research and Development Needs***

| ■ SHORT-TERM | | | | | | ■ LONG-TERM | | |
|---|---|---|---|---|---|---|---|---|
| **Q1** | | **Exploration** | **Q5** | | **Deep Water Offshore** (contd) | **Q1** | | **Exploration** |
| 1-3 | (51) | High-resolution seismic depth imaging | 5-12 | (11) | Workover | 1-3 | (27) | High-resolution seismic depth imaging |
| 1-14 | (46) | Advanced seismic acquisition | 5-14 | (11) | Hydrate prevention | **Q2** | | **Development** |
| **Q2** | | **Development** | 5-15 | (11) | Multi-phase pumps | 2-15 | (22) | Through casing logging |
| 2-2 | (45) | Computer-based 3D geological modelling | **Q6** | | **Arctic Region Activities** | **Q3** | | **Drilling and Completion** |
| 2-3 | (43) | Development-scale seismic applications | 6-3 | (7) | Development | 3-6 | (28) | Well productivity |
| 2-15 | (50) | Through casing logging | 6-4 | (10) | Drilling | **Q4** | | **Production** |
| 2-20 | (46) | Permeability logging techniques | **Q7** | | **Oil Processing and Refining** | 4-11 | (21) | Stimulation techniques |
| **Q3** | | **Drilling and Completion** | 7-1 | (22) | Catalysts with improved selectivities yields, lifetimes | 4-13 | (18) | Recompletion techniques |
| 3-3 | (49) | Advanced fracture techniques | 7-3 | (19) | Plant and process reliability | 4-25 | (19) | Near well bore stimulation |
| 3-6 | (47) | Well productivity | 7-16 | (21) | Energy efficiency of processes | 4-27 | (28) | Advanced recovery of natural gas |
| **Q4** | | **Production** | 7-17 | (19) | Energy efficiency of equipment | **Q7** | | **Oil Processing and Refining** |
| 4-11 | (53) | Stimulation techniques | 7-19 | (14) | Separations technologies | 7-1 | (14) | Catalysts with improved selectivites, yields, lifetimes |
| 4-25 | (49) | Near well bore stimulation | 7-21 | (10) | New approaches to refining heavy feeds | 7-16 | (15) | Energy efficiency of processes |
| 4-26 | (43) | New directional drilling | 7-27 | (10) | Performance characteristics of new hydrocarbon fuel compositions | 7-19 | (21) | Separations technologies |
| 4-27 | (39) | Advanced recovery of natural gas | 7-28 | (14) | Environmental characteristics of new hydrocarbon fuel compositions | 7-21 | (21) | New approaches to refining heavy feed |
| **Q5** | | **Deep Water Offshore** | **Q9** | | **Gas Gathering** | | | |
| 5-2 | (20) | Extended reach drilling or production | 9-1 | (30) | Compression | | | |
| 5-5 | (12) | Flowlines | **Q10** | | **Gas Storage** | | | |
| 5-6 | (13) | Flow metering | 10-3 | (11) | Reservoir management | | | |
| 5-7 | (15) | Subsea equipment | 10-5 | (9) | Base gas minimisation techniques | | | |
| 5-9 | (14) | Risers | **Q11** | | **Environmental and Regulatory** | | | |
| 5-11 | (20) | Drilling | 11-14 | (41) | Provide scientific basis for risk-based regulation | | | |

* Numbers in parentheses indicate number of responses.

Source: NPC, *Research Development and Demonstration Needs of the Oil and Gas Industry, Volume I: Summary and Discussion* (1995) p.5.

*Figure 3.2*
**Paradigms for Meeting RD&D Needs**

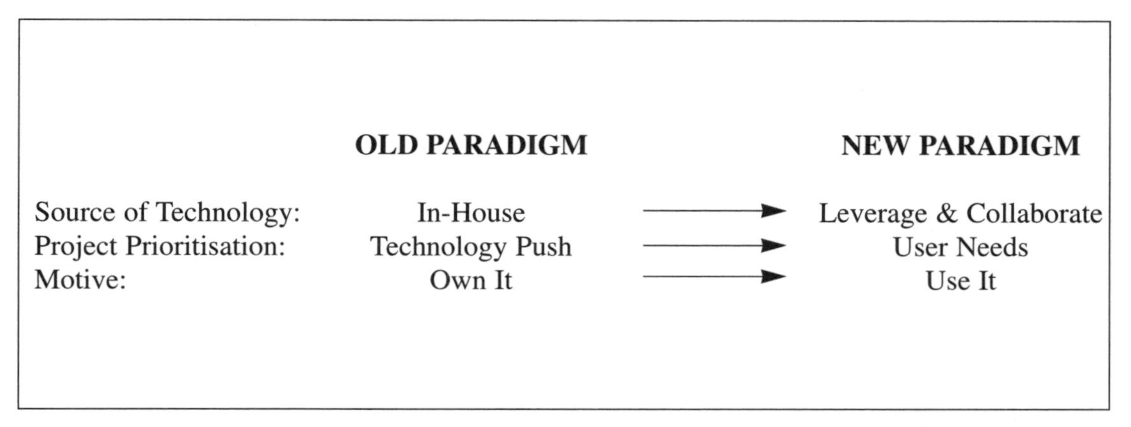


Source: NPC, *Research Development and Demonstration Needs of the Oil and Gas Industry, Volume I: Summary and Discussion* (1995) p.7.

### *Description of Significant Technologies*

Key technology areas in this IEA study are identified under the following headings: exploration; reservoir evaluation and engineering; drilling and well completion; offshore field development; field operations; transport systems; technology for Arctic regions; extra heavy oils, natural bitumens and shale oils. The reasons for selecting these specific technology areas are based on an assessment of the contribution of each to policy goals for oil and gas production, as summarised in Table 3.1.

a) *Exploration*

Exploration for hydrocarbons involves several technologies and scientific disciplines, especially the earth sciences of geophysics, geology, and geochemistry. Information technology plays a vital role in the manipulation and analysis of data, and in the design of reservoir and other databases. In the future, substantial finds of reserves of hydrocarbons will become less and less frequent in areas of the world that have been extensively explored. This may not necessarily be the case in other less explored areas of the world. Geological features trapping hydrocarbons are likely to be more subtle, and the volumes of hydrocarbons they contain smaller. As the scale of discoveries declines, the cost of exploitation will increase. Application of properly focused R&D in all aspects of exploration will help minimise the impact of this trend. Improved surface exploration techniques are also likely to help in the search for conventional natural gas fields that were missed when the object of most exploration was oil. In addition, smart drills capable of taking measurements, new bit designs and new materials for deep drilling can make formerly uneconomic fields (i.e. those with gas below 3 000 metres deep) feasible to develop. Both improved surface exploration techniques and improved drilling could help produce natural gas at competitive prices.

*Table 3.1*
**Main Reasons for Selection of Oil and Natural Gas Production Technology**

| Technology | Reasons for Selection |
|---|---|
| **Exploration**<br>• Geophysics<br>• Geology<br>• Geochemistry<br>• Information technology | • The discovery rate is declining because the hydrocarbon traps remaining are complex, and the volume of hydrocarbons they contain will be generally smaller than in known reservoirs.<br>• R&D into new and improved techniques is necessary to mitigate this trend. |
| **Reservoir Evaluation**<br>• Fluid/rock interactions<br>• Structure assessment | • The goal is to preserve access to identified deposits while developing and testing technologies designed to overcome specific problems associated with reservoir structure and potential. |
| **Reservoir Engineering**<br>• Enhanced recovery techniques<br>• Artificial lift | • Much of the oil in a reservoir is left in place when a field is abandoned.<br>• Advanced secondary recovery and enhanced oil and gas recovery make valuable contributions to the security of supply. |
| **Drilling and Well Completion** | • Improvements in drilling technology will greatly reduce the cost of exploiting discoveries.<br>• Advances in a number of technology areas will be crucial for developing currently uneconomic reserves. |
| **Offshore Field Development** | • R&D will reduce capital and operating costs.<br>• Significant technology progress could radically change production installations. |
| **Field Operations** | • R&D is necessary to increase efficiency of operations.<br>• Cost increases are expected for activities related to safety or environmental impact mitigation. |
| **Transport Systems** | • Development of marginal fields and the production of severe fluids will require the development of multiphase flow technology and the application of advanced materials.<br>• Work on natural gas conversion to liquid products for transport should be advanced. |
| **Technology for the Arctic Regions** | • Large supplies will be obtainable from the Arctic regions with the development and deployment of appropriate technology. |
| **Extra Heavy Oils, Natural Bitumens and Shale Oils** | • There are very large reserves of these sources of hydrocarbons.<br>• Appropriate R&D will make them accessible and competitive. |

b) *Reservoir Evaluation*

The evaluation of reservoirs involves the use of all the earth sciences. At present, there is considerable activity in integrated computer modelling incorporating relevant scientific and technical principles. These facilities are expected to improve production forecasting and to enable optimal exploitation of reservoirs, from early appraisal through to maturity.

c) *Reservoir Engineering*

A significant portion (up to two-thirds) of the oil in a reservoir is left in place when the field is abandoned. New techniques for assessing the structure of reservoirs and for recovering more of the hydrocarbons will make valuable contributions to energy supplies. Advanced secondary recovery for oil and natural gas involves drilling and improved production methods based on sophisticated geological and geophysical interpretation. Enhanced oil recovery (EOR) includes the injection of chemicals, gases or heat to overcome physical barriers in the reservoir. Next-generation technologies are under development. Targets are reduced cost and increased assurance of the value and certainty of performance output.

Many EOR techniques, such as miscible, steam and chemical flooding and *in situ* combustion, are commercially available technologies. EOR may be one of the most productive areas for R&D investment. Presenting few problems of institutional adaptation, it directly addresses the most valuable form of energy (oil) and can help to place a cap on oil costs.

d) *Drilling and Well Completion*

Available technology now exists to drill high-inclination, high-curvature and horizontal wells at moderate depths. It is also possible to drill multiple well bores. Measurement, formation evaluation and production logging tools suitable for present conditions are available. Methods of automating the drilling process are being pursued. Between 5 per cent and 10 per cent of the cost of an exploration well is spent on conventional formation logging, requiring recovery of the drill string and running wireline tools in a separate operation. Measurement while drilling (MWD) tools exist, but a major drawback to this technology is the slow data transmission rate, which is inherent in the physics of the mud pulse systems, significantly limiting drilling rate, depth resolution, and the number of parameters that can be measured. The data transmission rate must be increased substantially before MWD can realise its full economic potential.

Environmentally benign water-based drilling muds are being introduced to replace oil-based muds, a source of pollution and environmental damage. Where oil-based muds are necessary, technology exists to remove or break down the oil-coated waste, (through biodegradation, distillation, solvent extraction and incineration). These techniques can also be applied to the oil-coated solids generated during the production process in the separation vessels.

e) *Offshore Field Development*

Fields are being developed, using a variety of available technologies, including fixed structures, jack-ups and floating production facilities. In the North Sea, sub-sea completions have recently been introduced, and some are installed in deeper water elsewhere. It is becoming possible to design smaller, more compact equipment and systems for separation of oil, gas, water and natural gas liquids. Examples are compact heat exchangers, membrane technology, cyclonic devices and enhanced mass transfer systems. Multiphase flow technology is an advanced technology under vigorous pursuit. Many different techniques and designs for multiphase pumping have been identified, and the most promising are under development, but, no single pump design appears ultimately superior under all conditions. While one or two pumps have reached the full-scale field trial stage, there are no truly operational and critical applications at present.

In addition to pumps, there are other areas of importance, such as hydrate formation in pipes, process/equipment designs that leave a smaller footprint, and improvements in platforms.

f) *Field Operations*

Field operations include production, as well as inspection, maintenance and repair activities. Most production platforms are manned, though there are some small unmanned gas (and oil) platforms. Helicopters are used for personnel movements. Sub-sea installations require divers, although remote operated vehicles (ROVs) are an available technology in extensive use for inspection and limited maintenance.

Pipelines are inspected by various means, including the use of intelligent pigs. Sub-sea valves are installed to separate pipeline sections for maintenance or emergency shut-down. Chemicals are widely used to inhibit corrosion and scale and prevent hydrate formation. Present well servicing techniques include through flow-line systems and dynamically positioned wireline/coiled tubing/workover vessels. Considerable R&D is necessary to develop next-generation technologies to increase efficiency of field operations. Inspection, maintenance and repair will be refined and automation progressively introduced. For activities with a safety or environmental impact, cost increases are expected, unless the risks can be mitigated by technical advances.

g) *Transport Systems*

Because of the corrosive nature of reservoir fluids, pipeline materials are a major concern. Carbon steel pipe material is by far the most cost-effective available technology. Methods to extend its use to more corrosive fluids, if applied correctly, can save significantly on the costs of a satellite field development. The scale of saving increases sharply with transfer distances.

The development of fields producing more corrosive fluids is leading to the use of materials near their performance limits and pipelines constructed of layered composite materials. Alternative corrosion-resistant materials such as duplex steel, clad steel or glass-fibre reinforced plastics are available technologies, and are increasingly used. Methods of protecting pipelines against the corrosive effects of the environment, particularly the sea, are well established.

Several projects to develop next-generation multiphase flow boosters are being pursued and are approaching the industrial stage. Rotodynamic, as well as different positive displacement types, are under testing, with support from oil companies in joint ventures. The offshore loading of stabilised oil is a well-known technology and has been in use for about two decades. Recent developments tend towards simpler offshore loading systems, without large above-water structures. It is expected that this trend will continue.

h) *Technology for the Arctic Regions*

Significant supplies of hydrocarbons are likely to be obtainable from Arctic regions. For onshore operations, a continuous evolution of next-generation technologies is required to reduce operating costs and compete effectively with low-cost producers. For offshore operations, some of the most important issues involve the interaction of ice with vessels and structures.

i) *Extra Heavy Oils, Natural Bitumens and Shale Oils*

Currently, over 90 per cent of world oil production is in the form of light and medium crude oils. However, these crude oils account for only 25 per cent of world petroleum resources. Heavy oils account for most of the remaining 10 per cent of world production, with nearly half (1.5 mbd) coming from Venezuela. The magnitude of extra heavy oil reserves is similar to that of heavy oil, but production is much lower because of higher development costs. The world also has vast resources of natural bitumen and oil shale which could have a significant impact on future petroleum supply. But these resources have seen only limited development because oil prices have not yet justified vigorous development. Most of the world's natural bitumen reserves are located in Canada, the United States and the Russian Federation. The reserves are mainly produced by *in situ* steam stimulation and displacement processes or by surface oil sand mining and extraction.

Several promising next-generation technologies for surface extraction of bitumen from oil sands are being investigated. The present hot water processes will eventually be replaced by cold water techniques requiring less energy. Other programmes are under way to develop solvent extraction processes, primarily for lower grade oil sand, especially in the United States. In addition, sand retorting processes offer several potential advantages, including reduced process water requirements and disposal, also production of a pipeline-quality product. Hydraulic mining methods for miscible deposits are also being investigated.

The available technology to exploit oil shale involves surface or underground mining, followed by various retorting procedures. Another method involves the extraction of kerogen from a mixture of ground shale and solvent by subjecting it to ionising radiation. The viscosity of extra heavy oils, natural bitumens and shale oils must be reduced to facilitate pipeline flow. Usually, gas condensate or refinery naphtha are blended with these oils to achieve pipeline specifications. But using high-value oil to transport a lower-value product is expensive. Several processes capable of partially upgrading viscous oils and bitumens to increase pipeline flow are in development.

With regard to natural gas, concern has been expressed that reserves might prove to be limited within a few decades. Drilling R&D and subsequent improvements will facilitate deeper gas recovery. In addition, it now appears that unconventional gas technology under development, or relatively new gas technology, may make available large reserves of gas at two to three times present wellhead prices. The four major forms of unconventional or less conventional gas sources are tight sands, Devonian shales, coal seams and geopressured brines. In the United States, natural gas production from tight gas sands is an area of growing commercial importance. Recovery from tight sand formations would be expedited by research in characterising the reservoirs and by gas stimulation through hydraulic facturing. Devonian shales are also a major resource for the long term. Many wells have been drilled into Devonian shales, but gas recovery is slow and uncertain. Further R&D is needed on gas flow in the shale and on stimulation techniques. Coal seams are another source of gas. Recovery of this resource could provide valuable energy. Coal-bed methane production is a successful production technique in the United States, Australia, Poland and China.

Advances in a large number of very specific technology areas will affect the economics of future natural gas supplies and their environmental impacts. Examples include:

- low- or sub-quality natural gas upgrading and the potential effect of membrane technology on upgrading sub-quality resources;
- cost and environmental impact reductions via slimhole drilling technology;
- the effectiveness of high rate-of-penetration drilling systems in improving the economic recoverability of poorer quality reservoirs;
- technology advances in well stimulation, formation damage, and air drilling;
- technologies to remove contaminants through processing of natural gas and so reducing atmospheric pollution.

### *Priority Assessment*

a) *Exploration*

High-impact technology advances are possible through geophysics and related scientific disciplines. Technology advances are sought to: increase resolution of geophysical data; improve the quantification of hydrocarbon charge and migration mechanisms; and facilitate rapid access to and manipulation of data. The ability to define geophysical configurations trapping petroleum in the substrate remains one of the primary goals in the industry. Research in theoretical and experimental geophysics is important to achieve this breakthrough. Continued research into seismic excitation sources is required. Borehole seismic and tomography are other areas of frontier research. Shear wave seismic has the potential to deliver greater resolution. Research in the last stages of processing, attribute analysis and image processing will provide a greater impetus in interpretation.

Developments in organic geochemistry have increased understanding of the way hydrocarbons are generated within source rocks. The volumes of oil and natural gas generated during a source rock's maturation history can be predicted, but this subject requires further refinement. The next major breakthrough will be in predicting volume of hydrocarbon generated versus volume entrapped. To achieve this goal, source rock kinetics and generation profiles require extensive investigation. The reasons for the variation in composition of hydrocarbons in reservoirs is not well understood. This is important since variations in composition have implications for the processing equipment required for production.

In well explored basins, the remaining hydrocarbons are often discovered through evaluation of data on wells already drilled. The ability to retrieve, process and manipulate large, complex databases is a key to economic success. Research is needed to develop and build computational tools for field exploration. Expert systems are already being manufactured, but development should be accelerated. Standards are necessary for data storage and format specification, in order to facilitate international co-operation in the exchange of data.

b) *Reservoir Evaluation*

Critical R&D are associated with logging and with fluid, rock and geological analysis. Where logging is concerned, the main thrust of R&D should be real-time data acquisition. MWD techniques are in use, but need substantial improvement. Coring of intervals, identified as hydrocarbon bearing by MWD techniques, would be an important advance to allow detailed analysis at an early stage. This is critical since new reservoirs are likely to be smaller and experience more marginal yields than previous discoveries. Given this constraint, high-efficiency data acquisition is essential.

A programme of research into innovative techniques for determination of strata porosity and saturation is required. Post-development monitoring is also crucial. Continuous formation and fluid monitoring from the cased well is required to better determine fluid distribution under secondary and tertiary recovery. Advances in production logging tool design would also help describe variations in fluid production, and capability for downhole separation into constituent fluids.

In fluid analysis, fluid description will improve reservoir management and recovery. Little is known about gas condensate composition and behaviour, especially at higher pressures and temperatures. Since accurate component analysis is a prerequisite for prediction, development of appropriate pressure-volume-temperature apparatus for validation of calculation methods of the anticipated extreme conditions is called for, as well as improvements in the handling of high-pressure samples under minimum drawdown.

Regarding rock analysis, and to better assess whether EOR processes will be successful, it is essential to understand residual fluids distribution in the reservoir. Major difficulties still exist with replicating *in situ* conditions of a reservoir in the laboratory, both on a micro- and macro-scale. Improvements in the characterisation and knowledge of distribution of residual oil are essential. Fundamental research is required in the field of wettability. Other methods, such as nuclear magnetic resonance or seismic techniques, to determine fluid distribution directly, should also be pursued. With respect to geological analysis, understanding geological processes on the macro-scale has improved dramatically over the last three decades; and a combination of geostatistical techniques with improvements in the geological framework of geophysics should lead to improved intrafield description. Research is required in the field of stratigraphic and lithological analysis, based on geophysical techniques. The use of tomography is also expected to be fertile. Statistical analysis of modern-day geological systems, and development of systems modelling of well and field data, result in a detailed model of the field, greatly improving descriptive capabilities. The possible use of inexpensive drilling techniques for augmenting reservoir information, rather than for providing extra production points, requires careful investigation. The development of slim-hole drilling should be pursued for this purpose, though costs must be reduced if the technique is to be accepted. The development of a remote-controlled drilling mole could also prove fruitful.

c) *Reservoir Engineering*

Research over the next 30 years should concentrate on improving the cost benefits of enhanced oil recovery techniques and so secure their widespread acceptability. One fundamental issue concerns the difficulties inherent in successful transfer of EOR technology from one geological setting to another. A programme in the United States seeks to establish closer integration of geological deposition, structure, and transformation phenomena within engineering practice. This approach could be considered for extension to creation of an international database and to system evaluation, so that benefit could be drawn from a wider shared body of information and enhanced statistical power.

The reasons for the success or failure of chemical flooding techniques are unclear. A search for more effective surfactants is one approach, while increased efforts to understand and control the processes involved is another. It may be that both should be given high priority. Unless very low concentration floods become practical, this technique is likely to present continued cost problems. Basic research in the area may be the key to enhanced economics. Developments will probably continue to be constrained by the fact that surfactant costs are linked to oil prices.

Another example is $CO_2$ flooding. It is widely used in the United States, facilitated by available $CO_2$ reservoirs as a supply of gas. In the North Sea oil fields, reservoirs are more shallow and less densely injected, so large-scale sources of $CO_2$ are uneconomic. $CO_2$ recovery from flue gas is costly but costs could be offset by economic credits associated with removal of the $CO_2$ from the environment. Other types of EOR application are also more challenging in the North Sea than in many United States fields because logistics are more difficult, well spacings are wider, reservoir water is saline, and reservoirs are hot. Factors such as these have inhibited international co-operation beyond the research scale among major EOR-producing nations. Technical aspects of $CO_2$ flooding need further investigation, specifically with respect to volumes required, and the problems of supply, separation from the hydrocarbon products, and control. In the case of steam flooding, further development of downhole generators is a top priority. Improvements in separation techniques for the heavy oil/water mixture would aid economics.

For the North Sea, nitrogen and hydrocarbon gases are suitable EOR agents, given reservoir temperatures and pressures. Again, there are major uncertainties associated with unpredictable recovery factors which may merit increased research in fundamental science. For nitrogen injection, the cost of generating and separating nitrogen poses problems. And there is limited confidence that plants of the required size can be built offshore. For hydrocarbon gas, the economic incentive at the present time is to sell gas where possible rather than re-inject it for longer-term EOR projects. Large-scale gas injection requires gas that is cheap and readily available.

In some gas displacement applications, sweep efficiency can be improved by reducing effective gas mobility. This may be done by co-injecting water (or alternating gas and water injection). An alternative is to consider foams to reduce gas mobility. R&D is needed to improve confidence in the use of foams. Polymer injection has potential to improve oil recovery. The main problem in offshore applications is the instability of polymers in hot, saline environments. Development of more stable polymers is thus required. Polymer gel systems might also improve the cost effectiveness of polymer flooding. This technology would advance if more basic research were conducted on gel reactions in porous media.

Use of microbiological techniques for cracking oils or generating polymers and surfactants under controlled factory conditions is likely to be a more attractive target. Microbiological techniques are at a very early stage of development and will require advances in genetic engineering and reservoir technology.

There are also possible techniques to improve recovery from fields with more viscous oils. In unstable viscous oil displacements, sweep efficiency introduces a basic uncertainty that needs further investigation. Heavy crude reservoirs often require thermal stimulation to ensure economic production. Current technologies include steam injection, hot water injection, and *in situ* combustion. Future technologies might include chemical, mechanical and electromagnetic methods of heating the oil. Heavy oil also tends to be produced from cool reservoirs. As the oil flows up the well casing, its viscosity continues to increase as it cools further. More economic means for insulating the well bore are essential. *In situ* combustion involves difficult technology and is unlikely to be applied to the offshore environment because of safety and space.

With respect to reservoir management, the objective is to fully explore reserves already discovered. The gathering of maximum information is required to do this. Future technological advances should encompass the ability to perform *in situ* measurements on a continuous basis over the field life, as well as a more accurate method of distinguishing variations in fluid ingress. Seismic techniques have traditionally been used to identify potential structures. These techniques are increasingly used to identify reservoir variations between wells. In addition, repeated use of seismic techniques can enable flood front monitoring throughout field life, thus enhancing yields. A promising type of EOR is geologically-targeted infill drilling (GTID). After an oil field has been exhausted by conventional production techniques, a substantial amount of mobile oil remains behind in inhomogeneous geological formations. Most of the remaining mobile oil could be recovered by drilling on an ever closer well spacing and by completing wells at ever smaller intervals. Improved field characterisation techniques would permit the cost-effective recovery of more of the unswept mobile oil.

Another area for development is improved modelling of the fracturing and propping process, leading to better planning of fracturing techniques. The ability to hydraulically fracture more permeable reservoirs is desirable; this requires development of suitable fluids and better understanding of the fracturing process.

d) *Drilling and Well Completion*

In this area, priority technologies to facilitate development of uneconomic hydrocarbon reserves include: horizontal and extended reach wells; casing while drilling; automated, ultra-deep, and deep water drilling; more effective and economical disposal of drilling and completion wastes; and other techniques directed at deep water, heavy crude, deep high-pressure and temperature condensate reservoirs, and small deposits of any hydrocarbon type.

Extended reach and horizontal wells will play a major role in maintaining energy production over the next 30 years. Horizontal drilling drains oil from the ground using a well that is vertical at the surface but horizontal at the level of the reservoir. More of the reservoir can be drained using this technique because more of the reservoir is exposed to the wellbore. In certain types of formation, it can increase recoverable reserves, reduce environmental damage and increase producers' economic efficiency. Horizontal drilling has become one of the most important technological developments of the 1990s.

Technology exists to drill high-inclination, high-curvature, and horizontal wells at moderate depths, but further development of short-radius horizontal well technology is needed. Major advances are needed to drill such wells in deep, high-pressure and high-temperature reservoirs or from deep-water platforms. Some of the highest cost items in deep-water production are sub-sea wellheads and trees, flow lines, structures to support surface facilities, and drilling costs. All of these could be substantially reduced by completing a single well to drain several formations and by multiple horizontal drainholes in each formation.

Technological improvements to accomplish the above objectives are listed below.

- Steering and logging tools must be upgraded to endure long intervals at high inclinations and the harsh conditions of temperature and pressure in deep, hot wells. As the drillstring gets longer, there will have to be faster, more dependable ways to get drilling information uphole.

- New, high-temperature downhole motors and steerable assemblies are needed. New technology, including two-way communication, is required to control the steering assembly downhole, particularly for extended reach or deep wells.

- New methods will have to be developed to clean and remove cuttings from long sections of highly inclined well bore, both for the drilling and to maintain well performance.

- The technology exists today for drilling multiple horizontal well bores, but completions pose a formidable challenge. Pressure isolation and methods for re-entering the well bore are areas that need to be addressed.

- If horizontal well bores are to be productive over the life of the reservoir, methods will have to be developed to provide observation and control of production at selected intervals.

The development of procedures for casing the well bore during drilling will be particularly cost beneficial. This process, linked perhaps to the flexible drillpipe, MWD, intelligent steering systems, and alternative cutting processes, would negate most problems currently encountered in drilling. For small holes in deep, high-pressure and high-temperature environments, MWD tools designed for these conditions offer the potential of a much more rugged system to support the high-risk, real-time decisions typically required during such operations.

Automation of the drilling process involves control of hoisting and drive mechanisms, manipulation of tubulars and control of mud and cement supply. The advantages are a reduction in personnel, also removal of personnel from accident-prone areas. It is unlikely that oil reserves (as distinct from gas reserves) will be located at ultra-deep levels. Substantial oil accumulations exist at underwater depths beyond those where either fixed platforms or sub-sea wells have been installed. Successful drilling has been carried out in deeper water, but it is both technically difficult and costly to work at increasing water depths, and further refinements in equipment and techniques are required. Areas to be addressed include hydrate formation in drilling fluids and more economical well designs.

With regard to waste disposal, use of current technology generates a waste volume of four to six times the volume of the hole drilled. Replacement of oil-based muds with environmentally acceptable water-based muds, where feasible, is essential to reduce waste disposal costs, and may be required on environmental grounds in certain areas. It may be necessary to develop new chemical additives. Equally essential are enhancements in solids-control equipment to reduce the waste volume generated.

e) *Offshore Field Development*

The general aim in developing production facilities is to reduce both capital and operating costs. Extensive use of floating or sub-sea production facilities can be expected. Common trends will be simplicity and standardisation, coupled with reduced manning, ultimately producing sub-sea operations wherever cost-effective. Technological progress is needed to address environmental and safety concerns.

Important areas for technology development include: reduction in weight (and thus cost) of topside facilities and underlying structures; utilisation of new structural materials; system designs incorporating sub-sea and satellite facilities; improved instrumentation and control; and extensive application of multiphase flow equipment and concepts. Improved understanding of fluid behaviour and development of dynamic modelling techniques is leading to weight reduction in topside facilities and to parallel reductions in structural weight requirements. Dynamic modelling will support more cost-effective engineered designs to address fatigue, weather and design points, and to protect against extreme conditions.

The availability of large barge cranes will play an increasing part in the design of fixed structures. Installation costs represent a large proportion of a project's cost, and so the trend will be to reduce weights at the expense of fabrication cost to levels where crane installation is possible. Steel has been the primary structural material for many years, and its use will undoubtedly continue. Concrete structures can be viable alternatives for shallower water. Aluminium has some potential, especially for helidecks. The use of plastics has obvious potential benefit in weight reduction, but concerns exist with regard to fire resistance and possible emission of toxic fumes under exposure to heat. Lighter-weight materials are of considerable interest, provided concerns are met at reasonable cost.

Aside from attention to structural weight and cost, there is increasing movement in the direction of technology for sub-sea and satellite systems. This trend is likely to be centred initially on concepts for remote or small fields in shallow basins such as the North Sea, and then to translate to the Arctic and deeper fields in the Gulf of Mexico. Remote operated vehicles (ROVs) are being developed to install equipment under pressures of more than one tonne per square inch. Oil and gas from reservoirs in 600-1000 metres of water will be a significant part of offshore production by the end of the century and beyond. An important element in deepwater operations is the new flexibility allowed by recent advances in offshore technology. Tension leg platforms and floating production systems can help operators bring ultra-deepwater reserves on stream faster than is possible with traditional production schemes based on fixed steel-jacketed platforms. The application of diverless technology (automated and robotic) will be important here. Multiphase systems derived from North Sea experience could be used to tie back deepwater fields to shallower infrastructure.

A key parameter in sub-sea efforts is reliability. In the future, improved reliability will be realised through a reduction in the number of components, design improvements and improved quality control. State-of-the-art control systems, predominantly hydraulic, have limits on depths and response time, and take up valuable weight and space in production risers. Future research should investigate the use of other media, such as digital fibre optics, for transmitting control signals to the wellhead and other remote flow control devices. The aim is to introduce umbilical-free systems.

Satellite platforms are an alternative to conventional, large manned platforms and rely on automation or enhanced control systems to achieve better control of production facilities with fewer staff, lower operating costs and improved safety. Performance monitoring will lead to optimised maintenance schemes to further reduce operating costs through lower downtime and demanning. In general, however the industry will require achievement of all this with simpler rather than more complex instrumentation.

The market for onshore and offshore oil and natural gas production control equipment will be small, and core control engineering technologies will be driven largely by other markets. Specific needs for exploration and production will be satisfied by evolving technology and by developing elements unique to the oil-production industry. The ability to design and operate multiphase flow lines opens up new field development opportunities which will have a major impact over the next 30 years, namely:

- tie-in of satellite wells to existing platforms;
- unmanned wellhead platforms/sub-sea templates on new fields with transfer to existing processing platforms; and
- full field development with transfer to shore for processing.

To extend beyond current operating limitations, the industry must have transient multiphase design and simulation models, better understanding of, and measurement methods for, fluid properties and new multiphase pumps, flow measurement and sand detection equipment. Improved methods for selection and preparation of pipeline materials to prevent corrosion and erosion in multiphase flow pipelines are also required. A substantial R&D effort is already under way to develop suitable technology. However, parallel developments in fluid mechanics, and related effects such as hydrate control/prevention, are necessary to effectively implement multiphase production schemes. Multiphase metering concepts must also be advanced substantially.

A field trial of a sub-sea multiphase pump is expected in the next few years, followed by commercial applications of surface multiphase pumps. The latter part of the 1990s should see increasing use of multiphase pumps, including the first critical sub-sea applications. The following ten years will see further multiphase pump applications, possibly in remote and hostile environments.

f) *Field Operations*

The critical areas in field operations relate to: inspection, maintenance and repair; reductions in personnel requirements; and automated diagnostics and control. With respect to inspection, the need to improve safety will lead to enhancements in ROV capability for underwater structural inspections and simple tasks such as remedial grinding, to be carried out without divers. It will be necessary to improve manipulator hardware and supervisory control software, also, for work in poor weather conditions, to enhance tether management and deployment systems. There is a need for cost-effective and reliable inspection methods, such as real-time radiographic methods for piping systems and vessels. Current methods of pipeline inspection are considered adequate for large pipe sizes; however, methods for small bore and flexible flowlines need to be developed.

With respect to sub-sea maintenance and repair, development of methods and procedures can be expected, notably in those described below.

- Further remote intervention techniques for pipelines, sub-sea wellheads, templates and other sub-sea equipment at increasing depths. Although divers are now capable of performing at a depth of about 500 metres, it is desirable for safety reasons to minimise diver tasks.

- Development of wet welding techniques for structural repairs.

- Increased sub-sea well field serviceability for wells tied back to platforms, or to operating production facilities. Standardisation of such interconnection systems for serviceability will increase ROV capabilities, further reducing complexity and cost of control and well servicing systems.

Some technological spin-off from the remote intervention systems being developed for sub-sea use is envisaged for application to topside maintenance techniques within the next 30 years. This will facilitate operation of unmanned installations, and may reduce personnel requirements on large platforms. Use of helicopters for personnel movement is currently expensive. Development of tilt-wing or other improved aircraft may reduce operating costs and improve safety. Operation of large production platforms without on-site labour is considered impracticable over the next 20 to 30 years. However, reduced personnel requirements for operation, and the use of medium-sized unmanned facilities, controlled from other platforms, are likely to become common. Sub-sea development of small oil and gas accumulations tied to common facilities will also become more prevalent. Gas compression equipment is considered the most difficult type of equipment to automate, due to its complexity. Using dry gas seals makes it less complex, and these seals are being developed for higher, gas injection pressures. Other equipment enhancements will be required to reduce operator involvement and maintenance. Adoption of these evolutionary developments, together with expected instrumentation improvements, offer the potential for unmanned operation of compression equipment in the next 20 to 30 years. Alternatively, multiphase pumps may be used to transfer wellstream fluids to a mother platform for processing. This option is particularly attractive because it minimises facilities requirements on the satellite installation. Generally, demanning is more likely to be achieved through this type of process than by automation of facilities.

Experience has shown that automation does not necessarily reduce operating costs. Future gains may be achieved through:

- improved process design, using simulation and other techniques to effect systems requiring minimum control; and

- using field sensors which are simple in design, are fault tolerant and can be interrogated directly by a centralised control system, reducing the need for intermediate field transmitters.

If equipment maintenance costs are to be minimised, more sophisticated diagnostic techniques must be developed. All critical equipment on a platform will be monitored. Diagnostic routines would be installed on the centralised control system. Fire and gas protection systems need to be reliable, meeting functional loss-prevention requirements with minimal maintenance.

g) *Transport Systems*

New corrosion inhibitors for carbon steel pipelines, and better methods to evaluate their efficiency, are needed to avoid disruption to field operations. In addition to inspection of the inner steel pipe for possible cracks and corrosion attacks, penetration methods will be developed to detect failures or flaws in internal layers of a multilayer composite pipe. The need for these inspection tests will lead to developments in intelligent pigging. Better methods of leak detection are also required.

Improved scientific understanding and predictive tools are necessary to prevent environmental damage or unwanted exposure of the pipelines. Pipeline deployment in new unexplored waters, such as the Bering Sea or deeper parts of the Atlantic, will present new challenges. With continuous developments in the North Sea, and as Mediterranean traffic increases, the likelihood of pipeline hazards also increases. Better methods are needed for burial and trenching, inspection and *in situ* repair. Advanced automation and robotics, and use of mechanical couplings, would lessen stringent demands on pipeline alignment at the time of connecting. Such advances would also bring new remotely operated repair methods where a piece of damaged pipeline is cut out and a new piece inserted. Sub-sea pipeline valves are installed to separate sections of a pipeline for maintenance and as an emergency shut-down valve on the platform export riser. Further developments are needed on the control and operation of such valves, with focus on installation and retrieval for maintenance, corrosion resistance, bending resistance and piggability.

When new provinces are being developed, a pipeline infrastructure should be considered at the start, so new fields can be brought on-stream easily. A particular challenge is to put multiphase boosters into field service. Several projects are approaching commercial stage, with rotodynamic as well as different positive displacement types under testing. As multiphase transfer is extended to long distances and/or flowing wellhead pressures decline over field life, the need for boosting increases. Since the size of field and character of well fluids vary, the oil industry will need a variety of different multiphase pumps.

Natural gas conversion, including use for power generation, is prompting increasing interest. In energy equivalent terms, estimated undiscovered reserves of gas exceed those of oil. The oil and gas industry is thus presented with a major challenge to maximise the benefit of these reserves. In contrast with oil, natural gas must compete with lower-value alternatives in highly competitive regional markets. While plentiful gas supplies are forecast in some cases, there may be no local markets, and natural gas reserves remote from markets incur high transport costs. Gas conversion into economically transportable forms, high-value products or more compatible transport fuels is thus attractive. R&D should attempt to enhance current methods, or develop new methods to make natural gas conversion more attractive. As oil prices rise over the 30-year assessment period, natural gas conversion will become more economically feasible. But its use will still be largely dictated by market development and commercial considerations.

The possibility of *in situ* power generation, by converting natural gas (or oil) into electricity at the field site, has long been available to the industry and new technology is making this more attractive. Niche markets for fuel power might prove attractive in countries with remote onshore discoveries and no markets for gas. Advanced aero-derivative gas turbine technology with small footprint requirements, capable of simple-cycle efficiencies greater than 42 per cent (based upon low heating value [LHV]), can generate *in situ* electric power at competitive prices.

Today's tanker fleets are built on decades of experience and offer limited potential for improvements, but future transport of liquified natural gas is planned from Northern Europe to overseas ports. Shipping costs have a major impact on gas prices. To be competitive improved technology is required. This may involve new ship design as well as fuel-saving. These issues involving the transportability of natural gas are discussed further in Chapter 4.

h) *Technology for the Arctic Regions*

For onshore Arctic development, continued technology progress is needed to reduce operating costs to more effectively compete with worldwide low-cost producers. Improved pipeline coatings suitable for low-temperature application and service are needed. Intermittent permafrost is a difficult environment in which to control external corrosion of buried pipelines; cathodic protection is often ineffective. Available coatings are difficult to join or repair at low temperatures. Better thermal insulation is also needed. Lower-cost, more easily applied, thinner and lighter insulating methods would reduce development costs. Emerging ceramic matrix coatings have promise.

Next-generation multiphase wellhead metering and automated control would be ways to reduce operating costs and better manage well production. A meshing together of data gathering and automation into a single system with computer supervised control is desirable. Emphasis should be placed on low maintenance and calibration-intensive measurement devices. Similarly, low-cost, high-capacity and reliable communication systems will be essential. The application of more cost- effective multiplexed fibre optic systems for low temperature is a potential enabling technology.

Plastic piping is often more cost-effective than steel piping and is resistant to corrosion and erosion. Current materials are limited in their ability to operate and/or be installed at low temperatures. Advances in plastic formulations for low temperatures might expedite the use of this piping. Remote power source technologies would eliminate or reduce power distribution costs for low and moderate power consumption applications. Various possible technologies include thermal potential cells, nuclear batteries and small generators.

Disposal of drilling wastes is particularly difficult because of the remote and sensitive Arctic environment. Methods are needed to process waste material to be used as road or pad construction material and/or recycled as a drilling fluid additive or for other applications.

For offshore exploration and production, some of the major issues involve the interaction of ice with vessels and structures. Additional understanding is needed of the physical properties of ice and its distribution in various prospective regions, as well as the magnitude and nature of the forces resulting as ice interacts with structures. The extension of deep-water oil production technologies, such as tension-leg platforms or articulated columnar structures in marginal ice zones, is possible in the foreseeable future, providing hulls/pontoons can be designed to resist the impact of ice flows and moorings can tolerate some degree of ice pressure. Sub-sea satellite well technology and multiphase transport technology are also possible. In regions where multi-year ice flows and icebergs would present a more serious challenge, improved temporary disconnect methods are needed.

Although oil shuttle tankers will be practical in some locations, sub-sea pipelines will be required in others. Ice scour will require deeper burial, particularly in transition regions where pipelines come ashore. All aspects of this problem require further development. Possibilities include deep trench burial and modified horizontal drilling. More rapid and effective trenching techniques are needed, and development of accurate pipeline monitoring tools will be essential. It will be necessary to have the capability to deal effectively with oil spills. A primary requirement is a cost-efficient means of using and transporting Arctic natural gas. Options include pipeline, transporting in the liquid state, and conversion to a more readily transportable liquid.

i) *Extra Heavy Oils, Natural Bitumens and Shale Oils*

As noted previously, reserves of these materials are very substantial, but utilisation is inhibited by the current state of technology and by poor economics compared with other sources of crudes. R&D into pipelining of extra heavy hydrocarbons should be pursued. Forming emulsions is a promising technique, but there are technical problems to be resolved, including the large volumes of water and subsequent disposal problems, also the instability of emulsions during pumping.

For natural bitumens, cold water processes should be developed which require less energy than conventional hot water recovery. For the recovery of shale oils, fluidised bed retorting, offering simpler mechanical operations and higher thermal efficiency than fixed bed retorting, should be pursued. *In situ* retorting and solvent conisation are innovative approaches which should be explored further.

In general, lower-quality feedstocks such as heavy oil and bitumens have a lower hydrogen/carbon ratio and contain greater amounts of undesirable polyaromatic, sulphur, heteroatom and metal compounds that complicate refining and increase both extraction and processing costs. Shale oils and other kerogen-based materials may contain a higher nitrogen content and exhibit other chemical, physical and thermodynamic properties that also require special treatment during upgrading.

In all these cases the option exists to provide pre-refining steps. As the world oil market turns to more diverse sources to increase supply security over the next 30 years, economical treatment of such difficult and/or lower-quality crudes will become increasingly important. Here again, fundamental R&D may be needed to identify and develop feasible extraction, upgrading and processing steps to reduce economic penalties presently associated with their potential utilisation.

A summary of status and technical and economic potential for each major technology area considered is presented in Table 3.2. Areas of consistently high technical potential for productivity are in exploration, reservoir evaluation and drilling. In addition, a number of potentially high-impact opportunities have been identified to facilitate future operations in Arctic environments.

*Table 3.2*
**Technical and Economic Status of Oil and Natural Gas Production Technology**

| Technology | Status | Technical Potential | Economic Potential for Extending the Resource Base |
|---|---|---|---|
| **Exploration** | | | |
| • Geophysics | Demonstrated | H | H |
| • Source Rock Kinetics | Demonstrated | H | H |
| • Expulsion Efficiency | R&D | H | H |
| • Migration Efficiency | R&D | M | L |
| • Data Access | Demonstrated | M | M |
| **Reservoir Evaluation** | | | |
| • Measurement while Drilling | R&D | M | H |
| • Integrated Computer Facility | Demonstrated | M | M |
| **Reservoir Engineering** | | | |
| • GTID | Commercial | H | H |
| • EOR | Commercial | H | H |
| • Microbiological Enhanced Recovery | R&D | M | H |
| • Artificial Lift | R&D | H | H |
| **Drilling and Well Completion** | | | |
| • High Inclination, High Curvature, Horizontal Wells | Demonstrated | H | H |
| • Automation | Demonstrated | H | H |
| • Water-based Muds | Demonstrated | L | L |
| **Offshore Field Development** | | | |
| • Steel Structure | Commercial | M | M |
| • Concrete | Commercial | H | M |
| • Exotic Materials | Commercial | M | L |
| • Compact Equipment | Commercial | M | M |
| • Sub-sea | Commercial | M | M |
| • Multiphase Flow Technology | Commercial | M | L |
| **Field Operations** | | | |
| • Inspection, Maintenance, Repair | Demonstrated | H | H |
| • Chemicals | Demonstrated | M | L |
| • Well Servicing | Demonstrated | H | M |
| **Transport Systems** | | | |
| • Multiphase Flow Boosters | Commercial | H | M |
| • Corrosion-Resistant Materials | Demonstrated | H | M |
| • Gas Conversion | Demonstrated | H | M |
| • Diverless Connection of Pipelines | R&D | L | L |

Note: L, M, H represent Low, Medium, High

*Table 3.2 (continued)*
**Technical and Economic Status of Oil and Natural Gas Production Technology**

| Technology | Status | Technical Potential | Economic Potential for Extending the Resource Base |
|---|---|---|---|
| **Technology for the Arctic Regions** | | | |
| • Pipeline Coatings | Demonstrated | H | M |
| • Thermal Insulation | Demonstrated | L | L |
| • Multiphase Wellhead Metering and Automated Control | Demonstrated | H | M |
| • Multiplexed Fibre Optic Communications | Demonstrated | H | |
| • Power Source Technologies | Demonstrated | L | L |
| • Drilling Waste Disposal | Demonstrated | H | H |
| • Ice Surveillance Technology | Demonstrated | H | H |
| • Ice/Structure Interaction Research | Commercial | M | M |
| • Temporary Disconnection Methods | Commercial | H | H |
| • Spray Ice as Construction Material | Demonstrated | M | H |
| • Modified Horizontal Drilling Techniques | Demonstrated | H | M |
| • Rapid Trenching Techniques | Demonstrated | M | L |
| • Increasing the Accuracy of Pipeline Monitoring Tools | Demonstrated | H | M |
| • Oil Spill Treatment Technology | Demonstrated | H | H |
| **Extra Heavy Oils, Natural Bitumens and Shale Oils** | | | |
| • Hydraulic Mining Methods | Demonstrated | H | M |
| • Borehole Mining Techniques | Demonstrated | H | H |
| • Energy-Saving Development of Cold Water Processes | Demonstrated | L | L |
| • Development of Oil Sand Retorting Processes | Demonstrated | H | M |
| • Development of Solvent Extraction Processes for Lower-Grade Oil Sand | R&D | M | L |
| • Fluidised Bed Retorting | Demonstrated | H | M |
| • *In situ* Retorting | Commercial | H | M |
| • Solvent Ionisation | Commercial | M | M |
| • Upgrading of Oils and Bitumens to Improve Transport | R&D | M | M |
| • Production of Oil-in-Water Emulsions for Transport | R&D | M | L |

Note: L, M, H represent Low, Medium, High

## Technology Prospects and Markets

### *Market Trends*

The technological complexity and rising marginal costs of production of new oil and natural gas, combined with environmental and other risks of petroleum production, can act as constraints on new production. But in recent years the marginal cost of production has fallen in some areas, due in part to the use of improved exploration and development technologies. The challenge is to develop the technologies required to meet anticipated increases in demand for oil and natural gas in an era of flat prices. In this context, much of the technology focus identified by the oil and natural gas producers is related to reducing the cost of finding, producing and delivering oil and natural gas.

The bulk of the world's oil reserves with low production costs are concentrated in the Middle East. In other regions, reserves are frequently of heavier crude quality, often high in sulphur content, or located in environmentally hostile areas, such as deep and ultra-deep offshore regions and the Arctic, the result of which is higher production costs. The major impediment to significant further supply diversification is the high production cost and diminishing availability of undiscovered large or high-quality reserves. Heavy crude oils cost more to produce, transport and refine than light oils, due to their high viscosity and molecular weight. Many heavy crudes contain non-oil impurities like sulphur and metals, requiring extra refining steps for their removal. Operating in hostile and often fragile environments in Arctic and offshore regions requires more expensive equipment and it means lower labour productivity, as well as higher labour, transport, and environmental protection costs.

With current technology, there is often substantial economic risk in committing large investments to developing higher-cost sources of oil in competition with low-cost sources, as in the Middle East, where production costs can be a fraction of the price of internationally traded oil. Next-generation technologies which can more efficiently produce, transport and refine oil from difficult production areas could reduce this risk, but both evolutionary and breakthrough technology advances are required.

The present exploitable hydrocarbon reserves will gradually be exhausted and new sources of hydrocarbons must be discovered. Techniques for developing known reserves in difficult areas or in unconventional forms must be created. Research into all the areas described in the earlier sections will produce techniques and equipment necessary to exploit various types of reserve. The more difficult reserves will then become economical, as present lower-cost reserves are consumed and the cost of new oil and gas production gradually increases. It is important to ensure that R&D and resulting technical advances are pursued sufficiently early, so that the improved technology will be available when required.

### *Key Players*

Oil and natural gas production is a mature industry. The activities of the various organisations have been established for some time and, in general, they have served the industry well.

Governments may have a role to play in co-ordinating awareness of the needs of the industry, and in encouraging or stimulating R&D activity by funding appropriate longer-term and higher-risk R&D projects either alone or in co-operation with oil and natural gas companies.

The organisations primarily involved in the development of technology for the oil and gas industry are:

- oil and natural gas operating companies;
- equipment manufacturers and suppliers of engineering services used by operating companies;
- national (governmental) R&D establishments;
- R&D institutions and universities; and
- national and international entities concerned with stimulating and funding R&D activities.

The activities of all these organisations are well established. Many oil and gas operating companies have their own R&D facilities developing techniques for the companies' own use. The supply companies are continually developing new equipment to serve the requirements of industry, as exploration and production extend into more difficult areas, such as deep-water and high-temperature and high-pressure reservoirs. Universities and R&D institutions pursue fundamental investigation which forms the basis for future technology progress.

Given the maturity of the industry, the worldwide scale of its operations and the evident demand for its products, the most significant government actions to facilitate progress would appear to be associated, not with participation in conventional process development but with: areas characterised by high-risk, high-impact technology breakthrough opportunities; the societal responsibilities of enhancing environmental protection, safety, and helping to ensure an adequate cadre of scientific and engineering capability for its industrial base; and the balanced promulgation of market-based regulations and policies to enhance investment and promote risk-taking by the industry in responding to market needs.

In the United States, the NPC in its report *Research Development and Demonstration Needs of the Oil and Gas Industry* has tried to define the range of roles and motivations of both technology developers and suppliers. The private sector invests in the development of advanced technology to increase its economic margins and market competitiveness. Producers utilise technology to reduce operating costs. Only a dozen or so of the major producers (out of 8 000 domestic oil and gas producers in the United States) support in-house technology development. "More than 50 per cent of total US oil and gas is produced by organisations with essentially no in-house RD&D programmes." (NPC Study p.64.)

Refiners are similar to producers in that they use technology to reduce operating costs and their mainline business does not include providing a technology base to the industry at-large. Overall, private-sector technology development takes place in a highly competitive environment where knowledge is generally not shared and where effort is "skewed towards the short term with expectations for products within three years." Private-sector in-house RD&D tends to focus on the latter stages of research: product development, product demonstration, and technical service. According to the NPC survey the private sector will support selected longer-term, higher-risk programmes when the outcomes are vital to their future business interests.

In addition, in the United States, France and other countries, consortium RD&D organisations are an important component of industry's business strategy. These can take a number of forms, including RD&D pools, university research centres, basic research co-operatives, and industry R&D institutes.

Universities conduct very basic research that is targeted at providing the technology base for future products with characteristic time horizons extending towards ten years or more.

Federal and local government's focus (when they are involved in oil and natural gas RD&D) tends to lie between industry's shorter-term view and the university's longer-term perspective. Government's focus is on energy security, competitiveness and standard of living, to help ensure energy availability, environmental protection and future social benefits. Often, government efforts are not directed at the oil or gas industry, but support more basic, longer-term research which may have duel-use in helping meet the more general mission that they pursue.

### *Market Barriers*

The ability of IEA countries to confront the technology challenges in the area of oil and natural gas production depends as much on how wise they will be in coping with the mounting environmental concerns as it does on successful investment in skilled human resources. However, these environmental issues (including greenhouse gas emissions) must be taken in the context of the environmental performance of other competing fuels. Projected future growth to 2010 in the use of oil and natural gas is expected to contribute significantly to increasing greenhouse gas emissions. In that context, natural gas is viewed as relatively environmentally friendly as compared with other fossil fuels and this, along with its low price and efficiency, has encouraged its increasing use for electricity production as well as its current consideration as a transportation fuel.

Other important barriers relate to the general economic climate that generates the economic risk associated with oil and natural gas production. These barriers include political instability, price volatility, and the lack of investment capital or its high cost. With increasing proportions of oil and natural gas coming from exploration and development in non-IEA Member countries, these barriers may take on increasing significance.

Oil field developments have sometimes been delayed because of the absence of sound data about environment impacts. Some prospective lease areas have ceased to be considered, or delayed, because of environmental uncertainties and the desire to preserve natural wilderness. Waste disposal is a sensitive and important environmental issue. There is a special need for greater know-how in oil clean-up technology in pack ice or broken ice areas. The array of technologies needed in the next 30 years is uncertain. New and improved technology must reduce total hydrocarbon discharge into the sea and minimise the disposal therein of drilling and production solid wastes.

Oil and natural gas field development and operation must co-exist with commercial fisheries and the subsistence needs of the indigenous population. The effects of oil development on Arctic fishing and native ways of life are not well understood, due to the lack of reliable data. Northern natives are naturally concerned with preservation of their way of life as well as the environment. The development of economical technology to assure caribou passage through the onshore Arctic oil field is necessary. Arctic wetlands created by the intersection of permafrost and sub-surface impermeability must be protected. The wetland waterfowl habitat must be protected from field construction impacts.

Offshore exploration is particularly affected by environmental concerns. Unless the Arctic National Wildlife Refuge is opened for development, pipelines and support bases for potential fields in the United States Eastern Beaufort Sea have no nearby access to land. The remoteness and harsh environment of the Arctic makes the transport of crude oil and the delivery of supplies and equipment expensive and technically challenging. Mobilisation and demobilisation are a significant cost factor. The operation window for access of non-ice-capable vessels may only be a few weeks out of the year. Continuous winter re-supply by ice-breaking boats is uneconomical in many regions, thus requiring large storage areas. Situations or operations normally dependent on emergency support for marine equipment may need to be avoided in the winter months unless an alternative emergency response capability can be provided. Perhaps the greatest socio-economic concerns relating to development of petroleum resources in the high Arctic are the possibility of pollution resulting from well blow-out or from marine transport, as well as disturbance of marine life along tanker routes. Even for conventional tanker traffic, and the associated loading and unloading operations, oil spills are of increasing concern. While major spills draw worldwide attention, small and mid-size oil spills occur much more frequently. These smaller spills, although less noticeable, are not necessarily less harmful overall to the immediate local environment.

Initial damage assessment from major oil spills frequently pinpoints the immediate harm to shorelines and to marine, plant, and animal life. Prohibitions on commercial fishing create immediate economic costs as well. But the long-term environmental fate of an ecosystem after a major oil spill is less clear. After a period of time, visual evidence of oil spills begins to recede. Mechanical clean-up removes some of the evidence. Bio-remediation offers a potentially more effective clean-up technique. Forces in nature play their part in removing and dispersing oil from the water and beaches. For small spills, the visual impact recedes even more quickly. However, the removal and dissipation of the short-term impact of oil spills, which is immediately apparent, is only one aspect of their full environmental consequences. There is insufficient understanding of the long-term effects of major oil spills on the environment. Similarly, the impacts of small spills in diverse settings are not well understood. The ability to make more accurate assessments of environmental impacts in areas experiencing oil spills needs to be strengthened, and this strengthening will in turn support more effective remediation of environmental damage. Better assessments of the long-term consequences of oil spills should identify appropriate clean-up approaches, as well as priorities for those approaches.

A different problem is the removal of the offshore oil production platforms when the wells run dry. The International Maritime Organisation sets the legal framework for abandonment. Structures must be removed to provide a water clearance of 55 metres to ensure there is no risk to navigation. Any platform in water depth of less that 75 metres must be removed entirely. But, in the deep water, cheaper solutions can be adopted. These might include removing the topside accommodation and processing units and cutting the steel support structure, the "jacket", to the required depth or toppling it to lie on the seabed. These options are opposed by environmental groups anxious to prevent the sea from becoming an underwater scrap-metal yard, while fishermen are concerned about damage to their nets. Research is needed to find cost-effective solutions.

Safety will be increasingly important in design of new facilities and in the continuing usefulness of existing facilities. Rapid and major progress in design of explosion containment or relief is appropriate here. Further studies using advanced mathematical models need to be performed on blast behaviour of unconfined vapour clouds. As the industry learns more about the design of blast-resistant platforms, this knowledge will be incorporated into risk analysis techniques. Confidence in the ability to design platforms which will survive a major incident will thus be further enhanced. De-manning may also be an important factor in increasing safety. More involvement of professional societies in review of safety issues, as well as the technology transfer of standards applied in other industries, may also contribute to further advances in safety.

Specialist training of personnel is essential for the future of the oil and natural gas industry in the area of field operations. Demographic trends will result in reduced numbers of engineering graduates and other skilled personnel. As a result, there will be an increasing need to develop journeyman skills of young people joining the industry, for retaining older people as employment requirements change, and for multi-disciplined technicians. To help meet these needs, development of international competence standards for jobs in the industry is likely to progress, with encouragement from government bodies.

There is also a growing recognition of the need for more sophisticated management skills. This will be heightened by developments in exploration, production and information technology. Structural and demographic changes will challenge managers to control and make effective use of a set of increasingly scarce resources. Rapid transfer of new and emerging technologies, including the results from current research and development, will be needed. Education and training in these endeavours will help cultivate the required technical and managerial skills. Significant effort must continue to be directed towards safety training for offshore employees and contractors. Availability of skilled craftsmen and operators is a particular concern. This will be negated to some extent if multi-disciplinary work practices are adopted, together with equipment standardisation and automation. Moreover, the application of emerging technology will create a need for engineers and technicians with systems experience, rather than narrow specialisations. This should also facilitate safety awareness.

## Technology Policy Issues

### *Role of Governments*

Government regulatory and economic policies can help set the economic climate for private-sector decision-making and can make significant contributions, directly to promote security of petroleum supplies and indirectly by the promotion of appropriate energy technologies.

Past government intervention has included price controls and taxation which have made both the oil and natural-gas industries sensitive to the role of government. They prefer a less prescriptive approach which would utilise market-based approaches. Policies may promote long-term increases in petroleum supplies by influencing the amount of exploration, encouraging development of discovered fields, and securing maximum economic recovery from producing fields. Such policies will, in turn, sustain vigorous efforts in technology advancement associated with an expanding market.

While primarily determined by geological prospectivity, oil prices and costs of exploration and field development, the amount of exploration undertaken is also responsive to the terms of licensing and taxation imposed by host governments.

Depletion policy sometimes appears in the form of intervention by a host government to limit the pace at which oil or gas reserves are depleted. The idea of prolonging the life of discovered reserves has an obvious link with the maintenance of energy security.

The discovery and economical exploitation of petroleum reserves can be enhanced by the development and timely deployment of appropriate technologies. This requires investment in R&D. The fiscal system provides suitable incentives and disincentives, according to how it allows expenditure relief. When multinational investors undertake central R&D work, they generally wish to spread the cost among their operating subsidiaries in several different countries. Both parties benefit from this. Other government policies, such as direct government support for R&D, the provision of tax incentives for R&D and direct tax credits, can directly influence the amount of R&D undertaken by oil and natural gas companies. In some countries, one of the criteria for the award of licenses is the contribution that the investor proposes to make to appropriate R&D in the country concerned. In some countries, clauses regarding the transfer of technologies by the international investor are often included in petroleum agreements. The inclusion of training commitments by international investors as part of petroleum agreements should benefit both parties in the long run.

The pricing of oil and natural gas can significantly affect its production, consumption and R&D. In general, petroleum, like other products, should be priced at its market value. This is the economically efficient price because it then reflects its opportunity cost. Oil and natural gas prices have sometimes been controlled below market levels for anti-inflation purposes. This is generally inefficient as it encourages wasteful consumption by consumers, and thus contributes to reduced energy security. Crude oil and natural gas price controls act as a disincentive to exploration, field development, maximum economic recovery and to the development of new and improved oil and natural gas technologies. Removing price controls can encourage the development of enhanced technology.

### *Role of International Co-operation*

Because oil utilisation depends on supplies from a world market responsive to supply and demand, actions taken by one government can have an impact on the others. Thus, where oil is concerned, energy, environmental and technology policy is a particularly amenable area for international co-operation, both within the IEA and between it and non-Member countries. As noted, however, the maturity of the oil and natural gas production industry and the capabilities of large producing organisations, as well as effects of market competition, all tend to reduce the significance of government involvement in collaborative efforts for technology development associated with mainstream activities. Nevertheless, major areas for direct R&D and indirect involvement remain. A wide variety of technology targets were identified in the United States' National Petroleum Council's report discussed earlier. These opportunities are associated not only with acceleration of progress in areas of potential technological breakthrough, which would enhance future energy security by assuring both expanded supply and further diversification of sources, but are also associated with important environmental protection needs. Technological advances enable these needs to be met more surely and at affordable cost.

The primary technological requirement identified in this assessment is a strong scientific base in the domains of geology, materials, multi-phase flow, and information management. Such a base is essential, not only to support advances in exploration, reservoir evaluation and engineering, field management and multi-phase flow technology, but also as a source of new concepts facilitating extension of these activities to more difficult environments and ensuring more complete resource recovery. This is a classic arena for government involvement, and one well suited for international collaboration. In addition, breakthrough opportunities exist in high-risk or heretofore intractable areas where the effectiveness of national involvement can be strengthened through international collaboration. From the standpoint of the first technology priority – that of increasing access to economically exploitable oil and natural gas reserves – promising area of work include:

- measurement while drilling (MWD) technology applied to both reservoir evaluation and drilling;
- advanced enhanced oil recovery (EOR) and closer integration of geological and engineering disciplines to advance know-how and application in reservoir evaluation, engineering and management;
- drilling technology to allow economical access to current uneconomical reserves, such as deep water, heavy crude, deep high-pressure and high-temperature condensate reservoirs, and small deposits of any hydrocarbon type;
- exploration, production and transport technology for the Arctic, with an emphasis on environmental impact analysis and mitigation; and
- technology for an economic capability to recover and upgrade extra heavy oils, natural bitumens, shale oils, and other difficult crudes, to acquire access to the large resource volumes of these materials worldwide.

Concerning the second technology priority (that of lowering environmental impacts and risks involved in production processes), there are important and continuing environmental and safety issues associated with large-scale oil industry operations. These issues are the focus of ongoing industry activity, though they appear to merit government attention in order to foster technological advances. Also well suited for international collaboration, they are:

- improved prevention and technological response to oil spills; and
- minimisation and disposal of drilling and production wastes.

Increasing the supply of oil and natural gas from diversified sources may involve greater focus on issues of technology transfer to producing countries not yet fully utilising modern technology. It may involve planning assistance to newly industrialising countries, seeking to expand their resource base, and focusing on effective economic and regulatory policies and technology options for progress in exploration, reservoir evaluation and expeditious field development.

IEA Member countries have already entered into collaboration in a task-sharing Implementing Agreement on Enhanced Oil Recovery. This collaboration has functioned as a mechanism for the exchange of technical information and experience concerning fluids and interfaces in porous media, surfactants and polymers, techniques for miscible flooding, and thermal recovery. Its scope has been widened to cover dynamic reservoir characterisation. Wells have been drilled, and simulations and measurements have been made for experiments with $CO_2$ mixible flooding. In addition, R&D on pipeline transportation is under study within an IEA Implementing Agreement on Fossil Fuel Multiphase Flow Sciences, which has addressed oil-gas mixtures flow in pipelines.

## Approach

The world's hydrocarbon resources can be divided into four types: known reserves of oil, natural gas and condensates in those accessible areas of the world currently being exploited; reserves in deep water areas; reserves in Arctic regions; and natural bitumens and oil shales. With the exception of natural bitumens, shale oils, and unconventional natural gas resources, each resource type has similar basic R&D requirements, with some necessary variations. Each requires a focus on exploration, drilling, field development, reservoir evaluation and engineering, transport, and operations. The most important technological breakthrough expected during the coming decade is utilisation of horizontal wells and multi-phase transport. These technologies will facilitate use of existing processing installations, increase reserve accessibility, and lead to important economic consequences for the industry. This being the case, development of related technologies can be expected to evolve in a number of ways.

Sub-sea technology will be simplified and standardised to reduce costs associated with such systems. With respect to mature fields and present techniques for reservoir management, a large proportion of the oil is left in the reservoir after normal production has ceased. Significant benefit will be achieved in the supply of hydrocarbons through improvements in enhanced oil recovery techniques. These cover a wide range, from well understood $CO_2$ injection to speculative microbiological processes. In exploration, and in reservoir evaluation in particular, substantial benefits could accrue through wider availability of information from operating fields through seismic survey, drilling and reservoir production monitoring. Use of sophisticated computer search and analysis on this combined data is likely to reveal hard-to-find hydrocarbon traps in complex geological structures. Indeed, in all aspects of oil field technology, increased sharing of data would be beneficial.

IEA governments can facilitate this co-operation through policies promoting the sharing of data, through technology information exchange, and establishment of data standards to ensure dissemination and assimilation.

It must be ensured that the environment is protected during exploitation of all forms of hydrocarbon reserves, and it is important that new technology developed should not cause damage. Current technology for solid waste management deserves greater attention. Improved methods to prevent and mitigate oil spills must be devised, and a better understanding of longer-term consequences of past oil spills must be obtained.

To meet the technology priorities for oil and natural gas production identified in this chapter, IEA Member countries may therefore wish to contribute to and co-operate in a technology strategy and collaborative R&D programme aimed at the measures listed below.

- Supporting fundamental scientific R&D, education and training which underpin all these technology options and prospects, including geophysics and hydrocarbon geology, measurement while drilling technology, remote operation, multiphase flow, solvent extraction, and microbiological recovery.

- Facilitating technology progress and R&D partnerships with industry in the areas of hydrocarbon exploration, reservoir evaluation and engineering, enhanced oil recovery, horizontal drilling and well completion, offshore field development and operations, and fluid transport systems.

- Enhancing environmental protection during all phases of the hydrocarbon exploitation cycle, including technology for solid waste management, water treatment and re-use, and methods to prevent and mitigate oil spills.

- Searching for breakthrough opportunities to gain increased economic access to fragile frontier regions and difficult sources of new crudes such as extra-heavy oils, oil shale and tar sands.

- Sharing technology information and experience, and developing principles for effective application of government regulatory and economic policy tools to facilitate technology transfer and aid diversification of new sources of supplies.

*Appendix*
## National Research Council
## Identification of Long-term RD&D Targets Having Potentially Moderate or High Impacts*

| Research Area | Description |
|---|---|
| Exploration | Multi-component seismic techniques; 3D paleostructural restoration; Geophysical fracture-detection methods; 3D visualisation tools; Advanced seismic acquisition; Amplitude versus offset (AVO) in 3D; Specialised seismic processing; High-resolution seismic depth imaging. |
| Development | Rock physics; Geostatistical reservoir descriptions; Advanced reservoir analog models; Advanced well testing and interpretation; Advanced attribute processing; High resolution borehole imaging logs; Fluid-rock interaction; Cross-well geophysical imaging; Reservoir property identification; Advanced reservoir simulation modelling; Permeability logging techniques; Seismic/log/core calibration; Deep investigation techniques; Development-scale seismic applications; Computer-based 3-D geological modeling; Through casing logging. |
| Drilling and Completion | Slim hole drilling; Unconventional drilling technology; Under balanced drilling; Cementing; Innovative bit and tubular technology; Drilling fluid design; Coiled tubing drilling; Advanced fracture techniques; Measurements while drilling; Multilateral technology; Perforating and well bore cleanup; Well productivity; Horizontal well bore applications. |
| Production | Modification of reservoir fluid mobilities; Injection water treatment; Compact processing on offshort platforms; Oil/water/gas/separation; Produced water treatment; Gas compression techniques; Corrosion control; Paraffin control/removal; Scaling inhibitors; New directional drilling; Advanced recovery of natural gas; Recompletion techniques; Near well bore stimulation; Stimulation techniques. |
| Deepwater Offshore | High pressure systems; ROV systems; Multi-phase pumps; Structures; Produced fluid disposal; Workover; Flowlines; Hydrate prevention; Drilling; Extended reach control systems; Extended reach drilling or production; Subsea equipment; Risers. |
| Arctic Region Activities | Drilling; Transportation; Mobile Ice; Production; Exploration; Development. |
| Oil Processing and Refining | Reactor engineering and modeling; Risk assessment methodology; New materials for construction; Solid acid catalysts; Performance characteristics of new hydrocarbon fuel compositions; Techniques for integration of environmental solutions into process and plant design; Advanced computational modeling of processes/reactions; Hydrogen production and recovery; Environmental characteristics of new hydrocarbon fuel compositions; Energy efficiency of separations; Advanced control and information systems; Energy efficiency of equipment; Relating chemical compositions to process and product performance; Plant and process reliability; Separations technologies; New approaches to refining heavy feeds; Energy efficiency of processes; Catalysts with improved selectivities, yields, lifetimes. |

* Note: Targets are listed in generally increasing order of importance but not in likelihood that they would be commercially available between 1999 and 2010. Targets with high potential impacts are shown in bold.

*Appendix (continued)*

**National Research Council**

**Identification of Long-term RD&D Targets Having Potentially Moderate or High Impacts***

| Research Area | Description |
|---|---|
| Gas Processing | Acid gas removal; Gas dehydration; Separation of high concentrations of impurities (nitrogen, $CO_2$, $H_2S$, etc). |
| Gas Gathering | Multi-phase metering; Compression. |
| Gas Storage | Gas migration control; Leak detection and mitigation; Unconventional development techniques; Well deliverability restoration; Reservoir management. |
| Environmental and Regulatory | Leak detection; Disposal methods for drilling fluids; Compliance with stationary source issue; Remediation technology; Effluent and emission monitoring, minimisation, and control; Treatment and disposal of produced fluids; Provide scientific basis for risk-based regulation. |

* Note: Targets are listed in generally increasing order of importance but not in likelihood that they would be commercially available between 1999 and 2010. Targets with high potential impacts are shown in bold.

# Chapter 4

## NATURAL GAS AND ITS TRANSPORT

### Goals and Rationale

Natural gas is a source of energy that offers substantial benefits. In its natural form, however, natural gas is about a thousand times more voluminous than oil, for the same energy content. Because of this reduced transportability per energy unit in comparison with competing hydrocarbon fuels, and the long distances between remote gas fields and users, the challenge is thus to increase natural gas transportability and market access. Natural gas must be delivered in a form which can satisfy the needs of end-users. In principle, natural gas can be delivered through a pipeline or gasduct, or transformed into liquefied natural gas (LNG) to be shipped, or compressed (CNG) to be delivered in tanks. Or it can be converted into some other chemical substance or fuel, or into electricity (Table 4.1).

*Table 4.1*

**Natural Gas Transportation Modes and Characteristics**

| Transport Mode | Energy Content Relative to Oil (% per unit volume) | Conversion Loss of Primary Energy (%) | Transportation Volume | Transportation Distance |
|---|---|---|---|---|
| Natural gas (at normal temperature and pressure) | 0.1 | | | |
| Pipeline (80 bar) | 8 | 2-3 | Small-Large | Medium |
| LNG | 50 | 10-12 | Medium-Large | Medium-Long |
| CNG (200 bar, tank transport) | 20 | 5-7 | Small-Medium | Short |
| Methanol/Oxygenates | 50 | 30-40 | Medium | Medium-Long |
| Gasoline/Diesel | 100 | 35-45 | Medium | Medium-Long |
| Electricity | n.a. | 50 | Medium | Medium |

n.a. not applicable

The infrastructure installed to bring gas to the market is enormous, in both physical and economic terms. In 1992, there were 702 716 km of transmission pipelines in IEA Member countries, and 25 liquefied natural gas regasification terminals. Total consumption of natural gas in these countries in 1992 was 1 023 bcm, and internal production was 884 bcm, of which 31.5 per cent was produced offshore. These figures compare with a world marketed production of natural gas of 2 106 bcm, of which 19.1 per cent originated offshore. Much of the potential supply of natural gas is located well away from end-users. Increased market access through new and improved transportation technologies is a prerequisite for security of supply and for successfully bringing natural gas to the forefront for new applications. Transport has accordingly been identified as a priority technology area within the natural gas fuel cycle.

Methane ($CH_4$), the main constituent of natural gas, is a greenhouse gas, like carbon dioxide ($CO_2$). Estimates of methane emissions from the natural gas chain vary. This is due to a fundamental lack of data, as well as different vintages of capital stocks and technologies currently in use, including types of production, transmission and distribution system. Leakage from a modern, continuous, all-welded, long-distance, transmission pipeline is negligible (approximately 0.001 per cent), while leakages from converted pre-war town gas distribution systems with screwed couplings are estimated to be up to 2 per cent or more in the worst cases. Methane releases can also occur in some oil producing areas of the world where natural gas is still vented. Methane releases can clearly be remedied, given the proper incentives. Natural gas combustion leads to the emission of other greenhouse gases, notably $CO_2$. But comparisons of total fuel cycle greenhouse gas emissions between the three major fossil fuels (coal, oil and natural gas) indicate that, per unit of energy produced, natural gas has the lowest level of emissions of the three.

The efficiency of the end-use technology is also important. For instance, industrial demand for a process motor drive can be served by two alternative energy paths: direct use of natural gas to generate electric power, or conversion of natural gas to methanol, which can then be transported for use in internal combustion engines.

Depending on the application, the source and cost of the fuel, and the type of fuel previously used, switching to natural gas could contribute to increased energy security (at least from a near to mid-term time frame) as well as offering the environmental benefit of some reduction in greenhouse gas emissions and contributing to the economic development of both producer and end-user countries. Here again, transport is a priority.

Priority goals for natural gas transport are thus to:

- increase market access for remote reserves of natural gas through alternative energy carriers and lower transport costs;
- enhance the diversity of liquid fuels through chemical conversion of natural gas to improve its transport and to encourage new transport sector end-use markets; and
- mitigate the environmental impacts and risks to public health and safety of natural gas transport and delivery.

The present chapter examines long-distance mobility but not local distribution, and it considers use of natural gas only as a provider of energy. Storage, although an integral part of the transportation system, is not discussed. Storage is needed to respond to daily and seasonal variations in demand and to serve as a booster in the event of potential supply disruptions. Further discussion of the use of natural gas for electricity generation, for transport fuels and other end-use purposes can be found in Chapters 8, 9, and 10.

## Technology Description and Assessment

### *Description of Significant Technologies*

a) *Natural Gas Transport*

With very minor exceptions, all natural gas is brought to the market in IEA Member countries either as pipeline gas or as liquefied natural gas (LNG). In one of the variants of the natural gas chain, gas produced offshore is transported to the mainland, processed onshore and then reshipped, through an offshore pipeline for example, to a landing terminal in another country. From the landing terminal it can either be sent through a domestic transmission pipeline or through an international transmission pipeline to a third country. At some stage, it would end up in a regional distribution pipeline before it was distributed in an urban distribution system or dispatched to a big final user such as an energy-intensive industrial enterprise or electricity producer. In some cases the transmission pipeline could be replaced, by a liquefied natural gas chain for instance, because transportation of the gas as LNG is more economical over very long distances. The key technology aspects and options are described below.

(i) Pipeline transportation

The transportation of natural gas in pipelines is a deployed technology. One anomaly exists, however, between onshore and offshore pipelines, where the latter often operate at a much higher pressure than onshore pipelines. Some of the natural gas is utilised for driving pipeline compressors. A typical gas "loss" will be 1 per cent of throughput in a 500 km high-pressure transmission line. A gas pipeline system is capital-intensive and inflexible once laid. It will then carry large amounts of energy, however, at low operating costs for 50 years or more. New and novel technologies could help to further improve gas pipeline operations. Pipeline infrastructure R&D can improve operational flexibility in the delivery and storage of natural gas. For example, new technologies for real-time metering and measurement, technologies for energy content and gas flow, and technologies to ensure pipeline safety are needed.

(ii) Liquefied natural gas

The production and transportation of liquefied natural gas (LNG) at -162°C is a deployed and efficient technology. When liquefied, the density of natural gas increases by a factor of 600. This compares with a volume reduction factor of about 80 for compressed natural gas at 80 bar and normal temperatures. The necessary links in the transport chain are a liquefaction plant at one end, a ship or vehicle for movement of the LNG and a regasification plant at the other end. An integral part of the chain is LNG storage in order to provide for the bulk nature of transport. Acid gas removal and dehydration are particularly important since all substances that become solid at LNG temperatures must be removed from the gas to avoid clogging the chain.

The LNG transport chain requires a substantial energy input, which is usually provided by the natural gas itself. Cooling and liquefaction, the heart of the process, are usually conducted in two separate stages by heat pumps, which work on the same principle as a domestic refrigerator. The first cycle reduces the temperature to around -30°C, the second to -160°C. This process requires very large quantities of cooling water and consumes the majority of the entire LNG chain's energy needs (which represent approximately 10-12 per cent of the incoming gas). While LNG plants function more or less continuously, ships arrive at intervals of at least two to three days. The liquefied gas must therefore be transferred to insulated holding tanks to await shipment. Designed to insulate and hold their cargoes at just below -160°C, LNG ships make up a small portion of the world fleet. The majority of the vessels were built to serve dedicated routes and have a capacity of around 130 000 cubic metres. The liquefaction of the gas requires approximately 8 to 10 per cent of the input gas. Boil-off during the ship voyage is in the range of 0.10 per cent to 0.15 per cent of the transport volume per day. The boil-off gas is either utilised for ship propulsion or reliquefied. The treatment at the receiving terminal is less complex and consumes far less energy than the liquefaction plant. Storage tanks work the same way as those at the liquefaction plant, but may be larger in order to accommodate variations in shipment size due to seasonal and peak demand fluctuations. Between 1 and 2 per cent of the LNG is lost through vaporisation before distribution to customers.

(iii) Compressed natural gas

The large-scale transport of compressed natural gas (CNG) in high-pressure tanks at between 150 bars and 250 bars involves available and next-generation technology. Road transport of CNG has been deployed on a small scale. Numerous studies of barge and ship transport of CNG have indicated that such methods are viable, for low to medium gas volumes, where the water route is preferable.

b) *Chemically Converted Natural Gas*

Difficulties associated with natural gas transport may be overcome by co-locating industries that use gas as a feedstock to sites closer to gas fields. The energy content of natural gas could be embedded in an intermediate energy form or end-use product and transported to distant markets. Local use of indigenous gas may be particularly attractive to newly industrialising countries, since it minimises investment in expensive transmission infrastructure.

An efficient next-generation means of increasing the transportability of natural gas lies in chemical conversion to liquids or to easily condensable gaseous products. Volumes of natural gas energy can be converted to methanol or other liquid products and made available to markets distant from remote on-site production. Natural gas can be converted into liquid products using two technologies. One is production of synthesis gas (a mixture of carbon monoxide and hydrogen) as an intermediate product. The other is direct conversion to a variety of final products. A summary of the major options is given in Figure 4.1.

*Figure 4.1*
**Options for Converting Natural Gas to Liquid Energy Carriers**

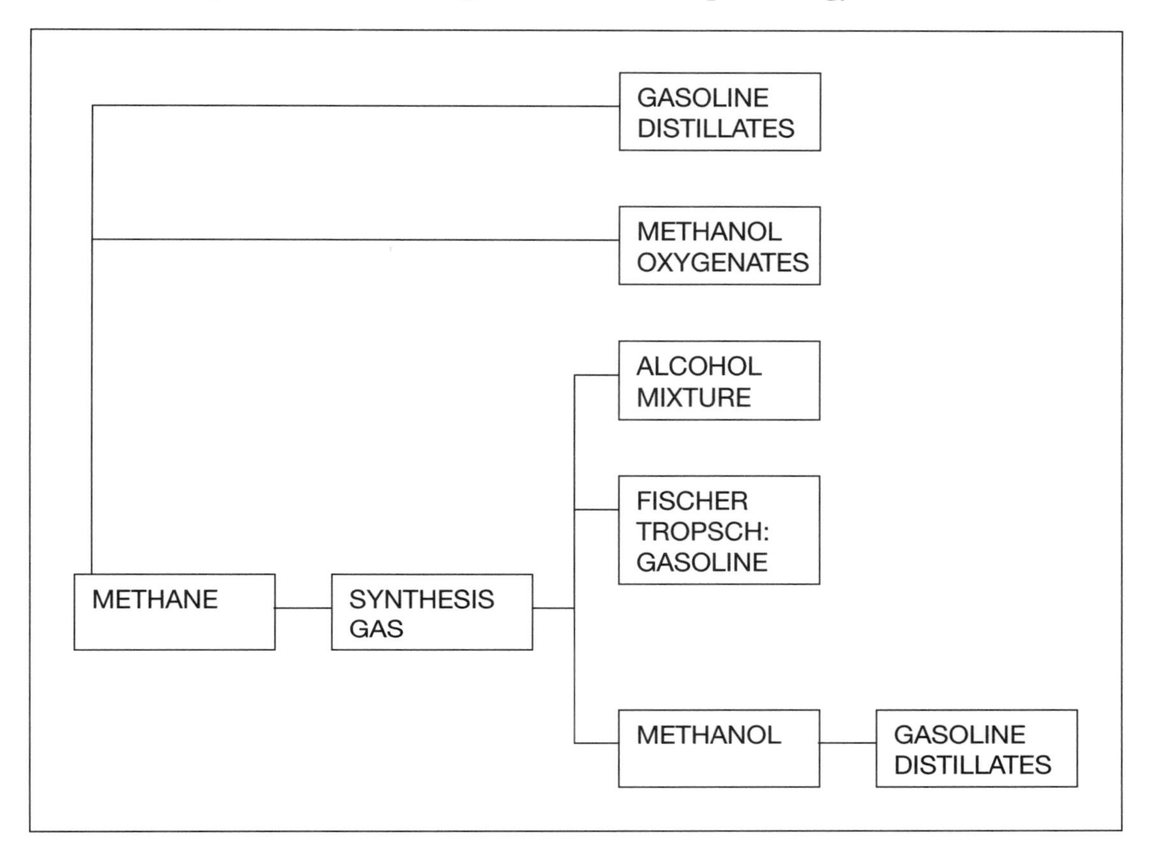


Note: The fine lines indicate technology options for the long term.

The synthesis gas or syngas (SNG) route is technologically far more advanced than the direct conversion route. It consists partially of processes that have been developed and deployed. The thermal efficiency of these processes is estimated to be 60 to 70 per cent. The direct conversion of natural gas, or the $C_1$ chemistry route, has a large potential. But optimal technical solutions have still to be found. If chlorine-based conversion processes are compared with oxygen-based processes, the former are definitely further advanced. Seen from a purely technical point of view, these processes could be installed significantly earlier than the oxygen-based processes. However, since chlorine is a focus of public concern for environmental reasons, installation of such processes would probably need very thorough documentation. In general, it seems that synthesis gas-based processes will constitute the first generation of natural gas conversion processes. However, at present it is very difficult to estimate the economics of the different conversion routes, since these are highly dependent upon locations. Combining conversion processes with other processes will make the overall economics more favourable. One such solution might be to utilise surplus heat from the conversion process for electricity generation.

(i) Conversion of natural gas via synthesis gas

The main disadvantage of the SNG route lies in the capital cost of the synthesis gas plant, which at present accounts for about 60 per cent of the overall capital cost. Processes involving methanol as an intermediate product offer the additional benefit of being flexible (methanol may be sold as such, or olefins, gasoline and diesel can be derived from it).

The primary energy products are methanol (and possibly higher alcohols) and Fischer-Tropsch (FT) hydrocarbons. These products can be easily transported as such, or after upgrading to fuels. Due to the cost-intensive synthesis gas step, all technologies involve costs in the high or medium-to-high range (although the combined process with heat exchange is somewhat less costly). A number of companies are working on new concepts for synthesis gas generation. The technologies can be classified in the manner shown in Table 4.2.

Relative levels of energy utilisation in synthesis gas production are difficult to quantify, since they depend largely on integration effects at the plant site and overall plant optimisation. An estimated energy efficiency rate of 65 per cent or above should be possible today for the total process from natural gas to a transportable liquid.

*Table 4.2*
**Technical and Economic Status of Synthesis Gas Production Technologies**

| SNG Technology | Stage of Development | Cost | Unit Capacity |
|---|---|---|---|
| Steam Reforming | Commercial | High | Large |
| Auto-thermal Reforming | Commercial | Medium-High | Medium |
| Partial Oxidation | Demonstrated | Medium-High | Small-Medium |
| Catalytic Partial Oxidation | R&D | Medium | Large |
| Combined Processes (without heat exchange) | Commercial | Medium-High | Medium |
| Combined Processes (with heat exchange) | R&D | Low-Medium | Small-Medium |

Note: All technologies shown give products that can be easily converted into gasoline, diesel or fuel alcohols. All processes involve high costs and aim at high-volume markets.

(ii) Direct conversion of natural gas

The main challenge in the conversion of methane to higher hydrocarbons stems from the fact that even the simplest product, ethane, is more reactive than the starting material. Substantial efforts are thus called for to keep the products from further reaction. The preferred intermediate products in a coupling process are ethylene or acetylene, since these can be transformed easily into other higher hydrocarbons such as petrol. Another challenge lies in the inertness of methane. Directly coupling methane to higher hydrocarbons requires temperatures as high as 1 000°C. Methane may, however, be coupled at lower temperatures using coupling reagents such as chlorine or oxygen. A summary of the factors involved in such direct conversion is given in Table 4.3.

*Table 4.3*
**Technical and Economic Status of Processes for Direct Conversion to Ethylene**

| Process Technology | Status | Capital Cost | Unit Capacity |
|---|---|---|---|
| KTI-Benson | R&D | Medium | Large |
| Oxichlorination | R&D | Medium-High | Medium |
| Partial Oxidation | R&D | Medium | Medium |

The KTI-Benson process comes in the category of next-generation technology. The reaction includes a non-catalytic chlorine to produce mainly ethylene and acetylene. Hydrogen chloride is a product which has to be re-oxidised to chlorine and recycled. The re-oxidation can be achieved with air by using existing technology. Approximately 40 per cent of the capital costs are associated with this step. An alternative version of the process has been suggested, where the hydrogen chloride re-oxidation step is eliminated. Ethylene may be oligomerised (converted) to fuels using standard, current technology. The process gives quite good yields in hydrocarbons.

The oxichlorination of methane is another next-generation technology. This catalytic, low-temperature (400°C) process has been proved feasible at the laboratory level. The process concept consists of reaction of methane with oxygen and hydrogen chloride in a first step to give methyl chloride and water. This step may give up to 100 per cent conversion of oxygen and hydrogen chloride. After separation of the water, the dry methyl chloride-containing feed is transformed into petrol, hydrogen chloride is recycled to step one and the petrol is further purified. The main advantage of the concept is that, theoretically, a very high conversion of methane to gasoline per pass is possible.

Partial oxidation of methane is another technology. The process concept is to use air/oxygen in the presence of a catalyst, or a regenerable stoichiometric oxidant, to give ethylene/ethane or methanol from methane. Ethylene may be further oligomerised to petrol. It has been indicated that the use of stoichiometric oxidant is not technically feasible. Too much solid matter has to be removed from the reaction zone to the re-oxidation zone and back per converted $Nm^3$ of methane. The reaction of methane to ethylene proceeds at 700°C over corrosive catalysts. Additionally, there seems to exist an upper limit of approximately 20 to 25 per cent yield with the present-day reaction mechanism. However, even though it may be possible to go beyond this limit, the problem may not be solved, since it is likely to be difficult to remove the enormous heat of reaction from the reactor.

Upscaling of the partial oxidation of methane seems entirely possible. However, at 20 per cent conversion of methane, 70 per cent and 30 per cent selectivity to higher hydrocarbons and carbon oxides respectively, is observed. This implies that 1.35 tonnes of carbon dioxide are produced per tonne of higher hydrocarbons. Since both methane and oxygen are valuable raw materials, the production of $CO_2$ constitutes a double loss. The catalytic partial oxidation of methane to methanol is theoretically possible, but it has not been shown to be a conceivable technology. It is suggested that capital costs constitute the bulk of the cost involved in a partial oxidation process, the separation and heat removal stages being the chief elements in the process. The process is probably not only self-sufficient in energy, but could drive a small power plant.

Production of hydrogen as a secondary provider of energy is also attracting support. Since hydrogen reacts with oxygen in combustion processes to form only water (and some $NO_X$), hydrogen is viewed as a possible future clean fuel. At present, the production costs are much higher than for fossil fuels. The least expensive current method for production of hydrogen is steam reforming of natural gas. One such application is the chemically recuperated gas turbine (CRGT) power cycle referred to in Chapter 8. The CRGT cycle incorporates methane steam reforming as a means to recover gas turbine topping cycle waste heat, while producing a design fuel of principally hydrogen and carbon monoxide that has very clean combustion characteristics. Expected cycle efficiency is 55-60 per cent, depending upon technology progress. Hydrogen produced by steam reforming can also be transported in existing natural gas pipelines without modification. However, the energy carrying capacity for a given pipeline would be only 60 per cent of that of natural gas, because of the lower energy density of hydrogen at pipeline pressure and temperature.

c) *Natural Gas Conversion to Electricity*

Two transport options exist. One is to transport the gas closer to the place of consumption and convert it to electric power there. The other option is to convert the gas to electric power at the gas source and then transport the electric power to the consumer. To determine the best means of transport under differing conditions, the most important factors are:

- volume to be transported;
- transport distance; and
- environmental or other relevant considerations associated with the location of the generating source.

Table 4.4 shows an example of how transmission costs compare between natural gas converted into electric energy at the location of consumption and gas converted at its source. The assumptions are: transportation distance of 500 km, use of alternating-current high-voltage transmission lines and available gas combined cycle power plant technology. For these medium distances, electric power transmission would be the preferable solution for low power flows, while gas transmission represents the economic alternative for volumes above 12.5 TWh. It has been observed that, for medium to long distances, the gas pipeline shows a larger cost advantage, while direct current (DC) transmission has moderate potential for reduced transport cost compared with AC transmission. In the future, electricity transmission costs may be substantially reduced through higher power plant conversion efficiencies and use of superconducting materials that may reduce dimensions and weight of equipment and transport losses. The main technology alternatives for a natural gas-fired power plant are utility turbine systems and fuel cells.

*Table 4.4*
**Natural Gas Transmission Cost Comparisons**
(as of 31st December 1993)

| Transportation System | Equivalent Volume Transported (per year) | | |
|---|---|---|---|
| | **5 TWh** | **12.5 TWh** | **25 TWh** |
| Gas Pipeline | 10-15 | 5-7 | 3-5 |
| Electric Power | 6-8 | 5-7 | 5-7 |

Note: TWh measures delivered energy

(i) Utility turbine systems

Available combined cycle plant technology can convert natural gas to electricity at 50 per cent efficiency based upon the lower heating value of the fuel. Next-generation power cycle technologies, such as the inter-cooled steam-injected gas turbine (STIG) and the chemically recuperated gas turbine (CRGT), have an expected technical potential of 55 to 60 per cent cycle efficiency.

The capacity of gas-turbine power plants can be increased using modular blocks of turbines, boilers and generators ranging in size from 20 MWe to 200 MWe. Thus, at each module, electricity unit costs remain relatively unaffected by power plant size. The technology is available, and continuous progress will lead to better performance, lower costs and higher conversion efficiencies.

(ii) Utility fuel cell systems

Fuel cells convert the potential chemical energy of the reformed methane (hydrogen or natural gas, plus air) directly into electricity. Individual cells are stacked in electrical series to increase the voltage output, and increased in area, to produce more current. A typical cell measures from 0.5 to 1.0 square metre and produces 0.5 kWe to 1.0 kWe. Fuel cells also generate co-product heat, which can be used directly or as input to a bottoming cycle to produce additional electricity. Early fuel-cell power plants are expected to be sized from several hundred kW to several MWe. A fuel cell power plant consists of three main parts, namely:

- a fuel processor that cleans and converts natural gas to hydrogen-rich gas;
- a power section with fuel cells that convert the hydrogen-rich fuel to produce direct-current (DC) electricity; and
- a power conditioner that converts the DC electricity to regulated alternating-current (AC) electricity.

Technical advantages of fuel cells include:

- very high efficiency of up to 60 per cent and more, which is sustained at part load;
- zero sulphur dioxide ($SO_2$) emissions and insignificant nitrogen oxide emissions (although, if natural gas is applied directly as fuel, through high-temperature, solid oxide fuel cells may produce small amounts of $NO_X$); and
- modular power blocks, easily matched plant to load, and small units with the same efficiency as larger units.

Conversely, high capital costs currently make fuel cells non-competitive in many applications. Lack of customer familiarity with fuel cells attributes excludes fuel cells from consideration in many prospective applications such as dispersed utility power generation and transportation. A number of fuel cell types are under development. Distinctions between fuel cells are primarily determined by electrolyte type, operating temperature, and fuel, as shown in Table 4.5.

*Table 4.5*
**Technical Status of Fuel Cell Technologies**

| Type of Electrolyte | Fuel | Operating Temperature (°C) | Technological Status | Application Issues |
|---|---|---|---|---|
| Alkaline | $H_2$ | 80-100 | Commercial | Small units in residences, transportation, and space flights |
| Solid Polymer | $H_2$ & Oxygen | 100 | Demonstrated/ Commercial | Small units |
| Phosphoric Acid | $H_2$ | 200 | Demonstrated | Dispersed utility power generation |
| Molten Carbonate | Methane | 650-700 | Demonstrated/R&D | General purpose |
| Solid Oxide | Methane | 800-1000 | R&D | General purpose |

Fuel cells operating directly on natural gas have an environmental and economic advantage over those requiring hydrogen. Thus, for general applications such as electric utility power, molten carbonate and solid oxide cells are the most attractive technology options for the long term, while phosphoric acid cells constitute another advanced technology, to be available shortly.

Phosphoric acid fuel cell power plants are at market-entry status for small, on-site power plants of 200 kWe. Power units now operating have reached 20 000 hours and more. The primary focus is on reducing costs in the near term from approximately US$ 3 000 per kWe to US$ 1 500 per kWe. Molten carbonate fuel cells have been scaled up to commercial-size cell and stack hardware, and they are projected to be ready for market entry around the year 2000. These systems must still be improved to increase performance, to reduce costs and to demonstrate that integrated systems can meet life and efficiency goals. Solid-oxide fuel cells are projected to be ready for commercial use within the next decade. Demonstrations using advanced, lower-cost modules of this type are expected to take place before the year 2000.

### *Assessment of Technical and Economic Potential*

a) *Natural Gas Transport*

Seen from a technical viewpoint, the potential of each natural gas technology to meet policy goals varies considerably. A summary of R&D needs and opportunities regarding natural gas-based technologies is presented in Table 4.6.

*Table 4.6*
**Natural Gas Transport Technologies: R&D Needs and Opportunities**

| Technology | Bottlenecks | Spillovers | R&D Requirements |
|---|---|---|---|
| On-shore Pipelines (higher pressures) | • Regulatory arrangements | • Manufacturing technology | • Materials and weldability |
| LNG-plants | • High capital cost<br>• Safety requirements and siting | • Membrane technology<br>• Centrifugal contactors | • High-performance membranes<br>• Mechanical contactors |
| LNG-transport | • Safety requirements | • Material technology | • Insulation<br>• Ice-capable LNG tankers |
| Direct LNG Fuel Use (stationary applications, ground vehicles, ships and aircraft) | • Technology demonstration<br>• Lack of LNG distribution systems<br>• Regulatory arrangements | • Space and hydrogen technology | • LNG engines<br>• Storage, insulation and fuelling<br>• Distribution technology<br>• Gas engines |
| CNG Transport | • Limits to CNG distribution<br>• Regulatory arrangements | • New materials<br>• Adsorbent technology | • Conceptual system design<br>• High strength materials<br>• Adsorbents/physics |

(i) Pipeline transportation

Technology developments that reduce pipeline costs include horizontal drilling under crossings and enhanced-strength steel for pipelines. Horizontal drilling under rivers or roads greatly reduces the disruption and environmental damage caused by digging trenches. As a result, construction permission can be obtained more quickly than for conventional crossings.

The material cost of a pipeline system is for the most part directly related to the diameter and thickness of the pipe. The use of a stronger pipe means it can have a thinner wall or be used for operation at higher pressure. The incremental cost reductions may, however, be offset by other factors such as more stringent environmental and safety regulations. It is probable that higher maximum pressures will be introduced for new onshore pipelines, especially those laid in sparsely-populated areas. Progress is expected with regard to materials and weldability of steel pipelines. While non-steel materials will be utilised increasingly for distribution systems, long-distance, high-pressure pipelines for dry gas will continue to be made from steel.

(ii) Liquefied natural gas

The cost of the entire liquefaction plant accounts for more than half of the total investment in the LNG chain. The volume to be transported determines the number of liquefaction units (also known as trains) required. The cost of adding new trains to an existing plant is considerably less than the cost of the first unit, since housing, sea terminal and offsite facilities are already in place. The cost of ocean shipping, on the other hand, is closely linked to the distance between producer and market, also the volume to be transported. The distance and volume determine the number of tankers required and their size, as well as the storage capacities at the liquefaction plant and reception terminal. A greater number of smaller ships means more frequent port calls and reduced terminal storage requirements. Economies of scale mean that larger carriers are preferred for long-haul routes.

Improvements will be needed in the areas of methane and $NO_x$ emissions for all links in the chain. Further improvements can be expected in the area of thermal insulation of LNG tanks, both onboard ships and onshore. Development of both larger and smaller LNG ships is needed to improve transport economics for new trades. Development of Arctic gas reservoirs may necessitate the development of ice-capable LNG tankers. For the LNG liquefaction process, there is potential to be exploited in the development of membrane technology, centrifugal contactors and other separation and purification methods.

Looking into next-generation technology, one may expect that LNG will be utilised in its liquid form as a transport fuel instead of being converted back to its gaseous state or chemically converted to liquids like methanol. The first generation of LNG-fuelled vehicles was demonstrated as early as the mid 1960s as "add-on" technology to conventional vehicles. LNG-fuelled trains are being evaluated, and a Russian (Tupolev) aircraft has been flown successfully using LNG fuel.

(iii) Compressed natural gas

CNG has a market potential for transportation of small/medium gas volumes over short to medium distances. It seems likely that commercial demonstration projects with ship or barge transport of CNG will be initiated in a short-term timeframe, most probably in an area lacking gas infrastructure. The safety issues associated with CNG must be addressed systematically at the design stage. The escape of methane from a CNG system should be low, and on a par with that of a regular gas pipeline system. Possible new technology includes more efficient materials for high-pressure tanks, the use of zeolites or similar gas adsorbents, and more efficient loading and unloading methods.

b) *Chemically Converted Natural Gas*

Although the end products may be the same, the technical potential for chemically converted natural gas to meet policy goals is dependent on the conversion system. In general, direct conversion offers a larger potential than SNG but requires more research and development because uncertainties remain.

(i) Conversion of natural gas via synthesis gas

The technical potential offered by processes using synthesis gas as an intermediate energy carrier is moderate to high. The technologies used for SNG production from natural gas present the advantages and challenges described below.

- Reduced capital investment. Once-through steam reforming with efficient heat exchange and new syngas technology are key factors.
- Maximum energy efficiency. Excess steam could be used in adjacent facilities or converted into electricity. Overall efficiency greater than 70 per cent can be achieved.
- Maximum carbon efficiency. Total $CO_2$ emissions should be minimised, preferably below 15 per cent of the carbon feed.
- Maximum product selectivity. Environmentally attractive products would be preferred.
- Feedstock flexibility. Rich gas as well as $CO_2$ mixture would meet feedstock requirements. Natural gas pressure should fit the synthesis gas concept.
- Process integration. Incorporation into a larger facility with multiple product slates or energy generation systems (e.g. CRGT), hydrogen and ammonia production, or even conventional refining and chemical processing, will increase performance.

Table 4.7 summarises technology barriers, possible spillovers and R&D requirements.

(ii) Direct conversion of natural gas

The technical potential of direct conversion of natural gas is high, and R&D needs and opportunities are shown in Table 4.8. Both the KTI-Benson process and oxichlorination approach are technically feasible, also on an industrial scale. No $CO_2$ is co-produced in either of these processes. $SO_X$ and $NO_X$ do not pose any problem, since no high-temperature burning of gases is required.

*Table 4.7*
**Natural Gas SNG Conversion Technologies: R&D Needs and Opportunities**

| Technology (Product) | Barriers | Spillovers | R&D Requirements |
|---|---|---|---|
| Methanol | • Fluidised bed and slurry reactor demonstration<br>• Catalyst technology | • Syngas reactor technology | • Improvement of syngas reactor performance<br>• Catalyst development |
| Gasoline and Diesel from methanol | • Fluidised bed reactor<br>• Catalyst technology | • Syngas reactor technology | • Process optimisation |
| Gasoline and Diesel from syngas | • Demonstration of reactor technology<br>• Catalyst technology | • Process engineering | • Process and plant optimisation<br>• Catalyst development |

*Table 4.8*
**Natural Gas Direct Conversion Technologies: R&D Needs and Opportunities**

| Technology | Barriers | Spillovers | R&D Requirements |
|---|---|---|---|
| KTI-Benson | • System engineering<br>• Material technology | • Environmental impact | • Chlorine balance<br>• Material development |
| Oxichlorination | • Chlorine balance<br>• Material technology | • New materials | • Process development |
| Partial oxidation | • Catalyst technology<br>• Reactor testing | • Membrane technology | • Catalyst and reactor development |

The main challenge lies in controlling the overall chlorine balance, i.e. not releasing any chlorine out of the process, for both economic and environmental reasons. Because of the corrosive character of chlorine and hydrogen chloride, special construction materials for the plant are needed. This may be expensive. Special technology has to be developed for the separation of small amounts of chlorinated products from hydrocarbon streams, as well as technologies for recirculation of these products.

Similar problems are already encountered in other areas of the chemical processing industry because of environmental issues. Extra impetus for eliminating the above bottlenecks may therefore be expected. These new solutions do not, in principle, require any basically new developments in chemistry.

Technology with regard to partial oxidation of methane offers significant economic potential for the future. Sufficient laboratory data exists to plan the first pilot plants. However, for the technology to be feasible on a large scale, integration with other processes is required. The energy generated in the coupling reaction is adequate to supply the whole process and also drive a small power station. The carbon balance can be optimised (and greenhouse gas emission reduced) by re-hydrogenating the carbon oxides to methane, but this is not a very economical alternative. Hydrogen is co-produced in the process.

Since only 20 to 25 per cent of methane is converted per pass, large amounts of methane have to be recycled. An important area for optimisation of existing technology is therefore the separation part of the process. However, major advances in the field will have to be made. The methane coupling reaction should proceed at temperatures below 500°C and essentially new chemistry will have to be found. This will, it is hoped, ensure better control over conversion/selectivity of the reaction.

It is expected that new related technology, such as membrane reactors, high-temperature membranes for the separation of methane/nitrogen or methane from the other products of the process, will add impetus to the development of feasible methane coupling. Since chlorine is a focus of public concern for the environment, installation of such processes would probably need very thorough documentation. On the other hand, these processes have a positive aspect since the amounts of CO, $NO_x$ and $SO_x$ produced are only minimal.

Oxygen-based processes have a large potential, but significant advances still have to be made. On environmental issues, $CO_2$ emissions must be significantly reduced. Technically this is possible, but expensive. Cheaper variants will call for new chemistry, the discovery of which is in principle both possible and probable. Such new chemistry would have a profound influence on all the oxygen-based processes, since new pathways for methane conversion would then be available. Other important bottlenecks concern cheap separation of oxygen from nitrogen, high (700-1000°C) and room-temperature separation of methane and nitrogen. Developments in the field of membrane technology will play a major role in resolving the above issues.

The development of solutions regarding the separation side of the processes would need initial short-term government support. As progress is made, industry should take over.

c) *Natural Gas Conversion to Electricity*

Electricity for power machinery and processes is an important element in industrial development, and natural gas can provide this in a very efficient and environmentally attractive way. Electricity can also be an efficient means of meeting heating demands. A fairly large share of fossil fuel is used for direct combustion heating. If electricity is used for driving heat pumps to pump low-value ambient heat from the outside to the inside, primary energy requirements can be reduced. An energy system based on electric power generation and distribution to local heat pumps will reduce gas consumption to half that required by direct combustion. Similar efficiencies can be realised through electro-magnetic induction and radiation process heating technology. It follows that $CO_2$ emissions will be correspondingly reduced. This example illustrates the importance of viewing transportation of natural gas by pipeline or transmission line in the context of the end-use as well as the context of the volumes and distances involved. Chemical conversion, on the other hand, provides a unique degree of freedom from high-cost and fixed-location transportation infrastructure, albeit with some cost differential likely.

Inasmuch as electricity production from natural gas is an established and mature technology, technical opportunities are well understood and under development by large equipment manufacturers and other research organisations. Particularly attractive are opportunities for increased efficiency through higher-temperature advanced gas turbines and their application in advanced power cycle configurations, as referred to above. In parallel with these gas turbine developments, fuel cell technology could conceivably lead to major new lines of development, with related learning curves, once the technology has achieved market entry.

## Technology Prospects and Markets

### *Market Trends*

Table 4.9 summarises market potential for the various natural gas transportation technologies. The impact on the market is potentially large in the case of some of the new technologies described. But increased utilisation of existing technology is equally conceivable.

For chemically converted natural gas, market penetration is assumed to be irrespective of the route chosen for conversion. Table 4.10 estimates market potential for the two major products, methanol and gasoline.

*Table 4.9*

**Comparative Market Potential for Natural Gas Transport Technologies**

| Technology | Time-frame (years) | Nature/Size of Market | Regional Aspects | Market Potential |
|---|---|---|---|---|
| Onshore Pipelines (higher pressures) | 0-30 | • Very large market | • Pipelines laid in sparsely populated areas | • Oil price rises and environmental considerations will be major driving forces |
| Natural gas liquefaction (LNG) | 0-30 | • Probable large increase in LNG trade for environmental and economic reasons | • Areas with an existing gas infrastructure | • As above |

*Table 4.9 (continued)*

**Comparative Market Potential for Natural Gas Transport Technologies**

| Technology | Time-frame (years) | Nature/Size of Market | Regional Aspects | Market Potential |
|---|---|---|---|---|
| Direct LNG Fuel Use (stationary, vehicles, ships, aircraft) | 10-30 | • Potential market is very large<br>• Actual market penetration in short and medium term is uncertain | • Countries which export, import or otherwise handle LNG<br>• Countries with own gas resources | • As above |
| CNG transport | 0-20 | • Low to medium gas volumes and short to medium distances | • Developing countries lacking large single markets<br>• Countries or regions lacking gas infra-structure | • As above<br>• Local environ-mental concerns may add momentum |

*Table 4.10*

**Comparative Market Potential for Products from Chemically Converted Natural Gas Technologies**

| Technology (Products) | Time-frame (years) | Nature/Size of Market | Regional Aspects | Market Potential |
|---|---|---|---|---|
| Methanol | 0-10<br><br>10-20 | • Small potential for develop-ment<br>• Moderate market penetration | • Market with strong government regulations | • Government action will be required to establish a methanol fuel market |
| Gasoline | 10-20<br><br>20+ | • Limited potential<br>• Large market | | • Oil price rise will be major driving force<br>• Environmental considerations favour diesel from natural gas |

Methanol could also be produced as an intermediate product to be used in the fuel market. Diesel fuel produced by FT synthesis may take significant market shares as environmental restrictions are enacted. It appears likely that new constraints on fuel composition will be imposed, such as removal of benzene and higher aromatics from gasoline, or reduction of total aromatics content in diesel to the 10 to 15 per cent weight range (today it is 34 per cent in the United States). In addition, sulphur will probably be restricted to between 0.05 and 0.1 per cent. Synthetic fuels typically contain no sulphur. All these factors will improve the prospects over the long term for transport fuels derived from natural gas.

For next-generation technologies to be competitive in comparison with crude oil refining, oil prices must rise substantially. If a technological breakthrough is made, methanol produced directly from methane may have a major market impact. Methanol is primarily used today as a chemical feedstock and, to some extent, in blended gasoline. M85, a blend of 85 per cent methanol and 15 per cent gasoline, is currently marketed by major oil companies in California. M85 or other alternative fuels will face stiff competition from reformulated gasoline produced through improved available refining technology.

With respect to the conversion of gas to electricity, gas turbine power plants have already made an impact on the energy market, and natural gas-based fuel cells are in the process of commercialisation. Conversion of gas to electricity and transporting it by conventional means will be preferable to transporting gas through pipelines, when the distance is short and the volume is small to medium. Economical transmission distances will increase significantly if the potential of superconductors is realised.

### *Key Players*

Key participants in determining the rate of progress in technologies for transporting natural gas include: gas utilities and transportation companies; shipping companies; technology and engineering suppliers; governments and inter-governmental organisations; regulatory and standard-setting institutions; environmental and other public interest groups. The most active participants can have an influence on technology progress at a strategic level and can directly affect the orientation and magnitude of progress.

From a technical viewpoint, natural gas transportation using conventional and accepted technologies is relatively straightforward and non-controversial. Natural gas transportation is governed by regulations and standards worldwide. The transmission and distribution of natural gas offer greater economies of scale than is the case for oil products. This has led to the emergence of local and national monopolies and regionalised market structures. But these market characteristics are changing, and one of the major driving forces for change is the search for more efficient energy markets. In the gas market, regulatory measures aimed at greater efficiency focus mainly on the transportation sector.

To a large extent, gas transportation technology is what determines the structure of gas markets and, as a consequence, market regulation. This often has a major effect on end-user prices and is growing in significance and complexity. The key players in building and operating a large natural-gas pipeline are typically the gas sellers, the transport companies, the technology supply companies, the government regulatory bodies, other standards-setting institutions, the environmental groups, land owners and, finally, gas customers. Depending on the circumstances, all these players can contribute to establishing how the technology evolves, including the pace of introducing new technology. Research in the long-distance pipeline sector seems adequately covered by existing private and government programmes.

In the case of liquefaction of natural gas, transport of LNG and barge or ship transport of CNG, additional players are involved. Alongside the owners of the transportation system and the sellers and buyers of the gas, the International Maritime Organisation is involved, as are national maritime organisations, classification societies, the landowners and the local population at the loading and unloading sites. R&D needs in the LNG sector are being met by the private and government players. As LNG transportation increases in international commerce, enhanced focus on the environment and safety may be needed where both transport and storage are concerned.

R&D in the CNG transportation sector is currently small-scale, in line with the present scale and mode of utilisation. The development of adsorbents and composite-material pressure vessels could, however, offer potential that justifies intensified R&D. Moreover, potential applications exist that could result in significantly increased use, CNG-powered vehicles being an example. As with LNG, current R&D commitments may thus prove inadequate as commercial applications expand.

Direct use of LNG as a fuel, with regasification immediately preceding combustion, is currently common practice among stationary users like generating plants located adjacent to LNG-import terminals. Its use as a fuel for buses, heavy trucks, private cars, locomotives, ships and even aeroplanes has been demonstrated. But these demonstrations are one or two decades old in many instances, and reflect neither current technology nor environmental concerns. Research on use of liquid hydrogen as a transport fuel has also been conducted. A methane economy could be regarded as an important forerunner of a possibly more flexible hydrogen economy, and it might utilise much of the same type of technology at a lower price and level of sophistication.

The players are numerous in a new technological chain for production, distribution and use of LNG as a fuel for vehicles. The major players are LNG producers and distributors, as well as sellers and buyers of the fuel. Others are technology supply companies, machinery manufacturers and government regulatory bodies. While R&D now conducted by both private and government bodies is clearly below the scale warranted by its technical potential, it reflects an awareness of difficulties in pursuing these concepts at relatively low energy prices.

Suppliers of chemically converted natural gas technology will play an essential part in advances in this field, since most technologies are in the prospective category or barely beyond the demonstration stage of development. In SNG-based technologies, the synthesis gas step accounts for about 60 per cent of the cost. This area has potential for improvement, and a number of companies are working on new concepts. Private-sector and public-sector R&D entities have identified promising technologies, and appropriate resources would appear to have been allocated.

Significant resources in private-sector R&D have been allocated to direct conversion. To pave the way to the technological breakthroughs that are required, further impetus will be needed for international programmes on methane conversion at low temperature, $C_1$ chemistry, and controlled oxidation of saturated hydrocarbons. The potential of chlorine-based processes has not been evaluated in depth. Some researchers have rejected this route because of safety concerns over handling and use of chlorine. However, a more detailed assessment of possible benefits, the issues involved and the chances of overcoming them appears warranted.

To achieve more efficient energy use through electricity generation, the chief players are the electrical utilities, governments and technology suppliers. The principal technological targets for sustained focus to promote natural gas use are combined cycle technology (including advanced high-temperature gas turbines, their application in advanced power cycle configurations such as the CRGT and STIG cycles) and fuel cells.

### *Market Barriers*

The major facilitating and constraining factors that can affect the development and market deployment of new and improved technologies to increase natural gas transportability are listed in Table 4.11.

*Table 4.11*

**Natural Gas Transport: Economic and Other Factors Affecting Technology Development and Market Deployment**

| Facilitating Factors | Constraining Factors |
|---|---|
| • General transition to hydrocarbons with lower $CO_2$ and other gas emission levels (Oxygen with higher hydrogen to carbon ratio)<br>• Taxation of fossil fuels according to emission levels<br>• Existence of long-term contracts offering stability in prices and energy accessibility<br>• Large resource potential in or near IEA countries<br>• Government-imposed technology development (such as the US Clean Air Act) | • Perceptions of limited availability, insufficient market competitiveness and transport infrastructure<br>• User perceptions regarding safety<br>• Lack of common-carrier principle in natural gas (and electricity) transportation systems<br>• Limited adoption of international equipment/ technology standards<br>• Inconsistencies between national, regional and international energy planning<br>• Trade protectionism, tax and price subsidies |

Some technologies, such as use of LNG as a vehicle fuel, are likely to prompt public concern and resistance unless they can be proved practical, safe and reliable. Resistance may also be expected from car manufacturers, from fuel distribution chains and others who could be affected financially by the introduction of a new fuel. Similarly, environmental concerns regarding diesel engine emissions may affect the potential market for diesel fuel, even though synthetic diesel is environmentally superior and diesel engines have a higher efficiency than gasoline engines. Further examples could be cited. The purpose of these examples is to stress the importance of attitudinal market barriers set against technological concepts that might radically alter the existing infrastructure. In such cases, and if the potential benefits to the nation are great, government leadership can significantly help to establish a secure market for technology commercialisation.

## Technology Policy Issues

### *Role of Governments*

Table 4.12 identifies government measures which may facilitate market penetration of key technologies for transporting natural gas. Technological innovations in transport for natural gas can be integrated into a national energy and industry strategy. When a new technology can contribute substantially to established goals, then governmental leadership, financial support and economic and regulatory policies can accelerate technological development that might otherwise be delayed because of the uncertainties of market response. Two factors are important in this respect: the transmission cost in gas transportation, and market regulation. In 1990, transmission costs in the United States constituted 33 per cent of the average wholesale price, and 20 per cent of the average end-user price. Transmission costs include haulage, storage and modulation costs. In addition to the economic benefit, new and improved natural gas transportation technology may affect market regulation and structure. As new technology options become available, IEA governments are increasingly reassessing their organisation of natural gas transport facilities and operations. From the standpoint that transmission facilities are natural monopolies and that society would not be efficiently served by parallel and duplicate facilities, many would see access to transportation as a prerequisite for introducing competition between sellers and buyers in the gas market.

Others would maintain that removal of monopolies and freedom to build pipelines is a more appropriate solution. As part of general energy market reform aimed at increasing economic efficiency, many governments are taking steps to increase competition generally in the utility sector, including the gas sector. Where gas transportation is concerned, this may mean allowing the construction of new pipelines to create competition and, in some cases, it implies forms of third-party access to transportation facilities, whether negotiated or mandatory. Increasing competition may encourage investments in new technology but could discourage R&D on longer-term, higher-risk technology options. Experience to date suggests that increased access to transportation facilities need not necessarily be incompatible with technology progress and long-term gas contracts.

*Table 4.12*

**Natural Gas Transportability: Government Role in Technology Deployment**

| Technology | Level of Market Activity | Need for Government Support | Possible Government Measures |
|---|---|---|---|
| Pipeline and LNG transport | • Largely covered | • Low, but could increase | • Focus on safety and environmental issues in R&D |
| CNG transport | • Largely covered | • Low, but could increase | • Exploiting market potential for the technology in industrialising countries<br>• Funding R&D |
| Conversion to liquid fuels via SNG gas | • Largely covered | • Low | • Regulatory support for industrial projects |
| Direct conversion to liquid fuels | • Long-term prospect | • High | • Funding of R&D on international co-operation basis |
| Moving energy-intensive industry to the gas source and adapting technology to that need | • Low, no clear market demand | • Moderate to high | • Establishing a policy framework to promote this strategy<br>• Exploiting market potential in industrialising countries |
| Expanding use of natural gas in the efficient energy end-use system to improve and reduce air emissions | • Increasing, particularly in the industrial and residential sectors | • Moderate to high | • Establishing a policy framework to demonstrate feasibility<br>• Funding collaborative technology projects |

***Role of International Co-operation***

To a large extent, expansion of the use of natural gas will be dependent upon international co-operation, both at government levels and between participants within the gas industry. Major areas for international co-operation are listed in Table 4.13. In the field of natural gas technology, international co-operation already exists on a wide scale in the form of multi-client R&D programmes, co-operative R&D projects with direct involvement of natural gas industries from different countries, exchange of research personnel and joint training programmes. The gas industry and the professional associations maintain a leading position.

*Table 4.13*
**Natural Gas Transportability:**
**Role of International Co-operation in Technology Progress**

| Technology | Prospects for Co-operation | Modes of Co-operation | Technology Transfer Issues | Potential IEA Role |
|---|---|---|---|---|
| General, at the strategic level | • Moderate | • Identification of policies and technologies that should be promoted | • Need for sharing of evaluation criteria and results | • Large |
| Specific technology at the sectoral level | • Moderate | • Involvement of natural gas industry<br>• preparation of standards<br>• information exchange | • Need for sharing of experience | • Moderate |
| Fundamental technology for conversion of methane to liquid fuels | • High | • Multilateral agreements between governments and other entities | • Need for technical co-operation while preserving intellectual property rights of participants | • Large |

The most important role to be played by the IEA is probably at the policy co-ordination level. This includes identifying areas and technologies that merit attention in terms of development and deployment potential, as well as fostering co-operation and technology information dissemination. An International Centre for Gas Technology Information has been created by IEA countries. The Centre was conceived to operate in a global context and to provide links between the existing national and regional technology information services in North America, Europe, and the Pacific region. The objective is to facilitate the establishment of a global R&D projects database and an international clearing-house for information on natural gas technology advances and new applications, including technologies for natural gas transmission and distribution. Adapting new technologies to meet local needs is essential, especially for countries of central and eastern Europe and the Newly Independent States. In the past, the former Soviet Union and other centrally planned economies gave priority to the development of technologies for the production and long-distance transportation of natural gas. Conversely, in the IEA countries the focus has been on developing technologies for energy-efficient consumption of natural gas. In the foreseeable future, as at present, priorities will be shifting in the IEA countries, where there is increased emphasis on technologies and methods that can contribute to efficient natural gas supply, while encouraging market integration and competition in gas transportation. In the former centrally planned economies, the priority is energy-efficient gas consumption and the introduction of free-market principles. In this changing context, the new IEA Centre may also provide IEA countries and others with an effective means of facilitating technology collaboration and transfer.

In the long term, the potential for R&D co-operation is great. One important area, which is technically difficult and yet promises high-value consequences if accomplished successfully, is the development of new, thermoneutral, low-temperature pathways (below 500°C, and preferably at room temperature) for activation and conversion of methane. This is a long-term objective requiring substantial and sustained commitment. A number of beneficial spin-offs associated with expanded knowledge of $C_1$ chemistry and the controlled oxidation of hydrocarbons can be expected. Chlorine-based processes are techni-cally further advanced and, from a purely technical viewpoint, could be installed earlier than oxygen-based processes. More catalyst development is needed, but efforts should be directed chiefly towards the separation and recycling of chlorine-containing hydrocarbons. Meeting these challenges would be highly beneficial to the chemical process industry.

The natural gas industry is a mature institution in many countries; and yet, even though it is a clean and low-cost energy source, natural gas is under-used. Clearly, high-value technological opportunities can be exploited through collaborative participation of government as well as industry in the fundamental sciences and in R&D to explore concepts for transporting natural gas as a liquid energy carrier. Because of the high capital cost of current pipeline and electricity systems, new interconnections between gas supplies and markets also merit attention, as do technological adaptations of systems to facilitate use of gas at the point of supply. Such applications could be of value to industrialising countries and could increase global energy security through reduced dependency on oil in regions where natural gas is available. International standards can assist in this process, and governments could well increase the focus on preparation of industry performance standards, particularly in relation to the environment and safety, and so reduce market entry barriers and investment risks. Effective and transparent standardisation is important in the near term in the area of technology for the transport and storage of liquefied natural gas, to the extent that it is increasingly becoming a commodity traded on a worldwide scale.

## Approach

According to the IEA *World Energy Outlook* (1996), gas demand and production, and dependence among the IEA countries on external gas supplies, will increase over the next fifteen years. Where natural gas transportability is concerned, this trend will call for new and improved technologies to lower infrastructure costs, while helping to extend natural gas applications into new market areas.

Available technologies for transportation of large volumes of natural gas over long distances, that is, via pipeline and as LNG, hold some potential for innovation or improvement. Major breakthroughs in the direction of satisfying policy goals will involve converting the natural gas before transportation. Chemical conversion of natural gas to liquid products and to electricity both have great potential in terms of transforming the gas at source into more readily transportable energy carriers. The approach using electricity as the vector still relies on fixed transmission infrastructure. Only the chemical conversion route offers the possibility of a major increase in flexibility. One alternative strategy is to move energy-intensive industries closer to the energy source, rather than moving energy to industries.

Pipeline transportation is an available technology offering large capacity and a degree of potential for improvement in a five-year to twenty-year time-frame. Although this technology is not expected to contribute significantly to lower transportation costs, it will probably be the preferred alternative for transportation of large volumes in the time-frame of this study.

The transportation of CNG in pressure vessels is available technology which may be improved by next-generation technology achievable within some ten to twenty years. The technology could contribute to reduced transportation costs for low to medium gas volumes and short to medium distances. The technology can be used for both sea and land transportation. Environmental impacts and safety risks are not expected to be a problem for a properly designed system. This could be a suitable technology for newly industrialising countries.

Transport of LNG is an available technology for large volumes. There is modest potential for improvement during the next five to twenty years. Ice-capable LNG vessels may be needed for exploitation of Arctic natural gas. LNG transport will probably be the preferred alternative for inter-continental transportation of large volumes over sea in a 30-year time-frame, provided the end-user requires the energy in the form of natural gas. As volumes in commerce increase, continuing technological emphasis may be placed on safety and environmental acceptability, including storage facilities.

The challenge regarding the indirect and direct chemical conversion of natural gas lies not in the transportation mode, but in the development of the conversion processes themselves. A wide spectrum of technologies exist, ranging from available technology to technology options for the long term. Available technologies are cost effective only in limited application. But, because of their potential, next-generation technologies are suitable targets for international collaboration. Synthesis gas-based processes will probably be available first. Direct conversion of methanol to gasoline and diesel fuel presents considerable potential. Additional R&D is thus needed in this area.

The most attractive concepts for natural gas-based electricity generation are likely to be low-emission power plants incorporating high-efficiency advanced gas turbines and electricity production from fuel cells. The former are mainly based on available technology and development of aero-derivative combustion turbine technology and system integration. While fuel cells have been demonstrated on a small scale, it is expected that they can be commercialised as a next-generation technology for large-scale application. Among the modes of transportation, transmission of electricity would be the preferred alternative to gas pipelines for short distances and small to medium volumes. In the long term, development and implementation of superconductive transmission equipment may substantially broaden the scope of electricity transmission by increasing energy volumes and distances, while reducing the associated cost.

To meet the technology priorities identified in this chapter, IEA Member countries may wish to contribute to and co-operate in a technology strategy and collaborative R&D programme aimed at the measures listed below.

- Stimulating technology advances and improvement on available and demonstrated natural gas transport and conversion systems, particularly technology relating to natural gas pipelines and liquefied natural gas, compressed natural gas, and natural gas transformation into electric power.

- Promoting the demonstration of natural gas conversion via syngas while supporting R&D on direct chemical conversion of natural gas into liquid hydrocarbons as a technology option for the long term, at the same time maintaining a special R&D focus on increased energy efficiency, process development and plant optimisation, chemical kinetics, and the preparation of new catalysts and materials.

- Facilitating inter-industry collaboration on technology progress to increase the safety, environmental compatibility, operability and maintenance of pipeline and liquefied natural gas transport systems.

- Exchanging information on environmental impacts of natural gas transportation technology and the technological means for reducing those impacts.

- Developing and harmonising regulatory frameworks and technical standards regarding the safety, management, and environmental performance of natural gas projects to promote continuing technology development and deployment.

- Enhancing technology collaboration with non-Member countries that have access to natural gas resources, in order to promote efficient transport and local use of natural gas, and thus increase fuel source flexibility and security, both nationally and internationally.

# Chapter 5

## NUCLEAR FISSION TECHNOLOGIES

### Goals and Rationale

Nuclear fission energy continues to make a substantial contribution to the diversification of energy supplies in the IEA region. It is a proven technology that emits no sulphur dioxide, nitrogen oxides or greenhouse gases in power generation, thereby providing one means of responding to a number of environmental challenges now confronting the planet. It also contributes to energy security. Uranium reserves, of which IEA Member countries have a major proportion, are abundant, widespread and not subject to depletion concerns. Nuclear power generation has contributed significantly to meeting increasing electricity demand. The IEA's *World Energy Outlook* (1996 edition) addresses current and future nuclear power generation. This is currently concentrated in OECD countries, which account for around 80 per cent of world nuclear generation. In these countries, it has played a major role in the marked reduction of reliance on imported oil. The report projects a continued slowdown however, in the rate of growth of nuclear generated power over the outlook period.

Since 1985, there has been a slowdown in the rate of growth of nuclear capacity. Indeed, as the rate of closures of nuclear stations increases towards the end of the century, and given the current low rate of addition to nuclear capacity, it is expected that nuclear power's share of total electricity generation may have reached a temporary peak. Given the serious public concerns over nuclear safety and waste disposal, nuclear's share may in fact decline. Despite aggressive Japanese plans to develop nuclear power, growth in nuclear electricity output in the OECD is expected to grow by about 1.2 per cent over the first half of the projection period to 2010 and to remain flat in the period thereafter, when the effects of current decisions for nuclear plant closures in OECD Europe and North America will be felt more strongly. Losing the nuclear option would reduce the diversification opportunities that enhance energy security, and could increase the difficulty of both meeting growing electricity demand economically and addressing global climate change.

Some countries intend to continue their nuclear construction programmes because they consider nuclear energy to be an important contributor to energy security which can play a significant role in reducing the growth of greenhouse gas emissions. Other countries are not developing nuclear power either because they have ample supplies of other fuels or because of perceived potential adverse health and safety consequences. Also, in some countries the economics of nuclear power have appeared less favourable, compared with other sources such as natural gas. In a number of countries, the development of nuclear energy technologies is effectively in abeyance as these issues are debated. The contribution of nuclear power in the industrialising countries will likely remain small in meeting energy requirements to 2010. The highly capital intensive nature of this energy form, its technological complexity, and the shortage of suitably trained personnel, imply a very high reliance upon external sources and a drain on resources and currency. Of these countries only South Africa, China, South Korea, Taiwan, India, Pakistan, Argentina and Brazil generated electricity from nuclear energy in 1992. However, all IEA countries agree on the necessity for continuing to apply the highest available standards of nuclear safety.

In this context, technology priority goals for nuclear fission energy are to:

- develop and deploy economically competitive nuclear power generating technologies with standard or modular designs while maintaining and enhancing safety;
- develop and deploy acceptable nuclear waste management technologies and systems;
- widen the safeguarded applicability of nuclear fission energy and expand its resource base.

These technology priority goals are broadly shared, both nationally and internationally, among nations with significant operating nuclear capacity. Nuclear accidents at Chernobyl in Ukraine on 26 April 1986, and at Three Mile Island in the United States on 29 March 1979 (Class 7 and Class 5 events respectively on an international scale of nuclear accidents and incidents) have significantly increased public concern over nuclear safety. IEA Member countries have good nuclear safety records and their successful experience in overcoming abnormal occurrences can be interpreted as a demonstration of the excellent employment of defence-in-depth measures. But there is a perceived need to allay public fears and build greater confidence in the industry's ability to protect public health as well as investments. In some countries, this has led to a desire to adopt technologies and other measures which would minimise the need for evacuation zones around nuclear power plants.

## Technology Description and Assessment

### *Description of Significant Technologies*

Current nuclear technology development can be considered under two headings: nuclear reactor systems (light and heavy-water cooled, gas-cooled and liquid-metal cooled reactors); and fuel-cycle technologies and radioactive waste management. The reasons for selecting these technologies are summarised in Table 5.1.

*Table 5.1*

**Main Reasons for Selection of Nuclear Fission Technologies**

| Technology | Reasons for Selection |
|---|---|
| **Reactor Technologies** | |
| Water-Cooled Reactors | • Prospect of more economic, less capital-intensive reactors.<br>• Less reliance on active safety systems.<br>• Development based on over 6 000 reactor-years of experience. |
| Gas-Cooled Reactors | • Potential for new applications.<br>• Alternative ways of using nuclear energy. |
| Liquid-Metal Cooled Reactors | • Prospect of 60-fold extension of fuel resource base. |
| **Other Technologies** | |
| Fuel-Cycle Technologies | • Improved economics of nuclear power.<br>• Extension of resource base. |
| Radioactive Waste Management | • Demonstration needed in certain countries to stimulate public acceptance. |

a) *Nuclear Reactor Systems*

The bulk of the world's current nuclear power generation utilises water-cooled and moderated nuclear reactors. IEA countries and certain non-Member countries have respectively accumulated 5 342 and 6 479 reactor-years of experience respectively, as of the end of 1992, and there have been no accidents with these reactors leading to significant off-site releases of radioactivity. Electricity production with a high degree of availability and high load factors has been achieved. Over recent years, annual average load factors have been above 80 per cent in several cases. Four IEA countries using nuclear power report lifetime average energy availabilities above 80 per cent, and a further six report more than 70 per cent availability.

Most water-cooled plants are light-water reactors (LWRs), using enriched uranium as fuel and ordinary water as coolant. These reactors are of two main types: pressurised (light) water-cooled reactors (PWR), where the water in the cooling circuit is under sufficient pressure that it does not boil; and boiling (light) water-cooled reactors (BWR), in which boiling of the cooling water is allowed. Of all reactors in service, 62 per cent are PWRs and 22 per cent are BWRs. Pressurised heavy water-cooled and moderated reactors (PHWRs) use natural uranium as fuel and heavy water (namely water composed of two deuterium atoms and one oxygen atom) as the coolant and neutron moderator. Such reactors are best represented by those built and operated in Canada, under the CANDU (CANadian Deuterium Uranium). PHWRs account for 5 per cent of the electric utilities' operating reactors worldwide. Design variations on the dominant commercial reactor systems include those of Russian design deployed primarily in the former Soviet Union and in central and eastern Europe. These are known as the VVER, pressurised light-water cooled and moderated reactor, similar to the Western type PWR and the RBMK, a light-water cooled and graphite-moderated reactor.

In addition, some 10 per cent of world nuclear reactors are gas-cooled and graphite-moderated (GCRs). The major operating experience with this technology has been in the United Kingdom, with the original Magnox system in transition to the Advanced Gas Reactor (AGR). Increasing the efficiency of GCRs through elevated operating temperature has led to a separate and advanced line of development pursued primarily by Germany and the United States. This line is represented by the high temperature gas-cooled reactor (HTGR or HTR) which uses helium coolant and advanced fuel designs to enhance performance. Current fuel designs use uranium dioxide in the form of small spheres encapsulated in layers of pyrolitic carbon and silicon carbide dispersed throughout a graphite matrix. In the German design, the fuel elements are spherical and the core consists of a graphite and steel barrel (hence the term pebble-bed reactor). This design allows on-line refuelling, an important operating factor. In the United States design the fuel particles are hexagonal graphite prisms, pierced by cooling channels, compacted into channels, and lodged within a graphite matrix. Japan is constructing a high-temperature test reactor of this sort.

A very low failure rate of HTGR fuel elements has been demonstrated, and for thermal reactor powers of 200-350 MWe with modest core power density, designers are confident that no emergency condition would produce temperatures high enough to risk significant fuel failure. Fission products are retained within each nuclear fuel element during all conceivable operating conditions, thereby mitigating off-site radioactive emissions. Fission product retention also contributes to low operator dosages during normal plant operations, to a level one-tenth of that routinely achieved in United States LWRs, although levels have improved recently. As a next-generation technology, it appears technically feasible for HTGRs with such low releases to be co-located with industrial plants, to provide combined heat and power to industrial users.

A technology option for the long term, stemming from the above concepts, involves using highly enriched uranium and possible combination with thorium fuel. Because of concern for nuclear proliferation, however, there are substantial uncertainties regarding the utilisation of highly enriched uranium. Uncertainties regarding fuel processing and waste disposal of thorium-based fuels remain, as attention has been given predominantly to uranium based fuels with which experience has been gained.

About 1 per cent of installed nuclear power consists of reactors which adopt molten metal as their coolant. Such liquid-metal reactors (LMRs) represent a further technology option for the long term which can breed nuclear fuel to produce more fissile fuel than is consumed. Fast breeder reactors (FBRs), based on plutonium fuel and using fast neutrons for breeding additional plutonium in uranium blankets, with a liquid-sodium coolant, exist in France, Japan, Kazakhstan, Russia and the United Kingdom (although the reactor is now closed). FBRs can also reduce the ultimate volume of radioactive waste products, transmuting actinides (nuclei with atomic numbers from 89 upwards) into other substances.

b) *Fuel-Cycle and Waste Management Technologies*

Included in nuclear fuel-cycle technologies are all activities ranging from exploration, mining and uranium ore concentration, conversion, enrichment and fuel fabrication through to spent fuel transport and storage. Technically, these activities can be carried out within safety limits. The major concerns are with economics and the resource base.

Reduction and recycling of waste have been pioneered by the nuclear community since the early days of nuclear power. Because of the relatively small volumes of waste generated, the nuclear industry has been a leader in pursuing waste containment and disposal rather than a dilution and dispersal strategy.

The operations of the nuclear industry produce radioactive waste with varying degrees of contamination by a range of radioactive isotopes. The problems of disposal of this waste are posed most starkly by the materials resulting from the reprocessing of spent nuclear fuel, and by the decision in some countries to dispose of the spent fuel itself. These materials consist partly of high-level nuclear waste (HLW) containing actinides, with very long lives to radioactive decay, so that many thousands of years pass before the radioactivity falls to background levels. Moreover, shorter-lived fission products and other radioactive isotopes are in such concentrations that for several decades a large amount of heat is produced by the radioactive decay, so that special measures are needed to avoid damage to structures containing the wastes.

Current concepts to dispose of HLW require multiple barriers in which the last barrier is a geological formation of such stability that, should all else fail, it will prevent migration of radioactive species into the biosphere for the necessary length of time. Granite shields and salt deposits exhibit great stability over long geological periods, and are thus suitable candidates for waste disposal. Certain deposits of tuff and of clay are also under consideration.

The OECD Nuclear Energy Agency (NEA) has sponsored an international research project at the Stripa mine in Sweden, where an investigation of the properties of granite as a waste repository was undertaken. Other underground research and demonstration laboratories in Belgium, Canada Germany, Switzerland and the United States are included in a co-ordinated assessment programme. On the basis of this programme, the NEA's Radioactive Waste Management Committee has reaffirmed its confidence in the safety and feasibility of geological disposal of radioactive wastes. Accordingly, the primary emphasis in HLW management, in addition to evolutionary technical development, is on characterisation and selection of candidate disposal sites, and on the design, demonstration and implementation of conceptualised disposal techniques.

### *Assessment of Technical and Economic Potential*

#### a) *Light-Water, Heavy-Water and Gas-Cooled Reactor Technologies*

In several countries – particularly those which have benefited from series ordering – nuclear power is highly competitive with other sources. Thus, it is not surprising that many electric utilities and nuclear equipment manufacturers favour an evolutionary approach to reactor development. In this approach, which is already resulting in considerable improvement of reactor designs, the goals are to increase safety margins, to simplify and reduce the cost of nuclear power plant construction and operation, to shorten lead-times (partly by improved planning, partly by standardising designs certified in advance by nuclear regulatory authorities), and to reduce radiation doses to operators. An example of this approach is the Tokyo Electric Power Company order for two 1 350 MWe, advanced boiling water reactors

(ABWRs), to be operational in 1996 and 1998. These reactors have a volume of about 70 per cent of previous BWRs of similar size; they use internal coolant pumps to reduce piping and welding and the frequency of in-service inspection. Such features will reduce construction costs and, with design features oriented to easier service and maintenance, will cut worker radiation exposures and improve public safety.

A number of nuclear reactor concepts under development follow the evolutionary path a stage further. An example is the European Pressurised Reactor (EPR), which is jointly designed by nuclear equipment manufacturers in France and Germany to respond to new safety and operational requirements proposed by European electric utilities. Other evolutionary reactor concepts strive for the construction of containment that prevents the damages associated with meltdowns or other accidents. All water-cooled reactors rely to some extent on the so-called passive safety features. Some reactor systems have negative feedback between reactivity and temperature and between reactivity and void volume; some have convective circulation of cooling water in case of accidents. These passive safety features are more appropriate to smaller unit designs with lower power densities. There are designers who believe they can be built for the same or lower cost per kWe installed than larger current plant designs (i.e., US$ 1 300/kWe to $ 2 500/kWe). The objective is to shorten reactor construction time to three to four years, based on modular or standard designs and a high degree of factory assembly of systems and sub-systems subject to uniform licensing requirements.

These designs feature large water pools located above the core, to flood the reactor by gravity in case of accident. Their simplicity is evident in Westinghouse's AP600 which would require about 50 per cent less concrete, 50 per cent fewer large pumps and heat exchangers, 60 per cent fewer valves, 60 per cent fewer pipes and 80 per cent less control cable compared with a current-design 600 MWe commercial reactor. Similar efforts are underway in the evolutionary improvement of the CANDU reactor to increase safety margins and reduce construction costs. Reactor manufacturers expect that, given progress to date, these designs can be certified and licensed as meeting or exceeding today's safety requirements and should be available for ordering by the year 2000.

Some design changes are a reaction to complexities arising from the constant addition of new layers of regulatory requirements. In some countries, there are suggestions that such evolutionary improvements will not suffice to provide the demonstrable safety that investors and the public want. Several designs of a more radical nature respond to this requirement, including the Swedish Process Inherent Ultimate Safety (PIUS) reactor, the Japanese Intrinsically Safe Economical Reactor, the System Integrated Pressurised Water Reactor and the Safe Integral Reactor (SIR) which has been developed by an Anglo-American group; but all of these are currently in abeyance because markets have not developed. These approaches rely to a greater extent on thermo-hydraulic phenomena to ensure safety, with the intention of virtually eliminating any possibility of a core melt accident and the need for operator action during an emergency.

These new concepts will likely require full-scale prototype or demonstration reactors before commercial acceptance. Accordingly, they should be considered next-generation technology, expected to be available well after the turn of the century. The economics of these concepts are necessarily less certain than for other designs, but the overall cost, for example, of electricity generated from a 630-650 MWe PIUS is estimated by its designers to be close to that for a 700 MWe BWR plant.

Reactor-related developments to extend the resource base are also being pursued: uranium requirements can be reduced by fuel management, fuel design, reactor design and fuel substitution. Improved fuel management and design can lead to greater burn-up of the fuel, with extension from the currently common thermal energy of 33 MWd per kilogram to 50 MWd/kg or higher without reducing safety. Estimates vary as to the magnitude of the uranium savings, but these might be in the range of 10 to 15 per cent in the period 1985 to 2000. The use of higher burn-up with longer operating cycles can improve the overall economics by US$ 2 million to US$ 4 million per fuel cycle, or roughly 10 per cent of the fuel-cycle cost. The adoption of less absorbant materials in the fuel and reactor core can lead to economy in the use of neutrons, hence lower enrichment requirement and lower natural uranium feedstock use. Continuous progress in resource-base economics is being made in this way.

Current LWRs can take up to 30 per cent of their fuel as MOX (mixed uranium and plutonium oxide pellets with typically about 5 per cent plutonium), without departing from normal safety and control requirements. There are already plans to use MOX in 40 to 45 reactors in the IEA countries. A limit on the use of plutonium, so as to retain stocks for use in uranium-conserving reactors, is an option for the long term.

Designs are already under study for high conversion reactors in which a more energetic neutron flux drives the nuclear reaction further, producing internally – and consuming – more plutonium than in current uranium-fuelled LWRs. It is envisaged that these reactors can be developed by only partial replacement of core internals, and that only a small cost penalty (perhaps 1 to 2 per cent in one case) over current capital costs would be incurred for a reduction of roughly 10 per cent in fuel-cycle costs in a first stage. Other, less tested concepts envisage flexibility of use of plutonium and uranium, with uranium requirements cut by up to 33 per cent. If uranium prices give adequate incentives, these changes could be initiated with a lead time of less than 10 to 15 years.

The greatest economic opportunities with respect to reactor design appear to lie in capital cost reduction, both directly and through reduced construction periods, rather than in fuel-cycle cost reductions. On the other hand, from the perspective of security of energy supply, there is currently more to be gained by continuing emphasis on safety of nuclear reactors generating electricity than by seeking to expand the role of nuclear power into new market areas. All of the primary reactor concepts – LWR and PHWR, GCR, and LMR – are moving towards similar technical objectives, albeit from different levels of experience base. All display both the technical and economic potential to make significant progress towards lower cost and higher safety characteristics, in both an evolutionary and step-wise manner. A further major technical area for attention in existing plants, beyond that of accident-free routine operation and maintenance, is careful design (and implementation) of appropriate life-extension programmes, to achieve further economic benefits while maintaining present safety limits.

Conventional nuclear plants are already quite safe. Indeed there has never been a major release of radioactivity into the environment from a nuclear power plant in IEA countries. There was a strong public reaction, however, to events at Three Mile Island (where the release of radioactivity was extremely minor, though the threat of a major release existed for some days) and to Chernobyl (where the release of radioactivity was major, but Western equipment, procedures, and safeguards were not in force). That reaction suggests that broad public acceptance of substantial nuclear power growth worldwide will require extended periods of accident-free operation.

Given the prevailing state of mind, high priority should no doubt go to the design, development, demonstration and deployment of simplified, standardised (and possibly modularised) plants with extensive use of passive safety features. Such plants appear to be achievable within the economic boundaries established by current technology, even with a reduction in average plant size. Their introduction may also lead to further cost reductions, including the simplification of the licensing process. This approach could conceivably increase the margin of safety in nuclear power production considerably. Such nuclear plants would be likely to reduce the probability of a complete reactor coolant failure by a factor of roughly ten; they would also increase reaction time for preventing such a failure from leading to meltdown and associated radioactive release into the environment by another factor of roughly ten, so that overall safety could increase by a factor of roughly one hundred.

The LWR and PHWR concepts sketched out above aim at improved safety and economics, including reduced investment risk, but other operational objectives might be considered. There has already been some use of process heat from the CANDU reactor at Bruce, Ontario; and in Switzerland waste heat from BWRs has been used for district heating. But the steam temperature produced by water-cooled reactors limits their application in the field of process heat, and their generally large size, as well as public perceptions of their safety, limit their use in district heating. Canada has developed a very small passively safe reactor, the SLOWPOKE, specifically for space heating markets, as the reactor should be licensable for siting very close to heat loads (such as large hospitals). The idea of developing nuclear-powered desalination plants may also be revived.

Propulsion based upon LWRs is of crucial importance in naval submarines and other warships. Apart from some ice-breakers developed by the former Soviet Union, such reactors have not achieved widespread use in civilian fleets, although, during the early 1970s, the feasibility of commercial exploitation was demonstrated. In principle, there appears to be no technical barrier to the use of reactors in marine propulsion, but their economic competitiveness must be proven and safety demonstrated to the satisfaction of regulatory authorities, as well as public opinion.

Meanwhile, a number of evolutionary designs are being developed for GCRs. There has been a particular emphasis on modularity, small unit sizes (as low as 133 Mwe) and reduction in siting restrictions by relying upon passive safety features. Because of its compatibility with modular design, the HRTGR concept may be amenable to substantial off-site fabrication, lowering costs both directly and through shorter on-site construction periods. Modularity, achieved without significant loss of economy of scale compared with larger conventional units, has a number of important potential benefits. Multiple units may provide higher assurance of operating continuity. In particular, small units offer the possibility of incorporating passive safety features more difficult to design into larger units. They also permit capacity additions to keep pace with demand growth (thus reducing investment uncertainties) and may reduce the financial costs through shorter lead times from construction decision to commercial operation.

b) *Liquid-Metal Cooled Reactor Technologies*

Breeder reactors using liquid-metal coolant were conceived in the very early years of civil nuclear power, when uranium was considered scarce, for large-scale recourse to nuclear power. The introduction of breeder reactors has not been seen as urgent for some years but, on reasonable assumptions about the continued use of nuclear power, it seems likely that all the world's uranium from low-cost conventional sources (less than US$ 130 per kilogram of uranium) will have been committed to reactor use well before the middle of the next century. Enhanced use of nuclear power to mitigate greenhouse gas emissions could lead to major price rises for uranium before 2030. Many reactors in use will need replacing in the period 2010 to 2030, and their owners will be faced with judgements as to the economics of either replacing them with a second generation of reactors using a once-through fuel cycle or the alternative of switching to breeder reactors. Current development of these reactors is aimed at presenting them as a credibly safe and economic long-term option by about 2010-2020, so that a timely decision can be made. Various specific aspects of their potential to ameliorate the disposal of radioactive waste are being explored.

A 1200 MWe sodium-cooled FBR has for some time operated at full power in France. France has meanwhile operated the 233 MWe Phenix since 1973, and the United Kingdom operated the 250 MWe Prototype Fast Reactor from 1975 to 1994. Germany has built, but not yet operated, the 295 MWe SNR-300. All three countries have prepared design concepts for a power station in the range 1300 MWe to 1500 MWe using a pool of sodium as coolant, and have combined their research, development and design efforts since 1988 into one co-operative programme.

The United States has designed a 1100 MWe fast breeder plant consisting of nine reactor modules coupled to three turbines. This modular approach uses simple designs and series production to offset the diseconomy of scale and the extra material. Safety is assured through passive means, although highly reliable, automatic control systems are also integrated in the design. Plant economics would be better than for the HTGR under development, and such reactors would compete with advanced LWRs. Both the pool and loop plant types have been designed with good safety margins that allow limited or no operator response to prevent coolant boiling or fuel melting in emergencies. However, many research projects are continuing, in order to achieve high fuel burn-up, with a long-term goal of 150 to 200 MWd/kg, control of impurities in the coolant, and greater understanding of core physics, thermohydraulics (including passive decay heat removal) and material properties relevant to the safe and efficient operation of FBRs.

One motivating factor in this research is the objective of lower capital costs, since monolithic FBRs are estimated by some to be about 50 per cent more expensive to construct than current nuclear reactors. But French and German studies suggest that considerable savings can be made by a 20 to 30 per cent reduction in the weight of materials for the nuclear steam supply system (NSSS). Further savings can be made in the balance of plant[1] by enhancing reliance on passive safety features in the NSSS. Fuel-cycle costs can already be predicted to be comparable with once-through fuel costs with burn-up levels already achieved (using current prices for uranium and fuel-cycle service costs expected for routine large scale operations). Nevertheless, efforts continue to improve the efficiency and cost of reprocessing. In the United Kingdom and French programmes, closure of the fuel cycle has already been demonstrated with satisfactorily high recovery of plutonium (greater than 99 per cent) using the PUREX chemical separation process on the oxide fuel.

An alternative fuel-cycle proposal, developed in the United States, envisages a metal fuel (plutonium-uranium-zirconium alloy) which would be reprocessed by melting and electrolytic separation. Experience with test rigs and research reactors suggest that this fuel can be expected to be highly reliable in operation, and test burn-ups of 170 MWd/kg have already been achieved. The thermal-conductive and neutronic properties of the metal fuel have been shown in test reactors to provide wide safety margins regarding coolant boiling and fuel failure in accidents involving the loss of coolant or loss of heat sink. The fuel-cycle costs could be less than for the oxide PUREX cycle. One of the arguments adduced in favour of any fuel cycle involving reprocessing is that the volume of highly radioactive, heat-producing wastes is considerably reduced, thus presenting an easier disposal problem than for spent fuel itself. One advantage claimed for the breeder concept is that the actinides produced in the reactor can be retained in the recycled fuel and consumed, so that the radioactive toxicity level of the remaining waste decays to background levels of radiation in about 300 years, rather than the thousands of years otherwise required.

The significance of near-term LMR development obviously depends on the magnitude, timing and rate of current nuclear power additions, relative to the uranium resource base and to its potential role in enhancing the LWR spent fuel disposal challenge. The longer-term significance may depend on the degree of progress made in other power technologies which also strive to capture a significant share of future electric generation markets.

c) *Fuel-Cycle and Waste Management Technologies*

Fuel-cycle costs account for about one-fifth of total levelised nuclear generation costs. The total cost is not susceptible, therefore, to major change as a result of the modified cost of a single element in the fuel cycle. This can be expected to remain true even for a new generation of reactors with lower capital costs. Nevertheless, there are commercial forces opening the way to a wide variety of developments, particularly for enrichment and fuel fabrication.

Enrichment of uranium in the isotope $U^{235}$ (from its natural level of 0.7 per cent to between 2.5 and 4.0 per cent for currently operated LWRs) was first performed commercially in gaseous diffusion plants. More recently, ultra-high-speed centrifuges have been used, with a

1. Balance of plant – Contracts for a nuclear power plant are often divided into Nuclear Island and the Balance of Plant. The former is usually considered to include all systems needed for the safe operation of the plant, although the precise definition of the boundary may vary between different contractors. Balance of Plant can therefore be considered to refer to other parts of the plant.

view to exploiting lower electricity demand for a given amount of separative work. The plant size for economic operation tends to be lower with this technology than for diffusion plants. Both technologies appear competitive at current prices of about US$ 100 per kilogram of separative work unit (SWU). Limited effort has been put into developing a chemical and a fluidics technology, but the most important alternative currently under development is based on the excitation of $U^{235}$ atoms by laser light (atomic vapour laser isotope separation). This development has been pushed furthest in the United States, so that it is likely to be available for commercial introduction before 2000 at a production cost of about US$ 70/kg SWU. Centrifuge proponents indicate that centrifuge costs can be lowered to a similar extent.

All fuel manufacturers strive to improve the reliability and utilisation of fuel through changes in materials and configuration. Reactor manufacturers and utilities contribute by modifying the operating cycle and core management to obtain higher burn-up of fuels. The effectiveness of this kind of approach can be illustrated by the 10 per cent fuel cost saving achieved by Electricité de France in its 900 MWe reactors through increased fuel enrichment and burn-up. Substantial economies can be achieved by consistently operating a reactor close to its operating design limits. The introduction of improved in-core instrumentation is thus also considered important, as is the improvement of reactivity control by introduction of burnable poisons into the fuel.

While uranium exploration and extraction technology advanced significantly up to the mid-1970s, recently there has been little pressure for advancements. Uranium is already derived from very low grade resources. The technology for exploitation of more costly resources is fundamentally available, although it may need adjustments in order to cope more economically with even lower grade resources, particularly when they are not associated with other economically useful metals.

The technical problems of disposing of low and intermediate level waste arise more from their bulk than from the intrinsic difficulty of containing them. Therefore attention is being given to compaction methods (such as electrolytic refining to separate radioactive isotopes from steel structures recovered from reactor cores, or incineration of low level wastes such as paper, clothing and other material). As yet, no permanent repository is operating for intermediate level wastes, but several countries have low-level waste repositories which give no problems in terms of radioactive releases.

Conversely, HLW management efforts are concentrated on identifying suitable repository sites and implementing demonstrations of disposal concepts. Even when waste repositories have been operated for a few years, it will still not be possible to assert solely from the experience gained that the repository will perform as required for as long as needed. Considerable effort is invested in setting up and refining methods of assessing the performance, based on models of repository behaviour, supported by major effort to develop data on relevant physical and chemical parameters (e.g., thermochemical and adsorption data). The performance assessments extend to consideration of human intrusion into a waste repository. The reliability of the engineered barriers is studied, including methods of conditioning spent fuel before disposal. Two materials for the first barrier, the matrix containing the HLW, have been developed: a borosilicate glass and a synthetic rock. Reprocessing companies in France and the United Kingdom are already producing discs of glass for containing HLW on a commercial scale. Another line of research, commensurate with the very long time-scales which have to be considered, is to study natural analogues, natural deposits of radioactive material where the effects of dispersion processes, such as leaching by ground-water, can be investigated after geologically long periods. The Alligator Rivers Natural Analogue Project in Australia was set up under the sponsorship of the OECD-NEA for this purpose. The concept of international storage facilities may also offer several advantages. Such facilities could help provide the nuclear power industry with the time it needs to develop better technological and institutional final waste disposal methods.

A major motivation for the wide range of research work is the need to increase public assurance that radioactive waste can indeed be safely managed. It is true that refined understanding might enable repositories to be designed, constructed and operated at reduced cost. There is no globally valid estimate of the cost of disposing of nuclear waste, but the technical community does not doubt that it will be only a small part of the total fuel-cycle costs. For example, according to an OECD-NEA analysis in 1991, the cost of the back-end of a reprocessing cycle (after allowing credits for recycled plutonium and uranium) would be 1.75 US mills per kilowatt hour (mills/kWh) out of a total fuel-cycle cost of 8.56 mills/kWh. For a once-through cycle, the figures were respectively 0.97 and 7.78 mills/kWh. As noted previously, several countries have research programmes including underground facilities. Only the United States and Sweden have made firm plans for constructing final repositories, in both cases for spent fuel. Sweden plans to start operating a final repository by 2010. United States plans to have a federal repository operating before then have been delayed owing to opposition at the State level.

A less well known, or characterised, radical long-term option to dispose of HLW is based on accelerator-driven nuclear systems. These systems use nuclear particle accelerators to introduce high-energy protons into the multiplying medium. Spallation reactions then create a high-energy particle cascade to transmute actinides into shorter-lived products and generate a net amount of energy. The primary objective is to eliminate certain problem nuclides from the bulk of the spent nuclear fuel, so that the remainder can be packaged more easily with reduced heat load and shorter lifetime requirements for disposal in simpler geological or engineered repositories.

With regard to other waste management and environmental considerations, the main environmental impact of nuclear power plants under normal operating conditions is the emission of very low level radioactive gases and liquids. Emissions of gases are of roughly the same magnitude for nuclear power production as for mining and use of coal in fossil plants. Both gaseous and liquid emissions are strictly controlled, so that even a person living at the plant boundary would not suffer undue health effects. Overall land use requirements for fuel production, power plant, and waste disposal are comparable for nuclear and coal-fired electricity generation, though coal has greater requirements for the mining process, while nuclear has greater requirements for the disposal process. A major environmental advantage of nuclear power plants is that they do not emit greenhouse gases or acid rain precursors into the atmosphere. The negligible contribution of emissions of this character is associated with the manufacture of components, construction of plant, and supporting fuel-cycle activities. The French experience is possibly significant in this connection. As French nuclear power grew during the 1980s to supply over 70 per cent of all electricity, emissions of sulphur dioxide declined by 90 per cent and emissions of both nitrogen oxides and carbon dioxide declined by 85 per cent.

The technology of nuclear plant design and construction is preponderantly a resource developed in IEA countries. A large share of the known uranium resources is located in the IEA region, primarily Australia, Canada and the United States. France and the United Kingdom hold significant stocks of plutonium and uranium depleted in $U^{235}$ which can also be used as reactor fuel. Japan intends to build up its position in the use of plutonium. Thus there is a potential for very high energy supply security from the use of nuclear power, as well as potential environmental advantage. There is also a high degree of technical and economic potential. Such potential has not yet been fully realised, although continuing efforts to do so are being vigorously pursued by a number of governments.

A summary of the technical and economic potential of the various nuclear fission reactor systems and associated fuel-cycle opportunities is given in Tables 5.2 and 5.3.

*Table 5.2*

**Comparative Technical Potential of New and Improved Nuclear Fission Technologies**

| Technology | Safety | High Temp. Applications | Low Temp. Applications | Extension of Resource Base |
|---|---|---|---|---|
| LWR | | | | |
| • Advanced | M | L | H | M |
| • Revolutionary | M-H | L | H | M |
| PHWR | | | | |
| • Advanced | M | L | H | L |
| GCR | M | H | M | M |
| LMR | M | L | L | H |

Note: L, M, H = Low, Medium, High.

*Table 5.3*

**Economic Potential of Improved Nuclear Fission Technologies**

| Technology | Current Costs | | | Potential Costs | | |
|---|---|---|---|---|---|---|
| | Capital | Operating (incl. fuel) | Total | Capital | Operating (incl. fuel) | Total |
| LWR | 15-30 | 12-20 | 27-50 | 15-20 | 12-18 | 27-38 |
| PHWR | 15-25 | 10-15 | 25-40 | - | - | - |
| GCR | - | - | - | - | - | 35* |
| LMR | 40* | 15* | 55* | 25* | 15* | 40* |
| Fuel Cycle • reduction from current levels | - | - | - | -2% | -2% | -4% |

Notes: * Estimates.
Costs given in 1990 US mills/kWh; 30-year lifetime, at 5% discount rate.
LMR estimates were made by the OECD-NEA Secretariat.

## Technology Prospects and Markets

### *Market Trends*

Nuclear energy generated 15 per cent of world electric power in 1992, or some 2 027 TWh out of a total of 13 450 TWh. According to OECD-NEA figures, nuclear production in the OECD Member countries was 1 717 TWh, or 24.5 per cent of total OECD electricity production in 1993. These nations account for 82 per cent of world nuclear energy generation.

As of end-1993, there were 430 nuclear generating plants operating worldwide in 30 countries, representing a total nuclear capacity of 338 GWe. An additional 55 plants, with a total capacity of 60 GWe, were under construction. Of this amount, the total operable nuclear capacity in OECD countries was 274 GWe (81 per cent of the total), comprising 330 plants with another 23 GWe under construction. Only four of the OECD countries had nuclear energy generating plants under construction. Table 5.4 provides the key statistical information for the twelve IEA countries having operating reactors. As the table indicates, the majority of IEA countries with nuclear generating capacity obtain from 20 per cent to 78 per cent of their total electric generation from nuclear energy. Only Belgium and France rely predominantly (59 and 78 per cent respectively) on nuclear generation. Further nuclear growth has been placed under moratorium in a number of IEA countries, and is static in others. France and Japan have announced their intention to continue with active nuclear development and are proceeding with plans. At a worldwide level, a similar situation exists with a cessation or slowdown in nuclear energy growth in most countries and active programmes still in place for a few others.

The slowdown in nuclear power expansion is also due to the forecasted decline in the expected growth of electricity demand, which has affected orders for all types of generating plants. The prospects for nuclear power growth have also been affected by the continuing competitiveness of fossil fuel prices. Additionally, the potential availability of new, more fuel-efficient, environmentally cleaner fossil-fuel combustion technologies may remove some barriers to their wider use. The relatively short lead time for small-scale plant construction provides electric utilities with flexibility in timing their investment decisions and reduced financing costs.

In terms of resources for the foreseeable use of nuclear power up to about 2030, abundant resources of high and medium-grade uranium appear to exist, although considerable exploration and development would be necessary to ensure availability of those resources in a timely manner. If other IEA countries were to use nuclear energy to the same extent as France and Belgium, it seems likely that current estimates of high and medium grade resources would be committed to fuel reactors for their assumed 40-year life. Before that time, market forces would cause uranium prices to rise, thus prompting increased exploration. At some point prices would reach a level justifying decisions to pursue breeder technologies. Multiplying the energy derived from the resource base by about 60, through exploitation of lower grades of ore, possibly in modified fuel cycles, would be possible.

*Table 5.4*
**Nuclear Power Reactors in IEA Countries**
(as of 31st December 1993)

| Country | No. of Reactors | | Net Capacity (GWe) | | |
|---|---|---|---|---|---|
| | Operational | Under Construction or Planned | Operational | Under Construction | Total Electrical Generation (%) |
| Belgium | 7 | - | 5.6 | - | 59.0 |
| Canada | 22 | - | 15.5 | 3.5 | 17.2 |
| Finland | 4 | - | 2.3 | - | 32.4 |
| France | 57 | 4 | 59.0 | 5.8 | 77.7 |
| Germany | 21 | - | 22.5 | - | 29.7 |
| Japan | 47 | 7 | 36.7 | 6.6 | 30.2 |
| Netherlands | 2 | - | 0.5 | - | 4.8 |
| Spain | 9 | - | 7.4 | - | 35.6 |
| Sweden | 12 | - | 10.0 | - | 43.1 |
| Switzerland | 5 | - | 3.0 | - | 37.9 |
| United Kingdom | 35 | 1 | 11.9 | 1.2 | 26.7 |
| United States | 109 | 5 | 99.0 | 5.9 | 19.6 |
| TOTAL | 330.00 | 17.00 | 273.40 | 23.00 | 24.5 |

Note: National data on units under construction or planned are subject to change resulting from future public and regulatory decisions.

But a technical need of a more urgent nature is raised by the fact that a large number of operating reactors will reach the end of their nominal 30-year lifetime within the time period of this assessment. Decisions must be made to either retire this capacity or invest in life extension. The International Atomic Energy Agency (IAEA) identifies three internationally accepted stages of decommissioning. In the storage with surveillance stage, the first contamination barrier of the nuclear power plant is kept as it was during operation but the fuel is removed and mechanical openings are sealed permanently. The containment building is kept closed and under institutional control. The second stage is restricted site release in which the first containment barrier is reduced to minimum size by removing easily dismantled parts. The third stage is unrestricted site use, involving removal of all materials, equipment and parts of the plant still containing significant levels of radioactivity.

On the other hand, the technical feasibility and costs of extending the life of reactors may vary according to reactor type, original design, and regulatory and public climate. Certain plants that were designed for 30-year life have received approval for extension beyond those 30 years. Some analyses see 60- and 70-year plant lives as feasible under certain operation and maintenance regimes.

### *Key Players*

Nuclear power technologies interact in their development process with public health and safety, the environment, foreign policy and energy security, as well as the economy. As a result, nuclear programmes have increasingly cut across institutional lines within IEA Member countries' governments, regulatory agencies, nuclear vendors, electric utilities, nuclear fuel-cycle service providers, R&D centres and the general public. In some respects, nuclear power presents unique institutional problems arising from the original government monopoly in nuclear energy, the special risks of accidents and thefts, the risks of nuclear proliferation, and the complex of treaties and agreements that have developed in the field.

Government-industry relations in the nuclear power area are currently changing in some countries. The governments of several IEA countries have historically taken the leading role in nuclear technology development, originally conducted by a government monopoly or government-funded laboratory. Private firms were initially contractors or chosen instruments. Even today, nuclear power is not really a private enterprise in the generally recognised sense, since most of the governments retain a dominant role in areas such as uranium enrichment, waste management and R&D.

It is in the interest of IEA countries to let the market take the decisions regarding nuclear power growth and technology advancement. This does not, however, imply complete private R&D programmes, in view of the large capital requirments, the technical and economic uncertainties, and facilities security issues such as those relating to uranium enrichment, plutonium reprocessing or permanent waste disposal. Regulatory and siting policies are also an area of government responsibility in view of the need to protect populations from possible accidents. In some instances, IEA governments have created special new institutional arrangements to deal with problems of nuclear fusion technologies, or to assist in meeting nuclear power development targets. To assist the decision-making process, various structures have been employed in the field of nuclear power and its technologies, including: advisory, monitoring and inspection agencies, legal frameworks to resolve public interest conflicts, planning inquiries, public debates and hearings. However, it should be noted that these decision frameworks were those established during the 1980s and that they may not take account of the more recent slowdown of nuclear power programmes in IEA countries, or the movement towards a more competitive energy market or concerns over global environmental consequences of fossil fuel combustion.

### *Market Barriers*

The principal forces driving nuclear revitalisation forward are centred on its potential to enhance energy security and to remove or reduce concerns associated with the emission of greenhouse gases from the combustion of fossil fuels, while itself meeting publicly acceptable standards of reasonable cost, safety, and environmental acceptability. Both existing and potential new markets exist in abundance, particularly in industrialised countries, but public safety concerns limit access to those markets in a number of countries. In newly industrialising countries and in transition economies, additional market barriers are created by the capital intensity of nuclear power (and thus by additional impediments to investment), lack of adequate technical and institutional infrastructure, and restrictions associated with concern over nuclear proliferation.

Any power reactor is a potential source of fissionable materials that could be used for weapons, although other sources of weapons-grade material are generally more attractive. Technology can reduce the risks of proliferation or diversion but cannot eliminate them. Safeguarding measures can be improved, and reactor and fuel-cycle designs that minimise the opportunities for diversion of plutonium or other sensitive materials should be maintained or enhanced.

It has already been demonstrated in France and Belgium that it is feasible to supply some 60 per cent or more of electricity demand from nuclear power. This involves a degree of load-following which could conceivably be increased with further attention to selection of reactor and fuel design and materials. The limiting factors are more likely to be non-technical ones such as the diseconomy of providing highly capital-intensive plants for peak loads. On the other hand, should hydrogen become an exploited energy carrier, use of nuclear electricity might be envisaged to produce hydrogen as fuel for peaking plants, as well as for fuel cells and other transportable energy converters, thus increasing the share of nuclear power used.

Nuclear reactors could be direct heat sources for a variety of industrial, commercial and residential uses. Many of these heat loads are less than 200 MWt, and would require development of small power reactors and, for some applications, development of further heat transfer technology. A number of industries, including food processing, paper and textiles, could be serviced by water-cooled or liquid-metal cooled reactors. Others, including non-ferrous metals, heavy oil production, petrochemicals and coal gasification, would need the higher temperatures available from HTGRs. The necessary development work could be completed by 2010. By that time, there could be several sites worldwide where reactors in the range between 150 MWt and 250 MWt could be utilised, the number of opportunities increasing thereafter with growth in energy demand. But only a small proportion of such sites, if any, could be expected to put nuclear reactors in operation by the first decades of the next century. For example, a recent study by the IAEA points to a demand for additional sea-water de-salination capacity of 12 million cubic metres per day in the Mediterranean area and Middle East by 2000. That is a market where nuclear-produced heat could be exploited, if it were cost-competitive and properly safeguarded.

If safety and economic concerns were resolved, nuclear power could conceivably expand rapidly for the electric market, and possibly for heat applications as well. In the five years from 1980 to 1985, the peak period of nuclear power plant construction to date, some 80 reactors with a total capacity of 115 GWe were put into service worldwide. If currently planned nuclear plants were completed in the 1990s and the record pace of construction were reached again and maintained for the first two decades of the next century, capactity for roughly 550 GWe of nuclear power could be completed by the year 2020. However, the current pace of additions is much slower, and many plants now in service, with a design life of 30 to 40 years, would be retired by then, although others would have benefited from life extension programmes. Thus, it may be difficult for nuclear power to achieve net growth over the next two to three decades.

The successful management of nuclear wastes remains a predominant condition for public acceptance of nuclear power. As one point of reference, worldwide nuclear power production in 1993 generated more than 8 400 tonnes of spent radioactive fuel. Of all radioactive wastes generated throughout the entire nuclear fuel cycle, the majority are low-level (some 89 per cent) and intermediate-level (roughly 11 per cent), in installations where current performance and technology appear adequate and improving. Only about 0.1 per cent of nuclear wastes are high-level. For these, deep geologic disposal has gained wide technical acceptance. Nevertheless, repository siting for permanent disposal has encountered numerous setbacks and delays, and it may require several decades of demonstration before full implementation.

A number of newly industrialising nations have initiated nuclear power development programmes, most of them relying on transfer of technology from countries with well advanced programmes. Although there has been a core of scientists and engineers to guide these new programmes, the progress of many has been impeded by a lack of industrial infrastructure and insufficient numbers of trained technical workers. Significant nuclear development depends more on social and economic factors than on technological ones. Such development would entail the organisation of considerable technical training, and would need to start with the regulation of nuclear activities, the construction and operation of training and research reactors, and arrangements for the retention of the trained personnel in the country. The build-operate-transfer method (BOT) for establishing nuclear power plants in newly industrialising countries is expected to offer certain advantages; it has been discussed already for certain projects but seems unlikely to have a major impact on nuclear capacity in those countries. It seems likely, therefore, that nuclear power would be concentrated in relatively few newly industrialising countries (independent of technical advances in reactor design and safety) even if use of nuclear power became more widespread in the IEA region.

Evolutionary and advanced reactor designs could help alleviate real and perceived concerns about the safety and economic risks of nuclear power, paving the way for its re-emergence as a major generating option in countries where such concerns have hitherto slowed its introduction or expansion. For this to happen, electric utilities must be convinced that such designs can be built within a reasonably narrow cost range, and the public must be convinced that they are safe. The long-term prospects of nuclear power may thus depend not only on the success of design but also on the flow of information about the relative risks of energy sources. In any event, the prime requirement on the part of electric utilities, equipment manufacturers, nuclear vendors and governments is to assure continuing safe operation of existing plants. Because reactor designs in the former Soviet Union, transition countries and some other locations in the world have followed different pathways from those in the West, and because institutional infrastructures have similarly developed differently and may now also be in transition, it is essential for international co-operative efforts to enhance world confidence in the operation of these facilities and to assist in bringing them into conformity with world standards.

## Technology Policy Issues

### *Role of Governments*

It was governments who launched civil nuclear power and it is they who continue to make a large contribution to the development of new technology. An increasing fraction of the work, however, is presently instigated and supported by nuclear vendors and fuel manufacturers.

The proportion of government funding of R&D programmes varies from zero to total, but fuels for LWRs are usually developed by the manufacturers. Nuclear reactor vendors and manufacturers are taking the lead with most LWR concepts requiring major investment in prototype or demonstration, although national research institutions and utilities in some countries are closely involved. At the other end of the scale, breeder reactors and new uranium enrichment techniques have been developed for the most part by organisations wholly owned or funded by governments. There has also been some government support for the development of evolutionary light-water reactors and liquid-metal reactors, even though manufacturers and utility organisations are contributing considerably.

The major impediment to funding future development is the need to find organisations or consortia willing to finance demonstration or first-of-a-kind reactors. Electrical utilities are reluctant to proceed to the construction of reactors of new design without some assurance of regulatory authorities' acceptance of them and governments' support for nuclear development. Thus, even when electricity demand and the availability of capital favour investment, major constraints arise from political and public opinion, and possibly even divergence between national and local authorities, leading to difficulties in siting and obtaining operating licenses for nuclear plants.

Allaying public concern is a necessity, as is continuing demonstration of the economic viability of nuclear power. In many circumstances, it is the most economic source of electricity, but changing technical and regulatory requirements and evolving standards obscure or, in some countries, may have reversed its economic advantages. The economics of nuclear power could benefit, in some countries, from greater regulatory stability, which would provide a more sure context for investment planning in this capital-intensive industry. Steps have been taken to address these concerns so that they may diminish in the next century. Stability of regulation may have further economic benefits where design and engineering can be optimised in relation to well-defined goals. A major obstacle to introduction of new reactor types is diverging national approaches to regulation of reactor safety. This means that several design programmes and demonstration reactors could be needed for each concept. An ideal solution would be an international set of safety regulations, to give developers of a new reactor an assurance that the product, once demonstrated, would be acceptable in a wide international market. To date, national authorities have been reluctant to seek common regulations, although steps have been taken to harmonise the principles underlying safety regulation.

In summary, the future of nuclear power, unlike other energy technologies, will depend upon government action, both to determine a level of safety to satisfy public concerns, and to implement HLW disposal. Given the uncertainties in these areas, normal market forces cannot apply to the degree that they otherwise might. An integrated approach to energy policy is required to co-ordinate political, financial and regulatory support, which is visibly and directly responsive to public concerns. This approach is continuing to succeed in a number of countries; it is absent, or would benefit from strengthening, in others. In many cases, differing domestic approaches reflect differing potential benefits from country to country, differing costs of nuclear safety, and differing national priorities in applying limited resources. For countries electing to advance their degree of reliance on nuclear power, technical and economic assessments indicate that opportunities exist for substantial evolutionary and tiered advances toward standardisation, simplicity of design and enhanced inherent safety features. These advances appear achievable without economic loss and seem likely to lead to lower overall costs when associated with simplified and more certain regulatory processes and reduced construction periods. An emphasis on modularity, and on unit sizes closely matching growth requirements and other market factors, will help enhance system economics and open new markets.

***Role of International Co-operation***

IEA governments are subject to a large number of external influences in their role as promoters of nuclear technology and R&D programmes. These influences include those from international institutions such as the IAEA, the OECD, the OECD-NEA and the European Commission. International electric utility and nuclear industry associations also have an important role, as do multinational corporations, and national and international environmental groups, like Friends of the Earth and Greenpeace.

New LWR development will depend upon effective international collaboration between nuclear industries, government and non-government organisations. Information exchange and co-operation on FBRs and HTGRs has been extensive in the past and may provide IEA countries with examples to follow, but it has been suggested that wider and more formally based exchange mechanisms could be advantageous.

The European Fast Breeder Programme operates under the umbrella of an inter-governmental agreement, with further agreements between national utilities and development organisations, although some activities are now dormant. Japanese and American work related to fast reactors has links with the European effort. The aim of wider collaboration is to facilitate the preservation of expertise, the search for economies in the design of FBRs, the demonstration of actinide burning fuel cycles and the construction of further demonstration reactors; this is because a delay of at least fifteen years, and possibly twenty, is likely before commercial orders will be placed. In the case of HTGRs and HTRs, the aim might be somewhat different. A large part of the market envisaged for these reactors depends on their being considered safe enough to locate close to population or industrial centres. International collaboration to establish safety criteria and to assure that HTGR concepts satisfy them would be a useful but ambitious goal.

To some degree, the trends and suggested extensions outlined above are a continuation of the status quo and may not address the most critical near-term issues to ensure sustained contributions to meeting world energy needs from nuclear power. To the extent that these issues involve attaining widespread public and national agreement on acceptable levels of risk and safety, they revolve around the predominant reactor type, the light-water reactor, and its technology base, now comprising over three decades of experience. Unless such issues are addressed effectively on an international scale, even countries with strong and viable programmes may face future political difficulties and uncertainties.

In waste management, safety and decommissioning, there is a great deal of multinational co-operation through organisations such as the OECD-NEA, and through bilateral agreements. These exchanges can be extremely fruitful, possibly because they are far removed from commercial pressures. By definition advances in nuclear waste isolation take place over an even longer time. International co-operation is helping to facilitate individual actions, but continued policy support remains essential.

Specific and urgent safety concerns are associated with Soviet-designed nuclear reactors in central and eastern Europe and the Newly Independent States, where nuclear reactor concepts, operating entities and oversight institutions have acted outside the mainstream of international practices. It is ultimately to the benefit of all IEA countries to validate, retrofit, downrate or deactivate the operation of units where the level of safety is questioned for either technical or institutional reasons. Beyond this, as indicated previously, life extension of operating reactors should proceed with a high degree of technical assurance that current levels of safety will not be compromised, and may indeed be strengthened. These tasks can benefit from the increased public assurance that might result from international discussions among experts and indications of international agreement on broad principles within which national actions might proceed.

For the mid-term future, the technical scope for increasing safety would expand most rapidly, and to the benefit of all, if international agreement were reached on broad principles and if sponsoring countries and equipment manufacturers worked together to establish a positive climate for innovation and for the demonstration of benefits. While such actions can advance nationally, transferability and acceptance of the viability of such actions on an international scale would proceed fastest if taken in an international context from their inception. It is acknowledged that national and commercial interests have produced a number of designs potentially in competition, and that such interests may constitute a force for independent action or fragmentation of effort. Nevertheless, an emphasis on principles and concepts may accomodate variations in details and individuality of design, while providing broader recognition of increased inherent safety in a manner allowing transfer and benefits to all. With a strengthened base for nuclear utilisation and development, additional international co-operation in extending the nuclear market, and for longer-term concepts such as the breeder reactor, may also become more realistic.

## Approach

Nuclear energy generates a significant proportion of world electric energy and has much to offer in relation to energy security and the global environment. Concerns about operating safety, nuclear proliferation and the ability to implement adequate isolation of nuclear waste may continue to limit the realisation of these advantages. These concerns must be addressed in order to maintain the viability of the nuclear option. Actions which should be considered include: developing standardised and simpler designs and continuous attention to improving safety; ensuring that procedures for the safe disposal of radioactive wastes are not only technically feasible but also publicly acceptable; requiring adequately funded and publicly acceptable decommissioning of nuclear power plants; achieving uniform health and safety standards worldwide; and increasing public participation in development of new electric generating capacity and integration of energy security and environmental goals. Governments will want to continue the regulation of health and safety aspects of nuclear power, and may wish to continue supporting basic research, while leaving commercial development to industry. But government policy and regulations alone are not enough to ensure the continued viability of nuclear power. Industry holds responsibility for ensuring that nuclear plants are operated safely and economically and that the public has full access to information on this technology.

While several IEA countries generate between 15 and 75 per cent of their electricity from nuclear fission, only two countries have active development programmes, the remainder having either limited construction programmes or government moratoria on nuclear growth.

Operating experience over three decades of electric power generation has been good, but was marred by the Chernobyl and Three Mile Island accidents. Continuing positive experience is being generated at the rate of more than 400 reactor years per year. Evolutionary improvements are being incorporated in systems already under construction. But tiered implementation of advanced safety designs may require validation by governments to reduce market risks, as well as demonstration to ensure the desired benefits are being achieved and to foster the rapid dissemination of those benefits worldwide. Furthermore, reactor designs and institutions developed outside the scope of Western standards are a current source of concern. Even for the predominant group of Western-designed light-water reactors, there is a growing consensus over the need for subsequent generations of reactors to incorporate increased and passive safety features. The technical pathways to accomplish this are understood, and a large number of design concepts in several countries, using a number of common technical approaches, have been proposed.

The costs involved in some stages of the back-end of the fuel cycle, including decommissioning of reactors and facilities and management of high-level radioactive waste, remain uncertain in the absence of demonstrated and clearly defined national policies. Improved economics of nuclear power are needed and can be achieved through reduced capital costs and shorter construction periods, including the time required for regulatory requirements, and clarification of nuclear fuel-cycle cost. Factors other than capital cost reduction have only a minor influence on nuclear generation costs and uncertainties are of less importance economically. This is not widely appreciated outside the nuclear industry.

With respect to the objective of expanding the resource base, outlined above, national and international co-operative programmes on liquid-metal reactors are in place to make possible a 60-fold increase in use of the uranium resource base. The aim of these programmes is to validate nuclear breeder safety and economics, as a technology option for the long term.

To meet the technology priorities identified in this chapter, IEA countries may therefore wish to contribute to and co-operate in a technology strategy and collaborative R&D programme including the measures listed below.

- Encouraging the design and technology demonstration of advanced and evolutionary water-cooled nuclear reactors to maintain and further enhance the highest available standards of safety and cost effectiveness of nuclear power.

- Supporting R&D programmes aimed at preparing and testing next-generation nuclear reactor concepts and advanced nuclear systems as a long-term option, also at expanding the nuclear resource base and widening the applicability of nuclear energy.

- Commitment to technology and projects which can demonstrate the ability of the nuclear industry to cope economically and safely with the management of nuclear waste, in particular the disposal of high-level waste.

- Reducing uncertainty in the regulatory process by working out a government-industry relationship that helps create a clear basis for nuclear technology development and ensures dissemination of sound information to the public.

- Technology assistance to non-Member countries (including countries of central and eastern Europe and the Newly Independent States) to improve the safety and operation of their nuclear facilities while implementing adequate safeguard measures.

Progress in resolving issues of public safety and acceptance is beyond the scope and the capability of the non-governmental sector acting alone. The debate over the future of nuclear energy has become increasingly dominated by dedicated advocates and opponents of this source of energy. New and improved technologies can help place nuclear power and energy in a realistic perspective in relation to broader energy security, environmental and economic objectives of IEA countries, while also developing further opportunities and options.

# Chapter 6

## NUCLEAR FUSION

### Goals and Rationale

Nuclear fusion is an important element of the long-term energy strategy of IEA Member countries because of its many advantages as an energy resource. The successful application of practical fusion energy technologies at some point in the 21st century could help to enhance IEA countries' energy security, provide an environmentally acceptable alternative to fossil fuel combustion, and help to ensure continued economic growth through reliable electricity supply. Advanced research and development in fusion energy also could provide high-technology spin-offs in such areas as superconducting magnets, high-speed computing, high-power lasers, electronic diagnostic equipment, and high-power and high-frequency radio sources. Further, fusion technology developed within the IEA region could help to enhance the IEA countries' position as major suppliers of energy technologies in the world market.

The fuel for a fusion reactor consists of the less common isotopes of hydrogen, deuterium and tritium, which are readily available and essentially inexhaustible. The potential use of deuterium fuel (one heavy isotope of hydrogen) together with lithium to breed tritium could provide enough energy for thousands of years at current levels of world power demand.

The technology priority goals for the nuclear fusion technology are to:

- continue efforts toward demonstration of the technical feasibility of nuclear fusion power systems; and
- assess the potential impacts of fusion power on future energy supply.

The successful commercialisation of fusion energy (which could be realised by the middle of the next century) could ultimately change the overall pattern of electricity generation, as fusion power plants replace those now fuelled by nuclear fission power and fossil fuels. Because fusion power plants would not produce air pollutants that contribute to acid rain and could contribute to global climate change, they could minimise the environmental risks associated with the burning of fossil fuels and could substantially decrease demand for premium hydrocarbon fuels. Further, because fusion reactors would contain only small quantities of fuel at any time, they could eliminate the potential for runaway reactions that might lead to accidents.

At present, nuclear fusion technology is still under development, at a rate governed by the building and operating in sequence of a number of devices leading to a large-scale experimental reactor and then to a pilot-scale demonstration plant. At the same time, a number of technical issues should be addressed and resolved in complementary and specialised facilities. Table 6.1 summarises the basic arguments which contribute to the attractiveness of fusion power.

Under the terms of this study, fusion power should be considered a long-term energy technology option. R&D activities planned to eventually make this option commercially available involve a sequence of inter-related tasks:

(i) construction and operation of a power-producing next-step device such as the International Thermonuclear Experimental Reactor (ITER);

(ii) study and comprehensive resolution of all environmental and safety issues to guide technology progress;

(iii) preparation and optimisation of the power reactor technologies and low-activation materials as necessary;

(iv) continuation of the effort to explore, develop and verify the most promising confinement concepts for optimising the conditions of power production;

(v) updating of the conceptual design of a demonstration power reactor for proper orientation of the fusion development programme;

(vi) construction and operation of a demonstration power reactor; and

(vii) in addition to the next-step device and the DEMO concept for a demonstration nuclear fusion reactor, commitment of other facilities of lesser scale required to support and complement major facilities.

*Table 6.1*

**Attractiveness of Nuclear Fusion Power**

| | |
|---|---|
| **Fuel:** | • Fuels are plentiful and widespread<br>• Less than one tonne per year needed for one GWe<br>• Deuterium and lithium are neither toxic nor radioactive<br>• Tritium loop internal to the reactor with inventory small enough to avoid accidents with intolerable damage to public |
| **Properties:** | • Negligible atmospheric pollution and greenhouse gas emissions<br>• Limited use of land<br>• Small biological hazard potential (with low activation materials)<br>• High safety level, highly improbable destructive power excursions<br>• No volatile elements or actinides present in fusion waste |
| **Application:** | • Base-load electricity generation<br>• Potential for extended applications (possibly process heat) |
| **Development Potential:** | • Transition to low activation materials and to advanced fuel |

The pace at which this or a similar sequence of activities might be able to proceed, and the degree of success to be met at various stages of experimentation, cannot be accurately forecasted. Recently the growing scale of the facilities required for the development of fusion power has raised the costs to highly visible levels, in turn creating the need to proceed in sequence because of these costs. Thus, scale and costs have become important factors in determining the pace of fusion development. This pace has become slow compared to earlier expectations because, in general, larger-scale facilities take longer to construct and to exploit, and for fusion there is a close integration of scientific, technological and engineering development, and experimentation in each new facility.

## Technology Description and Assessment

### *Description of Significant Technologies*

Fusion power occurs when light nuclei are fused together to form reaction products, and the total mass of the reaction products is less than that of the initial particles, the difference having been converted into reaction energy. The energy released from these reactions is very great, about ten times greater than typical fission reactions, per gram of fuel. Since the electric charges of the nuclei provide strong repulsive forces, the energy of the particles must be very high for the fusion reaction to occur at a sufficient and sustained rate. This can be achieved in a high-temperature gas (plasma), and by allowing sufficient residence time for the particles to collide. In stars this is achieved in very large volumes, subject to intense gravitational forces. In very limited volumes, different mechanisms must be used to contain the particles and prevent them from escaping before they react. There are two mechanisms being considered to reach this goal, allowing large enough reaction rates: high magnetic fields (magnetic confinement) and very high plasma densities (inertial confinement). These mechanisms are considered in this chapter.

Scientists and researchers must bring fusion reactions to breakeven, the point at which at least as much energy is produced as must be input to maintain the reaction. Existing experiments are expected to reach this long-elusive milestone around the turn of the century. Beyond breakeven, there is the even more important task of creating high-energy gain. Once the scientific feasibility of fusion as a potential energy source is established, the engineering development necessary to develop fusion research must be completed.

Among the many possible fusion reactions for the production of nuclear fusion energy, practical interest is in: deuterium-tritium, deuterium-deuterium, and deuterium-helium 3 ($He^3$) reactions. All present efforts concentrate on the deuterium-tritium reaction which offers by far the highest gain. But nature has provided this reaction with three additional properties making its exploitation difficult:

- tritium is unstable, it does not exist in nature and has to be bred from lithium;
- one of the reaction products is a neutron which is useful for the just-mentioned in-pile breeding of tritium, but also results in activation of the reactor structure; and
- tritium is a radioactive gas which must be confined.

The deuterium-deuterium reaction involves lower radioactivity. It requires, however, about one order of magnitude higher plasma pressure to produce the same fusion power density as the deuterium-tritium reaction. The $He^3$ reaction has the potential to involve even lower, perhaps even very little radioactivity, but has the burden of requiring the creation of $He^3$ or its extraction from some extra-terrestrial source since it is unavailable on earth.

a) *Magnetic Confinement*

As currently envisioned, a fusion reactor based on the mechanism of magnetic plasma confinement would consist of a toroidal reaction chamber, surrounded by a lithium-containing blanket for power extraction and tritium breeding; both are embedded in a magnetic field produced by toroidally arranged coils. Deuterium and lithium are the basic fuel constituents. Since tritium is bred *in situ,* there would be no need for an external fuel factory. The power, in the form of heat, would be extracted from the blanket and coupled by a heat exchanger to a conventional electricity generating plant. The heat may be removed at high temperature, but the actual temperature is determined by the thermo-mechanical properties of the blanket.

International collaboration has concentrated on magnetic confinement. Magnetic confinement fusion research is carried out in 29 countries, including the European Union, Japan, Russia, and the United States. The world effort in magnetic confinement fusion R&D amounts to more than US$ 1 billion per year. The goals of these various programmes are to complete the scientific base of the tokamak approach, to optimise the confinement concept, and to address the engineering issues of fusion energy.

In the course of the last decade, progress in fusion power technology has been very significant. Development of fusion power has reached a state, given the use of the most powerful of the available devices, in which plasma conditions are close to those needed for reactor operation. This progress is measured by comparing the equivalent fusion power produced to the rate of heat loss from the plasma. Tokamak experiments have increased this ratio by a factor of over a million during the last 20 years, by raising plasma temperatures and improving the quality of heat insulation. A factor of 5-10 remains to be achieved to reach the ignition point, in which the plasma keeps itself hot by its own fusion reactions, while generating additional energy which can potentially be extracted from the system.

Based on data currently being acquired, next step devices are now being designed to demonstrate burning plasma conditions and to allow testing of reactor components. The four ITER parties (Euratom for the European Union, Japan, Russia and the United States) are committed to complete the engineering design activities of the next-step tokamak by 1998. In this worldwide collaboration, an engineering design will be established, research and development to support that design will be carried out, planning schedules for construction and operation will be developed, site requirements will be prepared, cost and resource estimates will be produced, and proposals for approaches to implement construction will be completed. In short, all the necessary information will be developed to allow a decision to be made on the construction of ITER to start operation early next century. Its unit size will be of the order of one gigawatt. It should then be followed by a demonstration reactor to prove that fusion power can be produced safely and reliably, and to provide firm grounds for the evaluation of the investment and running costs for the next power producing reactors.

b) *Inertial Confinement*

A conceptual fusion reactor based on inertial confinement utilises fusion energy from a very dense and high-temperature plasma generated in the center of a spherical reactor chamber with a lithium-containing blanket. The ultimate goal of inertial-confinement fusion is to demonstrate that a mixture of deuterium and tritium fuel in a small capsule can be compressed and sufficiently heated by means of a driver which can consist of a laser or of other particle beam energy to undergo an efficient fusion reaction, while the capsule is confined by its own inertia. Fusion energy yields of about 1 per cent of the driver pulse energy and compressions of hundreds of times of the original liquid density have been achieved. Due to the potential for weapons-physics research, inertial-confinement programmes in some countries have been conducted as elements of defence programmes, while in other countries R&D efforts have been concentrated in view of energy development research.

For energy applications using inertial confinement, there are three critical problem areas that must be successfully addressed:

- pellets must be designed that yield high gain, and can be cheaply produced, efficiently driven, and stably imploded;
- efficient, high-power drivers should be developed that can be operated at useful repetition rates;
- reactor chambers need to be designed to contain the micro-explosion products and to adequately protect the driver.

At present, based on demonstrated performance, inertial fusion is less mature than magnetic confinement. However, progress in inertial fusion has been rapid since its inception in the early 1960s.

***Assessment of Technical and Economic Potential***

Future nuclear fusion reactors appear to have a variety of attractive environmental and safety aspects. They would have no greenhouse gas emissions from their operation. The basic potential for fusion power is for large scale base-load electricity generation. Present concepts are limited to extracting fusion energy for electric generation via a heat exchanger from a blanket surrounding the reaction chamber. Predicted operating temperatures of steam or helium working fluids should allow Rankine cycle thermal conversion efficiencies of about 35 per cent. Higher efficiency may be possible if improved materials become available. Waste heat from the thermal cycle could be used in a similar manner to that from other power sources. Table 6.2 summarises the technical and economic potential of nuclear fusion systems.

*Table 6.2*

**Technical and Economic Potential of Nuclear Fusion Systems**

| Characteristic | Comparative Advantage |
|---|---|
| Thermal Efficiency | About 35 per cent (higher if advanced fuels or thermo-dynamic topping cycles, direct energy conversion become possible). |
| Emissions | Practically none during operation, except for waste heat, and minor tritium releases under accident conditions. |
| Materials | Reduced activation and possibility of recycling. |
| Cost of Power | Competitive with other base-load power sources. |

In a reactor plant, the inventory may be up to several kilograms of tritium which is bred *in situ* from lithium and burned to helium; however, only a few hundred grams of the tritium are vulnerable to releases under accident conditions. One safety feature of a fusion reactor in contrast to fission reactors is that the reaction zone contains only a small amount of fuel, equivalent to approximately ten seconds of a thermonuclear reaction, and fuel is fed as needed. Second, and more important, the reaction rate is self-limiting, and therefore the magnitude of any potential power excursion is very limited in energy and time. Third, the power density associated with after-heat is small. All these factors contribute to the expected safety of fusion reactors.

The volume of radioactive waste produced during the lifetime of a fusion reactor due to regular replacements of parts, and after decommissioning, would be comparable to that of an equivalent pressurised water reactor with a once-through fuel cycle. However, no actinides and no volatile, highly active reaction products are produced in fusion and thus the waste is less hazardous than fission waste. The volume of waste from decommissioning could be substantially reduced by using low-activation elements and by recycling the used materials.

## Technology Prospects and Markets

### *Market Trends*

In nuclear fusion, theory has not been able to provide a full understanding of confinement problems. Thus, empirical confinement scaling laws have to be used for performance extrapolations. Moreover, as plasma confinement relies on a fine-scale turbulence, experimental devices provide increases in confinement performances according to their size. Achieving ignition requires an apparatus similar in size to a power reactor. This implies that after successful conclusion of the development programme the results can be applied directly to market requirements. Based on these assumptions, nuclear fusion power could be ready to enter the marketplace by about the year 2050.

When fusion reactors are fully developed and accepted for base-load electricity generation, market penetration would be governed primarily by the replacement rate of electric power stations. Within this context, Table 6.3 gives the market potential for nuclear fusion reactors in the power sector. The market potential for other applications has not been estimated.

*Table 6.3*

**Market Potential for Nuclear Fusion Reactors**

| Characteristic | Nature/Size of the Market |
|---|---|
| Time-frame | Target year 2050 |
| Nature of Market | Base-load electricity generation |
| Regional Aspects | Start of introduction in IEA and other industrialised countries |
| Size of Market | Any desired share of base-load electricity |
| Marketability | Once accepted as a competitive source, the penetration of nuclear fusion plants will be governed mainly by replacement rate of power stations |

***Key Players***

In all countries, fusion-oriented activity is concentrated in government-funded R&D centres. This fact reflects both the need to construct and operate large-scale experimental devices and the inherently long-development timescale, which exceeds the planning horizon of private enterprises. As a consequence, the bulk of the nuclear fusion technology programme is ultimately dependent on the amount and continuity of government support. Active industrial participation remains essential in technology innovation and facility construction.

Industry has constructed the large research facilities needed in both physics and technology research programmes. Industry has also contributed through contracts to developing technology needed for short-term applications to experimental devices. In some specific cases, industry has carried out independent development of fusion technologies.

Fusion-oriented research exists in universities and associated institutes. In some cases, these groups collaborate directly with larger national fusion laboratories. These universities perform work of special interest in connection with innovative or fundamental issues of fusion research. This research is either fully or partially funded by larger national fusion laboratories, or directly by the co-ordinating or overseeing governmental organisations. These universities also serve to train future scientists and engineers in the field of thermonuclear fusion.

Countries operating more than one fusion laboratory have established or charged organisations to sponsor and co-ordinate national activities. This co-ordination is done by the Department of Energy in the United Statest and by the Science and Technology Agency and the Ministry of Education in Japan. Fusion-oriented research in the European Union is co-ordinated by the European Commission, and Switzerland has joined this European programme. In Canada all responsibilities lie with AECL, while in Russia the leadership has been assigned to the Ministry of Atomic Energy.

There are two major international organisations which are important for efficient and widely practiced international collaboration in the fusion field. They are the IEA and the International Atomic Energy Agency (IAEA). The IEA is operating mainly via research and development Implementing Agreements on well defined topics, whereas IAEA supports broad information exchange in fusion research. Further, IAEA has recently become more involved by providing the auspices for the ITER EDA.

### *Market Barriers*

The pace of development of nuclear fusion power is governed by the breadth and intensity of the R&D effort, and by an acceptable level of risk in moving from one experimental step to the next. Since there are time requirements that are relatively fixed (such as the time for constructing and operating experimental devices, and the time needed for development of technologies), the rate of nuclear fusion development has clear upper limits.

Driving factors for development of specific technologies arise from a prospective view of future energy scenarios. Recognition of the challenges ahead may lead to increased pressure in further exploring promising technologies. The driving factors advancing nuclear fusion power, besides the challenge of mastering the source of energy which drives the whole universe, are:

- long-term energy independence and security;
- low environmental impact;
- low fuel cost; and
- possible economic competitiveness.

Conversely, factors which tend to constrain the pace of nuclear fusion power development are:

- capital intensity;
- cost of the necessary demonstration steps; and
- time required for each demonstration step.

Further constraining factors may arise from uncertainties as to the full economic potential fusion has to offer, and the value of this potential in the long-term future.

## Technology Policy Issues

### *Role of Governments*

Nuclear fusion is a conceptual technology for future energy supplies which embodies many unique characteristics compared to present sources of energy. It is one of the very few options combining wide-spread, plentiful fuel reserves and power generating capability with minimum environmental impact. It promises both energy security and environmental benefits compared to other base-load power technologies, but still requires extensive development, in terms of both cost and time. If the pathway presently visualised can be followed, and if favourable results are obtained, an environmentally attractive and competitive system could be available for use around the year 2050.

Because of the long development path, and the large scale of developmental devices, steady support from governments is necessary for effectiveness and success. Continuing support of nuclear fusion research and development means an investment decision which must balance the remaining uncertainties and risks associated with the long time periods involved against perceptions of future benefits which may be uniquely obtainable through this technology development. The prioritisation of this activity should reflect both awareness of its long-term desirability and uniqueness, and the existence of significant nearer-term energy supply, use and environmental issues which compete for limited resources. The nature of fusion power development is such that it is particularly amenable to co-operative actions among governments, resulting in sharing of knowledge, resources and burdens.

### *Role of International Co-operation*

Fusion research in the field of magnetic confinement is an outstanding example of international co-operation. An impressive and unprecedented effort in international collaboration and R&D programme co-ordination and information exchange has gone hand-in-hand with progress in scientific and technical achievements over several decades.

In this context, ITER represents a major technical challenge and an unprecedented level of international co-operation and management of a large, advanced technology project. The IAEA provided the ITER programme with a means of initiation and is now providing basic services during operation. The Implementing Agreements sponsored by the IEA provided an important base of experience through the demonstration over the last twenty years of a useful instrument for organising collaborative efforts among IEA Member countries on selected and well-defined research projects in nuclear fusion. As the nuclear fusion technology programme progresses in time, scale and cost, additional effort may be needed to increase the integration of ongoing national and international activities. The IEA is seeking to broaden the participation of non-IEA countries with significant fusion activities and to enhance further the concept of joint programme planning, with the role and significance of each element better visualised in terms of the total world effort. Such enhanced joint planning of a multinational character could be supplemented and further strengthened by joint evaluations which incorporate not only technical expertise, but also the relationships between technical progress and the resulting economic and industrial spin-offs.

## Approach

The potential advantage of nuclear fusion power is to be able to supply base-load electricity in an environmentally acceptable manner and to increase energy security while allowing reactor operation with practically no emission of conventional pollutants and greenhouse gases. Applications of nuclear fusion beyond the power sector might also become feasible. Nuclear fusion, albeit not likely to represent a widely available power source in the next 30 to 50 years, could thus turn out to be an attractive solution for power generation in a longer time-frame. This prospect makes nuclear fusion a fundamental component of any energy technology policy.

Progress made towards a deuterium-tritium fusion reactor is impressive and promising. Development of fusion power has reached a state where, in the most powerful of the available devices, plasma conditions are close to those needed for reactor operation. Thus the next feasible major goal for fusion research should be to achieve, in a next-step device, controlled ignition and extended burn of deuterium-tritium plasmas, while addressing substantial technological issues of reactor relevance. To this purpose, a fundamental contribution is expected from the ITER programme. The construction and operation of the ITER device would allow a number of technological issues to be addressed and would prepare the ground for a demonstration fusion reactor.

Advancement in nuclear fusion power technologies proceeded and is proceeding in the area of magnetic confinement. Inertial confinement research has to a large degree been undertaken as a supplement or contributing element to defence programme activities, in parallel with energy research projects. Inertial fusion is less mature than magnetic confinement in terms of demonstrated performance and possible application to commercial power production. Accordingly, magnetic confinement remains the priority approach for fusion power.

With a view to attaining the technology priority goals stated in this chapter, nuclear fusion technology programmes should:

- continue international collaboration and cost-sharing activities in the area of magnetic fusion confinement;
- develop materials that minimise radioactive wastes and design features that optimise safety and environmental advantages;
- conduct supporting experiments and investigate a spectrum of technology options to search for breakthroughs; and
- achieve early industrial involvement.

Fusion R&D requires adequate and sustained government support because of the long time periods required for the various stages of development needed. International collaboration is a valuable component of the current programme strategy. Future international co-operative efforts might usefully place even greater emphasis than at present on joint programme design and evaluation activities in order to sustain technical progress at an affordable level of resource commitment for participating nations.

IEA Implementing Agreements represent an effective means to promote joint design, the conducting of experiments and information exchange. Science aspects of this R&D are significant and basic research plays a more important role than in the case of other energy RD&D. Technology spin-offs should be further encouraged. Due to the increasing cost of future activities, the role of international co-operation may expand. The exchange of ideas, data, concepts, personnel and equipment has resulted in an expanded technology base for magnetic fusion concepts, and progress toward development of the fusion option has been cost-effective. Actions taken towards the next-step device and beyond would be facilitated by continuing and extending co-operative activities on an international scale. The expected result will be considerable cost-sharing of major design and facility expenses among participating nations, and eventually technological progress will be accelerated.

# Chapter 7

## RENEWABLE ENERGY

### Goals and Rationale

Renewable energy technologies use resources generally not subject to depletion, such as heat and light from the sun, the force of winds, organic matter (biomass), falling water, ocean energy, and geothermal heat from inside the earth. About one thousand times more energy reaches the earth's surface from the sun than is released by all the fossil fuels consumed. Though the large stores of primary energy exploited are often scattered, they can be converted in various ways to usable heat or power. New and improved technologies are being developed and tested with different technical and economic attributes, degrees of maturity, and potential in future energy systems. While not a major contributor to total primary energy supply in IEA countries, new renewable energy sources could become increasingly commercially competitive with conventional energy and power. During the last fifteen years, intensive work by industry, national laboratories and R&D centres has steadily increased the performance of renewable energy systems, while dramatically lowering their costs.

Increased use of renewable energy technologies can contribute to meeting environmental and energy security goals. Since few depend on combustion to generate heat or electricity, they offer substantial environmental benefits compared with conventional energy technologies. Renewable energy can also be used to make hydrogen, itself a potentially versatile fuel. To the extent that renewable energy systems tap large and dispersed resource bases, this energy can often be converted with minimal negative environmental impact. For the same reason, and because renewable energies are typically based on indigenous fuels whose supply is not easily disrupted, their development and use enhances energy security. However, some resources, like geothermal energy, are depletable over long periods and can have significant environmental impacts. Several renewable energy resources, moreover, are not uniformly distributed throughout the IEA countries but, taken together, the sum of the solar, wind, biomass and geothermal resources in the IEA region is ample to contribute appreciably to energy security, if adequately developed. Renewable energy sources thus have the potential to become an increasingly significant component of primary energy supply in the twenty-first century, in both IEA and non-IEA countries.

In addition to favourable environmental and energy security characteristics, renewable energy sources offer other advantages not commonly found in conventional energy systems. Most renewable energy systems are modular, allowing flexibility in matching load growth, and are suitable for use in decentralised energy production. In larger-scale applications, they are relatively capital intensive (compared with technologies against which they compete) and require major investment in equipment to capture diffuse energy sources. However, after the investment has been made, the economics of renewables improve in comparison with conventional competitors, since running costs are low compared with using conventional fuels, particularly if the latter are subject to large price increases. While some technologies, like hydropower, geothermal, solar water heating and wind energy, are already relatively mature and economic in specific localities today, improved systems will open up even greater potential for more widespread application in the future.

There are substantial prospects for improvements in efficiency, cost and performance, for both grid and off-grid applications. Advances will also be achieved through applications that take advantage of the many marketable benefits of energy from renewable resources, including off-grid and environmental benefits. Advances include the use of new materials, improved scientific knowledge and lower-cost components. For grid applications, the levelised cost of energy depends essentially on the facility lifetime and the operating and maintenance costs associated with sustained and reliable operation. However, some renewable energy systems are suitable for important niche markets.

The economics of renewable energy systems using intermittent sources such as solar and wind energy will improve with integration into existing energy systems, and as costs of energy storage decline. Energy storage is not seen as a major problem for renewable energy systems, but it should be noted that the "effective" storage consists in the already established network and fossil-fuelled generating capacity. This situation is tolerable only within a reasonable capacity contribution to the grid, beyond which grid stability issues become a problem. In the long term, cost-effective "storage" is necessary for large-scale market penetration of renewable energy technologies and systems. In fact, many studies have shown that the value of storage to a utility decreases if wind, photovoltaic or solar thermal equipment is added to utility systems where peaks occur during the day. Exceptions include small-scale wind-diesel hybrid power systems where batteries can reduce the operating time for the diesels. In many cases, well designed renewable energy systems for specific applications have been defined. Because technical and economic advances are still being made, opportunities exist to reconsider trade-offs involving different energy sources within total system design. Competitive renewable energy procurement in the United Kingdom and the United States in 1994 suggests that significant reductions in the cost of renewable energy have already been achieved.

This chapter focuses on the type of technology strategy and collaboration that can contribute towards the accomplishment of two priority goals, namely:

- improving the efficiency and economics of renewable energy systems; and
- expanding deployment and effective integration of renewable energy systems into existing or evolving energy systems, amid the widespread restructuring and privatisation affecting the energy utility sector.

## Technology Description and Assessment

### *Description of Significant Technologies*

Renewable energy technologies are at various stages of development. Some are relatively mature, as in the case of hydropower, the use of steam from geothermal wells, solar water heating, and the burning of biomass and waste. Others are new but already well developed; examples are the concentration of solar heat for passive-design systems, photovoltaic cells which convert the sun's light directly into electricity, the conversion of biomass into gaseous or liquid fuels, wind turbines, and the use of steam and hot water from geothermal wells. Still others are emerging concepts in the R&D or pilot-plant phase, as in the case of energy from hot dry rocks, power production from ocean tides, waves and temperature gradients, or hydrogen production. A summary of the technical status of renewable energy technologies described here is shown in Table 7.1.

a) *Active Solar Heating and Cooling Systems*

Energy demand in buildings accounts for approximately one-third of the annual primary energy requirements of the IEA countries. Large commercial and institutional buildings use between 20 and 50 per cent of their energy for heating, cooling and lighting. Residences and other small buildings invest nearly two-thirds of their energy budgets for space heating and hot water. To provide space heating or hot water, active solar heating systems use solar collectors in which air or liquid is heated and a fan or pump is used to transfer the heat to the living spaces, or to storage for later use. Active solar cooling utilises the sun's energy to help offset the net cooling load of a building (space conditioning or refrigeration), using solar collectors to drive absorption, desiccant, or Rankine cooling equipment. R&D on new and existing materials would help to improve the performance, durability, reliability and cost-effectiveness of solar energy systems. Active solar cooling, for its part, is not competitive with conventional options, but as a next-generation technology has significant potential.

The economic cost of solar energy for heating and cooling buildings depends on the solar radiation level, the efficiency of solar collectors, and the cost of equipment installation (including storage) and maintenance. The construction of very large solar collectors and the integration of solar collectors and equipment into the building shell are two alternatives for improving economy and increasing user acceptance.

b) *Passive Solar Heating, Cooling and Daylighting Systems*

Passive solar heating systems rely on the natural heat transfer processes of radiation, convection and conduction to collect, store, distribute and control, within a building, energy that has been received from the sun. Auxiliary power is not normally required for regular system operation. Simply put, with passive systems the building becomes the energy system. Passive solar cooling relies on building design to incorporate heat avoidance techniques, natural lighting and natural cooling to improve the indoor comfort level and, at the same time, reduce energy consumption. Natural cooling methods include natural ventilation, night cooling, and radiative cooling. Solar heating, both passive and active, is an available

*Table 7.1*
**Technical Status of Renewable Energy Systems**

| Technology | Status | Technical Feasibility | Unit Size | Conversion Efficiency[1] (%) |
|---|---|---|---|---|
| Active Solar Systems<br>• Heating<br>• Cooling | <br>Commercial<br>R&D | <br>H<br>M/H | 1-50 MWt | 25-50 |
| Passive Solar Systems<br>• Heating<br>• Cooling<br>• Daylighting | <br>Commercial<br>R&D<br>Commercial/R&D | M/H | 0.005-500 MWt | 25-50 |
| Solar Thermal Power | Demonstrated | M/H | 7-100 MWe | 15-30 |
| Photovoltaic Systems<br>• Grid-Connected<br>• Off-Grid | <br>Demonstrated<br>Commercial | <br>M/H<br>H | <br>1-7000 kWe<br>0.01-1000kWe | <br>10-25<br>10-25 |
| Biomass<br>• Fuels<br>• Power | <br>Commercial[2]<br>Commercial | <br>H<br>H | <br>n.a.<br>5-50 MWe | <br>n.a.<br>25-35 |
| Wind Power | Commercial | H | 0.02-1.5 MWe | 25-45 |
| Geothermal Energy<br>• Hydrothermal<br>• Dry Rock<br>• Magma | <br>Commercial<br>R&D<br>R&D | <br>H<br>L<br>L | <br>10-500 MWe | <br>10-16<br>n.a.<br>n.a. |
| Small Hydroelectricity | Commercial | M/H | 0.5-25 MWe | 80-90 |
| Ocean Wave and Tida Energy | Commercial/R&D | L/H | 3-10 MWe | n.a. |
| Ocean Thermal Energy | R&D | L | 100-1000 MWe | n.a. |

Notes: 1. Demonstrated or actual efficiency in use.
2. Wood combustion is commercial along with ethanol.
Mwt = megawatts thermal
Mwe = megawatts electric
kWe = kilowatts electric
n.a. = not applicable or not available
L, M, H = low, medium, high
Technical feasibility, conversion efficiency and unit size are based upon current views.
All of the tables shown are meant to convey a sense of progress and direction.

technology, developed and improved throughout the 1970s and 1980s, and a viable alternative or complement to traditional water-heating and space-heating systems. R&D efforts are under way to increase know-how in the design and performance of buildings using passive and active solar and conservation technologies, the interaction of these technologies, and their effective combination in various climatic regions. In northern countries, for example, central solar heating plant with seasonal storage may be the only option for solar heating if solar energy is required to make a large contribution to the annual load. Technical barriers to this technology concern the identification of high-energy-density media for storage and the need to predict the thermal performance of large-volume heat storage in the ground.

Daylighting consists in use of natural light as a source of illumination during daytime operation. Application technologies are available and used to level out peak lighting and cooling loads in commercial buildings, while simultaneously enhancing office productivity. Innovative passive concepts are available, particularly in the form of windows with variable or controllable radiation transmission characteristics and construction. Technological options include devices to improve the uniformity of daylight, such as light shelves, light pipes, mirrored louvres, holographic glazing and prismatic glazing. Coatings are under development for switchable glazing that can be controlled electrically or thermally to reduce solar heat transmittance, as required. In addition, daylight-linked lighting controls can encourage more thrifty use of electric lighting.

c) *Solar Thermal Power*

There are two basic ways to use solar energy for producing electricity, besides that of converting it into biomass. One is to use solar thermal power as it is; the other is to convert the energy directly through photovoltaic cells, which are discussed under the next heading. Solar thermal power systems use mirrors to redirect, focus, and concentrate the sun's rays onto a receiving surface, thereby achieving high operating temperatures. Thermal heat storage or back-up fossil fuel may be used to allow generation to continue when solar energy is not available. Typical systems range in electrical output from a few kWe to hundreds of MWe. Concentrating collectors are adopted most frequently for applications requiring high temperatures, such as electrical power generation, industrial process heat, production of chemicals, or chemical energy storage. The concentration may be performed by a number of means, including parabolic troughs, next-generation power towers and parabolic dishes. Parabolic trough collector systems are now available and commercialised; more than 1.3 million square metres of concentrating collectors are now installed in Southern California (United States), providing a capacity of 354 MWe of peak electrical power. An important technical priority for next-generation power towers and parabolic dishes is development of mirrors with flexible stretched membranes. Such membranes offer the possibility of light-weight low-cost collection systems. The Solar One solar thermal power tower in Barstow, California has been successfully demonstrated, providing on-line peak capacity of 10 MWe to the Southern California Edison system for five years. The United States Department of Energy and a consortium of electric utilities are retrofitting Solar One with a molten salt heat transfer and storage medium – Solar Two – to collect and store heat energy, replacing the earlier water/steam system in anticipation of future operations on a scale of 100 MWe to 200 MWe.

d) *Photovoltaic Systems*

Photovoltaic power generation involves direct conversion of sunlight into electricity using a solid-state device, the photovoltaic cell. The cell is composed of thin layers of semiconductor material that produce electricity when exposed to light. One may produce cells of just a few square centimetres, or combine modules into arrays of unlimited size. The cells are silent, produce no emissions, have no moving parts and incur very low operation and maintenance costs with currently available technology. Photovoltaic cells or solar cells are most commonly made from silicon, but next-generation cells may be made from more exotic materials like copper indium di-selenide and cadmium telluride. The predominant cell materials and types are monocrystalline silicon, polycrystalline silicon and amorphous silicon. Solar cells differ with regard to cell material, the material's crystallinity and the cell's structure, and they take the form of either wafer, ribbon, thin film or thick film. Cells are linked together and encapsulated into modules that are appropriate for a variety of applications. A comparison of present-day photovoltaic cell characteristics is shown in Table 7.2. Applications range from wristwatches to electric utilities or space vehicles. Photovoltaic units offer reliable, economical power where connection to the grid is difficult. New manufacturing processes continue to yield significant improvements in cell efficiency and cell lifetime, as well as major cost reductions. Solar cell efficiencies in the laboratory have improved from between 16 and 18 per cent in the mid-1970s to today's 29 per cent for a point-contact crystalline silicon cell, and 35 per cent for a gallium arsenide-gallium antimonide stacked junction cell (a cell with two layers that absorb different parts of the solar spectrum).

*Table 7.2*

**A Comparison of Photovoltaic Cell Characteristics**

| Cell Material | Theoretical Efficiency [1] (%) | Laboratory Efficiency [2] (%) | Commercial Efficiency (%) | Cost [3] (US$ per peak Watt) |
|---|---|---|---|---|
| Single-crystal silicon | 30 | 23.5 | 12 to 14 | 4 to 7 |
| with concentrator | 37 | 28.2 | 13 to 15 | 5 to 8 |
| Polycrystalline silicon | 25 | 17.8 | 11 to 13 | 4 to 7 |
| Amorphous silicon (including silicon alloys) | 17 | 13 | 4 to 6 | 3 to 5 |
| Polycrystalline thin films - cadmium telluride | 27 | 15.8 | 6 | n.a. |
| Copper indium di-selenide | 19 | 16.4 | n.a. | n.a. |
| Gallium arsenide | 28 | 27.6 | n.a. | n.a. |
| with concentrator | 39 | 29.2 | n.a. | n.a. |

Source: B. Weick (1995)

Notes:
1. Theoretical efficiency is evaluated at terrestrial level at a latitude of 45°N and ambient temperature of 20°C.
2. Laboratory efficiency is the ratio of the electric energy that a solar cell produces in direct sunlight to the energy from sunlight incident on the cell.
3. Cost refers to the sole module cost and does not reflect the cost of the balance of the system, which in most cases approximately doubles the total cost.

n.a. means not available.

Photovoltaic systems are in the category of available technology, having been used both in large-scale utility networks and in remote locations where conventional fuel sources are limited. Full commercial photovoltaic applications are found in professional areas such as navigation aids and telecommunications. Although these applications provide only a very small contribution to meeting total energy consumption, they nevertheless represent important business for the growing photovoltaics industry. For other applications such as home lighting and water pumping, there exists a potentially enormous market which is starting to develop. Grid-connected photovoltaics are attracting a lot of attention as building-integrated systems where photovoltaic modules form the roof or facade elements. A large market could develop.

Unfortunately, the cost of silicon wafers may not diminish sufficiently over the next ten to twenty years to allow the industry to become competitive in base-load grid-connected power plants. A cell's cost-performance ratio is also affected by expenses not directly associated with solar cell material. Balance-of-system costs include outlay on support structures, sun trackers, electrical interconnections, DC-to-AC power conversion, land use and energy storage. Indeed, large-scale generation of photovoltaic energy would require large land areas, perhaps as much as 2.5 square kilometres for a 100-MWe plant. Before photovoltaic complexes can start to provide base-load power, developers will have to find effective and inexpensive ways to store the electric power that solar installations generate. One approach involves passing electricity through water, splitting water molecules into hydrogen and oxygen. At night, or when solar systems are not operating at capacity, the stored hydrogen gas can pass through fuel cells to be converted back into electricity.

e) *Biomass Energy*

Biomass derives its energy from the sun and is produced from organic material such as wood and wood wastes, herbaceous and aquatic plants, agricultural residues, industrial and processing wastes, or municipal wastes. The *IEA/OECD Scoping Study: Energy and Environmental Technologies to Respond to Global Climate Change Concerns* concluded that the range of possibilities for major improvements through technology development is very large and very varied. Current biomass production on land represents the equivalent of over one billion barrels of oil equivalent per day, or more than five times the total present world demand for energy in all forms. Realising even a very small portion of this potential could make an important contribution to meeting future energy and environmental needs. The use of biomass as an energy resource for the future will require the development of better techniques that will increase the amount of feedstock available, enhance the efficiency with which it is used, and lower the cost of biomass energy to economically competitive levels. Throughout IEA countries, between 3 per cent and 15 per cent of primary energy is currently generated from wood and wood wastes. In Canada, for example, 7 per cent of primary energy is supplied in this way. Annually, hundreds of millions of litres of ethanol are produced worldwide from grains – primarily wheat and barley – for blending with gasoline.

Conversion is based upon biochemical processes such as fermentation (to produce alcohol) and anaerobic digestion (to produce a fuel gas), as well as thermochemical processes such as pyrolysis (to produce an oil), gasification to produce biogas, and combustion. In general, large efficiency improvements can be achieved by gasification of biomass and combustion of fuel gas in combined cycles. This technology is at the development and demonstration stage. There are thus two focuses for biomass energy: liquid biofuels and biofuels for power (which includes uses for district heating or plant heat).

(i) Liquid biofuels

Biomass is the only available renewable energy source capable today of producing high-value liquid and gaseous fuels such as ethanol and methanol. These alcohol fuels can offer versatile, renewable alternatives to premium fuels for transportation obtained from coal, oil, and natural gas (see Chapter 9). Biomass gasification and its use in combined cycles promises efficiency levels of 40 per cent.

Ethanol is produced by fermentation. Methanol can be obtained through biomass gasification, followed by the synthesis process. Vegetable oils are produced by processing rape-seeds, sunflowers, coconuts or soya. Despite the considerable investments that have been made in technologies to produce biofuels, there remains a wide range of other candidate crops for biofuel processes, and apparently considerable potential for future improvements. Among the various processes under development, the enzymatic process appears to hold the most promise. Cells and enzymes are capable of synthesising many organic chemicals of industrial interest, in addition to biofuels. More generally, biocatalytic conversions could provide alternatives for processing fossil fuels, for use in the synthesis of organic chemicals, for the conversion of biomass to chemicals, and for hydrogen production. These advanced systems can also be applied in environmental protection technology, particularly in innovative pollution-prevention chemical engineering.

A major advance likely to affect the use of biomass is development of improved crops. Biotechnology presents a wide variety of possible long-term options based upon photosynthetic and biological energy conversion processes. Genetic engineering may play a critical role in these efforts. For example, the development of high-efficiency plants that are then cloned and raised for feedstock for fuels and chemicals could carry industrialisation of biomass energy systems into a yet more advanced stage.

(ii) Biofuels for power

Energy recovery from industrial and municipal solid waste has the potential to gain an increasing share in IEA countries' overall energy production. Municipal solid wastes are those generated in residential buildings, commercial establishments and institutions such as hospitals and schools. The majority of waste combustors burn waste (at relatively low efficiency levels of between 15 per cent to 20 per cent) to generate electricity, but they also generate steam for heating and other industrial purposes. The remainder of waste-derived energy stems largely from burning methane emissions at landfills. Municipal solid waste can be burned in incinerators, or it can be digested to be converted to biogas through wet or dry anaerobic processes. The technology for burning municipal solid waste or converting it into combustible gas is similar to that for other kinds of biomass, though special environmental precautions must be taken against disease-carrying microbes and toxic chemicals. Pyrolysis of municipal solid waste has been tried in pilot plants, but few commercial-scale plants have been built.

Although the general trend in disposal of municipal solid waste is towards resource recovery and combustion, a high proportion is nevertheless still buried in landfills. Organic waste in landfills constitutes a sizeable potential energy resource. Dry anaerobic decay of buried organic compounds produces a methane-rich biogas, also known as landfill gas. A medium-sized plant based on landfill gas consists of up to 50 polyvinyl-chloride pipes sunk into the ground and connected by other pipes to the power unit. Most landfills use internal combustion engines or gas turbines, depending on the amount of gas available. In some cases, landfill gas is used as an auxiliary fuel in steam-generating power plant furnaces, or combined heat and power configurations. Most landfill sites can support several MWe of capacity, though a few sites in the United States have installed capacity of 10 MWe or more.

f) *Wind Power*

Wind power systems convert the kinetic energy of the wind into other forms of energy, more particularly electricity. There are two basic configurations: vertical axis and horizontal axis turbines. Both types comprise: a rotor with one or more blades; a drive train (usually including a gearbox and generator); a tower to support the rotor; and various subsystem controls (electrical support and interconnection). The amount of energy that a turbine can extract from wind is related to the wind speed. Below about four metres per second the wind is not strong enough to overcome the resistance of the turbine blades. Between four and twelve metres per second, the power output increases rapidly in pace with the wind speed.

Much R&D effort in recent years has focused on design improvements to generate more power from the wind. Significant progress has been made, mainly through better aerodynamic design and the use of lighter, sturdier materials for the blades. Two important parallel areas of R&D – energy storage systems and wind/diesel systems – could help expand the potential for wind-generated electricity. Both lines of R&D address the intermittency of wind power.

Nearly all the recent expansion in wind systems has been on wind farms, tracts of land where large numbers of wind turbines are linked directly to an electric utility grid. More than 20 000 grid-connected wind turbines are operational, with an estimated installed capacity totalling 5 GW at the end of 1996. The electricity delivered to consumers from these installations amounts to around 7 TWh per year. In addition, turbines are being deployed in increasing (though still relatively small) numbers in the off-grid wind-diesel applications. In isolated sites, moreover, turbines are now coupled with photovoltaics and other renewable systems. Wind energy systems can serve as a source of energy that is complementary to hydropower in some regions where water shortages limit the energy output of hydro projects. In these cases, deploying large wind power plants can take advantage of the fact that in many regions the strongest winds blow when there is least rainfall. Today there are more than 100 000 small turbines operating in China alone.

g) *Geothermal Energy*

Geothermal energy is heat stored in rocks and fluids inside the earth. Geothermal power systems use currently available technology to capture heat from the earth's crust to generate electricity through a steam cycle. To improve efficiency of high-temperature plants and utilise low-temperature resources, next-generation binary systems can be used, in which warm water heats a tube containing a different fluid which boils at a lower temperature. The number of sites suitable for conventional geothermal power generation is limited.

(i) Hydrothermal power

The conventional type of natural geothermal reservoir used for electricity generation is hydrothermal, consisting in accumulations of hot water (liquid-dominated) or steam (vapour-dominated) trapped in fractured porous rock. Dry steam power plants extract steam from vapour-dominated reservoirs and pipe it directly into a turbine. Flash steam power plants produce electricity from liquid-dominated reservoirs that are hot enough (above 200°C) to flash a large proportion of the liquid to steam. Binary-cycle plants – the most recently commercialised technology – and heat pumps are used in the case of liquid-dominated resources whose temperatures are too low to allow efficient flash-steam power production.

(ii) Hot dry rocks

As a long-term option, there is potential for more extensive exploitation of hot dry rock reservoirs. Here, a pair of wells is drilled in the rock, which is then artificially fractured; water is circulated into the injection well, and steam or hot water returns to the surface through the production well. The technical feasibility of the concept has not yet been demonstrated and development work is required on both the above-ground and below-ground arrangements. The economics of implementation of hot dry rock technology is dominated by drilling costs. Over the longer term, it might also be technically possible to drill through the earth's crust to capture heat from magma bodies relatively near the surface, but special materials need to be developed to cope with high temperatures and other harsh conditions involved in working with the magma.

Most of the IEA's available geothermal generating capacity is in Italy, Japan, New Zealand and the United States. Plants located in the western states of the United States provide approximately 2 750 MWe from hydrothermal resources. Principal technologies in current use are for dry steam and high-temperature fluid systems. The Geysers plant in California is the world's largest geothermal complex with an installed capability of nearly 2 000 MWe. United States geothermal resources generate approximately 20.9 TWh of electricity per year.

h) *Hydroelectricity*

Hydroelectric generators use available technology to convert the energy in falling water to mechanical energy and electrical power, using a turbine and generator. In run-of-the-river plants, water falls according to the natural flows of a river, usually with major seasonal variations. Pure run-of-the-river installations have almost no storage capacity, whereas reservoir facilities provide storage capacity for days or months before the water is allowed to fall through turbines as required. Unexploited large-scale resources in many countries are now limited, although there is capacity for very considerable expansion in Norway, the United States, Canada, and in many developing countries. Although still capable of incremental improvement, large-scale hydroelectric power technology is a mature technology. Adoption of new equipment and R&D advances to mitigate environmental impact are contributing to the upgrading of existing facilities and establishing the right balance between power and non-power uses of the waterways.

Large-scale hydro represents approximately 16 per cent of total electricity generation in IEA countries. In addition, both large- and small-scale hydro installations often have the ability to store large amounts of energy, which makes them very complementary with installations using wind and solar technologies.

Significant potential for expanding hydropower lies in small hydroelectric units. These units are low-head, high-flow devices which transform the kinetic energy of rivers and streams into electricity, and they are typically less than 0.5 to 25 MWe in size. Much uncertainty prevails about total energy resources available to small-scale hydropower. Conflicting and overlapping regulatory and environmental regulations make it difficult to aggregate national estimates. Small-scale hydro resources depend on geography and they tend to be widely dispersed. Requirements for mitigation of environmental impacts, and institutional issues such as electricity buy-back rates, can significantly affect the size of the cost-effective resource and can be subject to change. Small hydroelectricity also faces a number of purely technical barriers. Small-scale projects seldom have significant water storage facilities. Their output therefore depends on river conditions and they may not provide a source of reliable power. The technology is available, though, and work is in progress to identify new materials and plant configurations that offer cost reductions or cost-effective solutions for low-head applications. In some circumstances, the remoteness of a small-scale site from the power demand or from an electricity grid may decrease its economic attractiveness. Conversely, in some cases adoption of stand-alone control and operation can make small-scale hydropower the least costly energy source for isolated communities. Much wider utilisation of small hydro can be expected, especially in developing countries.

i) *Ocean Energy*

The ocean carries energy potential not only in its tides and waves, but also in the temperature difference between cold, deep waters and warm surface waters, in the salinity differences at river mouths, and in naturally occurring currents. Each of these offers opportunities for generating electricity. The cost of producing ocean energy is highly site-specific and depends upon a considerable number of technical factors.

Ocean-wave and tidal-energy systems convert potential energy of waves or tides into electricity using electromechanical generators. The only major ocean/tidal energy systems operating today in IEA countries are the 240 MWe La Rance Station in France and a unit in Nova Scotia, Canada, with an installed capacity of 17.8 MW which generates approximately 30 GWh/year. Tidal energy involves two distinct methods of energy conversion, namely tidal barrage and tidal current exploitation, and each requires quite different conditions. The former seeks to create a head of water and needs a location with high tidal range, while the latter depends on converting the kinetic energy of fast-flowing tidal currents and needs a location with relatively high current velocities.

Construction of large tidal barrages involves substantial capital outlay and long construction times. Possible projects examined in the United Kingdom would have build times ranging from two to ten years. Offshore wave energy converters are in the early stages of development. Of the many designs proposed in the 1970s and 1980s, only a few have led to prototypes. Most are either pressure-activated or surface-following. Some of the former use oscillating wave columns which can be mounted on a floating superstructure or on the seabed. Such devices can serve a dual purpose as a source of electricity and as a breakwater. The first testing of a floating oscillating water column device was carried out in Japan between 1970 and 1987. During 1997, a grid-connected wave-power station is due to be launched in the United Kingdom, capable of generating an average 2 MW, plus a further 500 kW from its attached windpower device.

In the case of ocean thermal energy conversion (OTEC) systems, electricity is generated by exploiting differences in temperature between cold seawater from depths of 600 metres to 900 metres and sun-warmed surface water. Although there are no commercial OTEC systems in operation, more than 90 countries are within 300 km of ocean thermal resources. Both closed and open cycles show promise for converting the thermal resources into electrical energy. The United States first demonstrated the production of net power using a 50 kWe closed-cycle OTEC plant. In addition, marine current energy, a much more recent focus of attention, may also be an attractive long-term technology option.

### *Assessment of Technical and Economic Potential*

The amount of energy currently contributed by renewable energy systems in most IEA countries is very small compared to the technical potential. An important need is methodology to properly assess and ultimately price renewable energy production from an energy systems perspective, which means incorporating environmental and off-grid benefits. Currently, potential is determined by the size of the resource base, which varies geographically, also by the extent to which the resource base's location renders its use practicable, and by theoretical maximum conversion efficiencies for the technology. Also to be taken into account are today's energy economics, market factors and institutional constraints. But, if national and social factors such as those reflecting environmental and security concerns were internalised in energy system costs, the economic potential of renewable energies would improve and these sources would contribute more. The supply of most renewable forms of energy depends on local conditions, so estimates of "typical" costs per kWh vary considerably, depending upon a plant's specific operating conditions. Estimates differ, moreover, according to financing methods and assumptions regarding capacity factors, operation and maintenance costs, and operational life. At all events, improved financing mechanisms are needed. The rankings of the technical and economic potential of improved next-generation technologies are presented in Tables 7.3 and 7.4.

Many technologies for using renewable energy are available commercially, but are not mature technologies and have yet to realise their market potential. Solutions need to be found to ensure lower costs for delivered energy, improvements in reliability, durability and lifetimes, as well as simplicity of design and manufacture. Information in Table 7.4 indicates that, under current market terms, the following renewable energy systems are cost-competitive or near-competitive: active and passive solar energy, waste and wind power, geothermal (hydrothermal) power and small hydropower. But care should be taken in making comparisons between technology costs since the table does not differentiate between various forms of energy, notably between low-value thermal energy and high-value electricity; nor does it take into account energy availability on demand. The table also shows that active and passive solar systems, photovoltaics, waste and wind power have significant prospects for cost reductions which may lead to competitive next-generation energy systems. These advances will not happen automatically, nor are they guaranteed. Substantial R&D, demonstration and testing have to be accomplished to increase competitiveness of renewable energy technologies and systems, as shown in Table 7.5. Technological spillovers to and from other energy systems should be noted, as should the fact that, due to technology progress, conventional systems are likely to improve and the respective technologies could either retain or lose their present competitive edge.

*Table 7.3*

**Comparative Technical Potential of Renewable Energy Systems**

| Technology | Expected Technological Breakthroughs | Environmental Impact | Resource Base |
|---|---|---|---|
| Active Solar Systems | M | L | Dependent upon geography, season and day cycle. |
| Passive Solar Systems | M | L | Dependent upon geography, season and day cycle. |
| Solar Thermal Power | L | M | Dependent upon geography, season and day cycle. |
| Photovoltaic Systems | H | M | Dependent upon geography, season and day cycle. |
| Biomass Energy<br>• Fuels<br>• Power | <br>H<br>L | <br>H<br>M | Dependent upon geography, agricultural progress. |
| Wind Power | L | M | Dependent on site, seasonal variations |
| Geothermal Energy<br>• Hydrothermal<br>• Hot Dry Rocks | <br>L<br>M | <br>M<br>H | Concentrated, dependent upon site, habitat. |
| Hydroelectricity<br>• Large<br>• Small | <br>L<br>L | <br>H<br>L | Dependent upon site, water use. |
| Ocean Wave and Tidal Energy | M | M | Concentrated (tidal), diffuse (wave), depending upon site and seasonal variations |
| Ocean thermal energy | M | L | Diffuse, unlimited resource base depending upon geography |

Notes: L, M, H = Low, Medium, High.
These are estimates intended to be indicative only and not to be used for direct comparison with non-renewable technologies.

*Table 7.4*

**Economic Potential of Renewable Energy Systems [1]**

| Technology | Current Estimated Cost | | | Estimated Cost of Next Generation | | |
|---|---|---|---|---|---|---|
| | Capital ($/kW) | Operating (cent/kWh) | Total (cent/kWh) | Capital ($/kW) | Operating (cent/kWh) | Total (cent/kWh) |
| Active Solar Systems | 2.5-3.0 | n.a. | 15-20 | 1.7 | n.a. | 11 |
| Passive Solar Systems | 1.2-1.7 | n.a. | 10-15 | 0.8 | n.a. | 7 |
| Solar Thermal Power | 3000 | 2.0 | 20-25 | 1500-3000 | 1.8 | 6-8 |
| Photovoltaic Systems | 7000 | n.a. | 25-35 | 3000-5000 | n.a. | 15 |
| Biomass Energy | | | | | | |
| • Fuels | n.a. | n.a. | 30-35 | | | |
| • Power | 1700-2000 | 4.5-5.5 | 7-15 | 1000 | 2.0 | 4-6 |
| Wind Power | 900-1400 | 1.0-2.0 | 5-10 | 760-1000 | 0.5-1.0 | 4-7 |
| Geothermal Energy (Hydrothermal) | 1500 | 2.0-2.5 | 7-10 | 900-1000 | 1.5 | 4 |
| Small Hydro-electricity | 1000 | 1.0-1.5 | 5-10 | 1000-4000 | 1.0 | 5-10 |
| Ocean Wave and Tidal Energy | 1400-2500 | 4.0-5.0 | 15-20 | n.a. | n.a. | n.a. |
| Ocean Thermal | 10 000 | n.a. | 30-40 | 5000 | n.a. | 20-30 |

Notes: 1. The estimates presented here are intended to show the relative progress expected between selected current technology and new or improved technology that would be available in the future.
All costs are expressed in US dollars per kW of peak electric power, while operating and total costs are in US cents per kWh of electric energy delivered. Estimates refer to grid-connected installations, 30-year system life, 7 per cent real discount rate per year. For passive and active solar heating, capital and total cost refer to thermal power and energy respectively. Biofuels costs are provided per litre of ethanol derived from biomass priced at US$ 3 a gallon.
One dollar = 100 cents.
n.a. means not applicable or not available.

As we have seen, resource bases for renewable energy systems are large. However, there are technical and economic constraints. For example, present use of bioenergy depends on the collection of waste produced in the agriculture, forestry, industrial and urban sectors. Where municipal solid waste is concerned, the present increase in energy production from waste combustors is expected to continue. But the potential of waste as a source of energy production is limited by the volume of waste generated, the energy content of the waste stream, and the technologies used to convert waste to usable forms of energy. Also, energy savings through the recycling and re-use of waste materials are possible only if the energy costs of using reprocessed waste materials compare favourably with the energy costs of harvesting, extracting and processing virgin materials. An anticipated future direction for bioenergy is cultivation of short-rotation, high-energy-content crops specifically for their energy value. The limit to this resource is likely to be competition for land use (urbanisation versus agriculture). If deforested lands can be converted into energy farms in newly industrialising countries, significant reductions in greenhouse gas emissions could be achieved. Waste-to-energy systems may be more widely used if institutional problems and environmental concerns are addressed.

*Table 7.5*

**Renewable Energy Systems: R&D Needs and Opportunities**

| Technology | Possible Bottlenecks | Related Areas | R&D Requirements |
|---|---|---|---|
| Active Solar Systems | Efficiency<br>Ease of technology applicability | Architectural design | Materials and designs<br>Cost and performance of collectors<br>Cost-effective, solar-driven cooling components<br>Long-term stability of working fluids |
| Passive Solar Systems | Technical issues related to development of codes and standards | Architectural design | New glazing materials<br>Thermal storage technologies<br>Training and technology transfer |
| Solar Thermal Power | Efficiency<br>Scale of unit | Hazardous waste disposal | Optical materials<br>High-temperature receivers<br>Tracking systems |
| Photovoltaic Systems | Storage technology<br>Manufacturing improvements and cost reduction | Microelectronic industry<br>Water services | Power conditioning equipment<br>System design software<br>Energy storage for remote, stand-alone and hybrid applications<br>Improved cell efficiency<br>More cost-effective modules, through improved efficiency and lower costs |
| Biomass Energy | Efficiency<br>Feedstock availability | Coal conversion technology | Improved sustainability of short-rotation, fast-growing trees<br>Development of harvesting, de-watering and preparation equipment<br>Demonstration of gasification processes<br>Evaluation and development of innovative refuse-to-fuel processes |

*Table 7.5 (continued)*

**Renewable Energy Systems: R&D Needs and Opportunities**

| Technology | Possible Bottlenecks | Related Areas | R&D Requirements |
|---|---|---|---|
| Wind Power | Power output and unit size<br>Demonstrated lifetime<br>Unfamiliar technology | Power electronics and aircraft industries | Reduction of noise<br>New high-strength blade materials<br>Aerodynamics and structural dynamics research<br>Wind and diesel hybrid system designs<br>Fatigue analysis and lifetime demonstrations |
| Geothermal Energy | Long-term sustainability<br>Conversion cycle designs | Gas and oil exploration | Binary fluid cycle<br>Advanced hot dry rock, magma and geopressure technologies<br>Improved drilling technology<br>Improved approaches to mitigate environmental impacts |
| Small Hydro-electricity | Environmental | Civil structure design | Habitat compatibility, transport function of waterways<br>Aspirating and cross-flow turbines<br>Modular designs |
| Ocean Wave and Tidal Energy | Resource access<br>System performance | | Improved operational and design modelling techniques<br>Construction techniques and field tests of wave power concepts<br>Improved lifetime and reduced maintenance costs<br>Environmental studies for tidal power |
| Ocean Thermal Energy | Resource access<br>System demonstration<br>System performance | Mariculture industry<br>Heat transfer technology | Cold-water piping and heat exchanger technology<br>Turbine technology for open-cycle systems |

So far as solar heating, cooling and daylighting are concerned, there are two key elements determining technical and economic potential: the availability of solar radiation and the rate of investment in the building market, for both new buildings and refurbishment. Accurately predicted and measured solar radiation data enables architects and the solar engineering industry to design, test and operate solar energy systems more efficiently. In the buildings market, domestic housing tends to be replaced in IEA countries at a rate of around 1 per cent to 2 per cent per year, and commercial buildings at a slightly higher rate. The passive solar resource available through new buildings is therefore limited, and the potential for adoption of active solar systems through retrofitting is much greater, but costs must be reduced. To lower the cost of direct-thermal and daylighting applications, R&D should be continued on new building energy technologies, on innovative building materials, and on incorporating photovoltaic systems into building design. R&D should be used to help validate new concepts in a variety of climates, and to help advance the commercial availability of technologies and make them more cost-competitive with other conventional heating, space conditioning and lighting technologies.

With regard to solar thermal power, existing parabolic trough technology is currently cost-competitive in certain markets; expanding the market will call for improved technology, higher efficiency and lower costs. In addition to parabolic trough technology, other approaches such as dish-Stirling and power tower technologies appear promising. R&D should focus on lower-cost collectors, advanced receivers that convert solar energy into heat energy, advanced heat engines, and advanced materials and components for all technologies.

In the case of photovoltaic systems, although these constitute an established technology for a variety of remote applications such as water pumping, communications systems and off-grid residences, and although these applications represent a major market opportunity for photovoltaics in the short to medium term, their costs are too high for basic utility electricity generation. Niche market opportunities do exist, notably in the market where the cost of the distribution cable and transformer exceeds the cost of the photovoltaic system. A second niche market would use photovoltaic systems to strengthen the utility's distribution system, thereby providing distributional value in addition to providing energy. A third niche market would be grid-connected residential and commercial building systems of 1 kW to 100 kW per site. This niche market would be larger in areas where the current cost of electricity is relatively high. Beyond these three niche markets lie the much larger peaking and bulk power markets.

While cost has in the past been a major hurdle for market deployment of photovoltaic systems, there has been a very significant fall in the cost of these modules over the past ten years, as a result of intensive research and development in Japan, the United States and the European Union, also as a result of cumulative production of more than 400 MW of photovoltaic power generating capacity. Stand-alone photovoltaic applications are already cost competitive, and roof-mounted systems replacing existing building materials and components are particularly promising. Furthermore, the architectural community sees aesthetic benefits in using photovoltaic modules as part of the building fabric. Most long-term energy assessments see photovoltaic power generation making a large contribution to world electricity supplies in the coming decades. Scope exists for building alliances between utilities, the photovoltaics industry and government to deliver photovoltaics to developing countries. Meanwhile, efforts should continue on integrating photovoltaic technology into the utility grid and on developing profitable niche markets.

Where wind power is concerned, further cost reductions and performance improvements will, again, be needed before this power can expand into lower wind speed markets. The major requirements for making turbines cost-competitive on a broader geographical scale are to improve turbine designs so they last for 20 to 30 years without needing any major component changes, also to develop advanced components such as airfoils and to integrate these advances into cost-effective systems. A low-cost wind turbine technology could be developed that would ensure reliable operation without battery storage and use photovoltaics or diesel generators as backup systems. This would make power applications possible where grid connection is not practical.

If technologies using geothermal resources are to supply a larger share of new electricity supply, the cost of discovery and extraction of heat must be lowered, and methods for prolonging the life of resources must be improved. Better techniques are needed to map the boundaries of discovered reservoirs, determine reservoir properties and improve the success rate of production. Once reservoirs are located, better reservoir engineering is needed in order to reduce uncertainty and provide for more efficient reservoir use, notably through fewer and better-placed wells. The cost of drilling for geothermal resources must be lowered. Temperatures are much higher for geothermal than for oil drilling, and rock types in geothermal are generally harder and more abrasive than rock above oil and gas reservoirs. More effective and durable drill bits and other drilling components must therefore be developed. At locations where highly corrosive brines and gases are present, materials need to be developed for building equipment more resistant to corrosion in acid fluid environments. Because drilling accounts for a major part of geothermal electricity production costs, improvements in drilling technology and the locating of wells could make electricity generation using geothermal resources more competitive.

Hydroelectric generation, for its part, faces some of the greatest challenges to expansion. Many potential sites exist for conventional pumped storage and low-head hydropower; at the same time, it is essential to increase the generating capacity and electricity production at existing hydropower plants. A significant potential also exists, moreover, in the upgrading or rehabilitation of old or disused small hydro sites. Areas for improvements include automation and remote control, on-line diagnostics, environmental data collection and rehabilitation of existing power plants, where this is economically justified and environmentally acceptable. The availability and cost of long-term financing is particularly critical to hydroelectric projects. The economic costs of regulations are important in this area, where the cost of licensing and obtaining approvals for hydro schemes (as is the case for other forms of renewable energy) can represent a large portion of the overall costs. Technology can also play an important role in helping to reduce these costs. Improved technologies can enhance hydropower output while ensuring protection of the environment and wildlife and offering safety assurances.

## Technology Prospects and Markets

### *Market Trends*

To help identify priority areas for national and international action in the field of renewable energy technologies, this section considers the nature and size of markets for these technologies, and it examines influences on market entry and penetration. With the exception of large-scale hydropower, most renewable energy takes the form of non-commercial fuels not readily quantifiable for national energy balances, even though, in some countries, over one-half of the energy consumed is in this form. Non-commercial biomass fuels are estimated to account for some 15 per cent of world primary energy used. By comparison, a little more than 6 per cent of world commercial fuel is renewable, primarily hydropower. Thus, renewable energies may be variously calculated to provide between 6 per cent and 21 per cent of world primary energy, depending on the accounting. If non-utility renewable energy producers are included, total IEA installed capacity for non-hydroelectric renewable energy resources may increase from 5 GWe to over 15 GWe by 2010. This total consists of about 7.8 GWe of units fuelled by biomass (agriculture and forest residues), 3.2 GWe by geothermal, 1.8 GWe by municipal and industrial solid waste, 3.5 GWe by wind (this was estimated to have grown to well over 4 GWe by the end of 1995 and, in Denmark, wind systems produced 3.5 per cent of electricity used during 1994), plus about 0.3 GWe each by landfill gas, solar thermal and tidal energy. In 1992, the contribution of geothermal, wind, and solar-generated electricity to the output mix was some 27 TWh, or less than 0.5 per cent of total electricity generation. This success has been concentrated mainly in Europe and North America.

Electricity generated from these sources is expected to continue increasing substantially, though development of hydroelectric power in the IEA region as a whole is at a relatively mature stage. Suitable sites for both large and small projects are increasingly difficult to locate and, for hydrological reasons, they yield lower load factors than the average hydroelectric capacity currently in place. Furthermore, competition with alternative land and water uses is becoming more acute. All of these factors tend to increase the expected long-term marginal cost of power generated from this source, which makes a large proportion of the potential projects economically marginal or not economic at all. In addition, recent public resistance to hydroelectric schemes has grown due to the perceived impact upon the ecosystem. For these reasons, it is unlikely that hydroelectric output in the IEA countries will grow as quickly as electricity demand. Consequently, the share of hydroelectric power in total electricity production is likely to decline from around 16 per cent at present to less than 14 per cent by 2010.

Capacity figures for electricity generation should not be directly compared without bearing in mind the difference between dispatchable and non-dispatchable technologies. Energy from sun, ocean and wind is generated when the energy source is available and thus at times not necessarily coincident with electric loads. However, it is also true that no power station of any kind can be assumed to provide 100 per cent "firm" capacity, because any generating plant may go out of operation due to failures or scheduled maintenance. For example, a typical steam thermal plant has a mean annual availability of about 73 per cent, or the equivalent of about 6 400 hours of utilisation at full power, which can be taken as a measurement of the firm capacity it can provide. In contrast with availability at conventional plants, availability at some kinds of renewable energy plant is further reduced by the intermittent availability of the relevant source, and this means that such plants can be allowed a lower firm capacity value. For instance, according to studies carried out, the firm capacity value of wind generation would be around 30 per cent for the first plants connected to a large electric system, and would gradually decline as penetration of wind power plants rises to attain substantial percentages of overall system capacity. (But if wind contributions to the grid came from widely dispersed locations this decline in firm capacity value would be reduced.) It can nevertheless be stated that even an intermittent renewable sources such as wind or solar energy can provide some contribution not only to avoiding fuel consumption, but also to removing the need for installation of conventional capacity.

Technologies have progressed significantly over the past ten to fifteen years. If they are to be commercialised rapidly, approaches will be needed to implement what has been achieved through R&D, alongside continued and focused R&D programmes. Equally essential is the removal of market barriers to technologies for using renewable energy sources. The current situation regarding deployment is outlined below.

- Large-scale hydroelectric, waste and hydrothermal power technologies are mature and commercial technologies, but still subject to upgrading and further market expansion, particularly in the newly industrialising countries.

- Passive and active solar heating and cooling, daylighting, wind and small-scale hydropower involve demonstrated and available technologies that promise continuing technical progress, significant cost and performance improvements and thus increased market penetration.

- Photovoltaic systems, those using fuels from biomass and solar thermal power are gradually becoming cost-competitive with conventional fuels and power sources, and flexible, environmentally sustainable and largely deployable next-generation options can be expected as technology continues to advance.

- Technologies using hot dry rocks, ocean energy, hydrogen fuels and other emerging renewable energy sources are further options for the longer term whose prospects basically depend on the design and testing of prototypes to demonstrate their economic feasibility and potential as a preliminary to diffusion into the marketplace.

### *Key Players*

Each market sector, and in some cases each renewable energy technology itself, has a set of key organisations, institutions and industrial interests which determine, or at least influence, the pace at which a new technology moves in the marketplace. A host of players are involved in the future of renewable energy. These include government decision-makers (devising and implementing policies and encouraging technology transfer), private industry and utilities (developing and using renewables), financial institutions (funding appropriate projects), universities and national laboratories (undertaking effective, goal-oriented R&D) and the public at large (creating a demand through expression of informed opinion). In particular, electrical utilities play a critical role by demonstrating technologies, and by purchasing renewable energy. Oil companies play in important role by incorporating biomass-based liquids into fuels for vehicle use. The automobile manufacturers also have a key role to play by adapting car engines for the use of alternative fuels.

One of the central factors in moving new technology into the marketplace is industrial participation. The development and deployment of competitive energy technologies is primarily the responsibility of the private sector or nationalised energy production and engineering companies. But it is the government policy-makers who are responsible for creating institutional frameworks that will encourage serious consideration of new energy technologies. Institutional barriers associated with market entry of new fuel resources, infrastructure and systems, combined with the sheer number of players, continue to make the application of renewable energy sources highly dependent upon the success of government policy.

National renewable energy R&D programmes for the short term focus on technology transfer, on support for promoting and exploiting industrial opportunities, and on developing international markets. Many programmes encourage diffusion and export of technologies and products to countries with relatively high-cost energy markets. In the course of this activity, manufacturers can develop technologies and lower production costs.

Although the specialty and off-grid power markets are important, the most fruitful path would seem to be that leading to a significant role for renewable energy systems in the utility infrastructure and in meeting energy needs. This has been happening gradually, as a result of major technical advances in the emerging technologies and in response to incentives and institutional change. Many of these incentives have been introduced by governments in the form of obligations for the utility to purchase energy from wind power plants. This form of legislation has often parallelled broad institutional change in both structure and ownership of the utilities. The late-1970s Public Utilities Regulatory Act legislation in the United States and the more recent Non-Fossil Fuel Obligation in the United Kingdom are both examples where such steps have been of significant benefit to the renewables industry.

Institutional changes affecting the utility industries could do much to expand opportunities for renewable energy technologies. In the United States, for example, legislation has ended the virtual monopoly in the commercial generation of electricity that regulated utilities had held for half a century. The United States renewable energy industry has been a major beneficiary of this change, the addition of nearly four GWe of biomass-fuelled capacity, mostly from wood and municipal solid waste, being the result. Similarly, in the United Kingdom, the transfer of the electrical supply industry from public to private hands creates more dispersed and diverse markets that are likely to be more favourable for renewables. While a large percentage of deregulated markets would select power primarily on the basis of price, some customers may elect to pay a premium for power from renewable energy.

International markets for renewable energy technologies in developing countries are particularly important since their electricity demand is expected to expand much more rapidly than that of OECD countries.

Governments have provided the majority of the R&D funding for renewable energy technologies and systems since those programmes began in the mid-1970s. But financial contributions from industry, especially in the commercialisation phases, have been significant. Governments have frequently participated in cost-sharing of large projects. They have been instrumental in helping commercialise renewable technologies meeting the requirements of particular niche markets. Over the years, governments have reorganised their renewable energy institutions, and in some cases created new ones. In Japan, for example, a consequence of the oil crisis of 1979 was the creation of the New Energy Development Organization (NEDO) as the centralised R&D body for joint industry-university-government co-operation to promote new energy application technologies; and the New Energy Foundation was established to introduce, popularise and promote new energy technology.

### *Market Barriers*

Assessments of the market potential and deployment factors for the various technologies are presented in Table 7.6. In addition to technical feasibility and cost-effectiveness, the other factors noted in the table are widely recognised as important in determining the rate of uptake of new technologies, particularly those which are technically advanced but not very successful commercially. Precise accounting for all factors is clearly impossible, though it certainly appears that deployment prospects for new and improved technologies would be highly dependent upon factors such as:

- the rapidity and extent of technical and cost-effectiveness progress, in combination with the pricing of conventional fuels;
- assurances regarding the reliability, durability and lifetimes of renewable facilities, and thus levelised life-cycle costs;
- the existence of markets of sufficient size to attract investments to finance innovative systems, together with the infrastructure and component manufacturing systems necessary to achieve economies of scale and accumulation of experience; and
- the economic effects of global environmental and energy security concerns associated with continuing reliance on conventional fuels.

Analysis suggests that realisation of market potential through normal market forces is constrained by a number of factors and aided by others. Constraining factors may include:

- the perceived or real inability of the renewable energy industry to finance technology development due to inadequate economic return and immature infrastructure, as seen in the difficulties of smaller organisations in marketing their energy and the relatively small size of many producers of renewable energy equipment;
- subsidies for other energy technologies;
- lack of monetised credit for environmental benefits;
- institutional inertia;
- the degree to which renewable energy technologies are seen as reliable;
- inadequate information regarding technical and economic opportunities;
- adverse regulatory considerations; and
- the institutional challenge of integrating an intermittent energy source with conventional systems.

Approaches have been developed, or are being so, in a number of countries to overcome these barriers.

Facilitating factors that could accelerate development of renewable energy technology include a greater focus on key national priorities, such as energy security and environmental protection, also on areas where new and improved renewable energy technologies and systems could speed economic development. Concerns over energy security support arguments for greater use of domestic resources, diversification of energy supply and reduction of imported energy. The

*Table 7.6*
**Market Potential of Future Renewable Energy Systems**

| Technology | Nature of Market | Time-frame for Major Market | Constraining Factors | Facilitating Factors | Market-ability |
|---|---|---|---|---|---|
| **Active Solar Systems** | | | | | |
| • Heating | Buildings | Near-term | Institutional aspects | Energy prices Niche markets | H |
| • Cooling | Buildings | Medium-term | Technical and economic aspects | Energy prices Niche markets | M |
| **Passive Solar Systems** | | | Customer awareness of benefits | | |
| • Heating | Buildings | Near-term | | Energy prices Niche markets | H |
| • Cooling | Buildings | Medium-term | Economic aspects | Energy prices Niche markets | M |
| • Daylighting | Buildings | Near-term | | Energy prices | M |
| **Solar Thermal Power** | Utility and industry applications | Medium to longer-term | Economic and institutional aspects | Energy prices Modular designs Niche markets | H |
| **Photovoltaic Systems** | Buildings, utilities, industry and applications in developing countries | Medium to longer-term | Economic and institutional aspects | Energy prices Niche markets | H |
| | Off-grid | Near-term | | | |
| **Biomass Energy** | | | | | |
| • Fuels<br>• Power | Transport sector traditional uses and utilities | Medium to longer-term | System integration Economics | Regulatory and environmental | M/H<br>H |
| **Wind Power** | Utility and Off-Grid | Near-term | Economic and institutional | Energy prices Modular designs | H |
| **Geothermal Energy** | | | | | |
| • Hydrothermal<br>• Hot dry rocks | Utility and industrial applications | Near-term<br>Very long-term | Economic and technical<br>Technical risk, capital cost | Energy prices Modular designs Energy security | M<br>L |

Notes: L, M, H = Low, Medium, High marketability. Near-term = 0-5 years; Medium-term = 5-10 years; Longer-term = 10-15 years; Very long-term = beyond 15 years.

*Table 7.6 (continued)*
**Market Potential of Future Renewable Energy Systems**

| Technology | Nature of Market | Time-frame for Major Market | Constraining Factors | Facilitating Factors | Market-ability |
|---|---|---|---|---|---|
| **Small Hydro-electricity** | Utility | Near-term | Institutional<br>Regulatory | Economic and development aspects | H |
| **Ocean Waves and Tidal Energy** | Utility | Very long-term | Technical and economic | Developmental aspects<br>Energy prices | L |
| **Ocean Thermal Energy** | Utility | Very long-term | Technical and economic | Modular designs<br>Energy security | L |

Notes: L, M, H = Low, Medium, High marketability. Near-term = 0-5 years; Medium-term = 5-10 years; Longer-term = 10-15 years; Very long-term = beyond 15 years.

development of renewable energy sources can also foster economic growth by providing more cost-effective energy supplies and thus helping to expand the nation's industrial base. By displacing less environmentally friendly sources, renewable energy may be a very good option for mitigating build-up of greenhouse gases. In terms of electricity production, renewable energy systems have little or no net emissions, particularly those of $CO_2$, although some emissions within the total fuel cycle can still be incurred in manufacture of components and facilities. The consideration of other externalities such as environmental burden could also affect the use of renewable resources.

Clearly, market deployment of renewable energy systems would be favoured by a number of general approaches. These include: demonstrations of technical feasibility, new financing strategies, decentralisation and greater involvement of local energy interests in plant design, construction and operation; institutional restructuring of national energy systems; and fostering evolving niche markets and the modular structure of renewable energy systems.

## Technology Policy Issues

### *Role of Governments*

The renewable energy industry has made significant technical progress in the last fifteen years. The efficiency of single-crystal silicon photovoltaic cells has increased by more than 50 per cent to 23 per cent in the laboratory, while costs have declined by a factor of two or more. The cost of wind turbines has decreased from the range of between US$ 2 500 and US$ 3 000 per kWe of peak power in 1980 to between roughly US$ 900 and US$ 1 400 per kWe today, while system availabilities have increased from 80 per cent to more than 95 per cent over the same period. By comparison, a typical range of current costs for conventional power peaking and base-load generators is between US$ 600 and US$ 1 500 per kWe. Other renewable electric technologies have made significant advances. Further cost reductions and performance improvements in general require no scientific breakthroughs, but simply a succession of research, engineering and manufacturing improvements. Governments can take a number of measures in such areas as taxation, subsidies, regulation and procurement, which will not only help them meet their environmental and energy security goals, but also contribute to faster technological progress, the removal of market barriers, and economic development.

Such possible government policies facilitating progress in the maturing and increased deployment of renewable energy systems include:

- establishing an analytical framework and energy accounting structure for comparison of all sources of energy from resource to use, which provides the basis for internalisation of national and social costs within the market prices of energy, fuels and systems;
- providing long-term support for basic underlying research on advanced technologies and systems that clearly demonstrates the potential value of renewable options in the context of an environmentally sustainable economy for the longer term;
- reinforcing government assistance for basic science in areas relevant to new renewable energy systems and sponsoring programmes of R&D in collaboration with industry;
- taking steps that alleviate risks associated with new ventures in demonstration of new cost-effective renewable energy systems, and so helping to promote technology transfer and commercial uptake;
- informing investors, decision-makers and the general public about technological change and alternatives to conventional energy;
- based on results of ongoing comparative analysis, in general supporting development and use of all economic renewable sources of energy that can be produced, supplied and used efficiently, while meeting safety and environmental criteria, thus fostering diversity of supply and reducing the risks associated with over-dependence on one source of fuel;
- ensuring that legislation (laws, regulations, standards) and relevant fiscal incentives (tax credits, depreciation allowances) provide an institutional framework that encourages the development of renewable energy technologies and processes, their integration into conventional systems where this is appropriate, and their deployment on a competitive basis into a marketplace where customers are encouraged to use them.

A summary of government action and initiatives that may be considered in the market deployment of new and improved renewable energy systems is shown in Table 7.7.

Any governmental programme should open avenues for renewable energy systems when appropriate, as determined by the state of the technology, relative competitiveness and the prevailing economic climate. Although the potential contributions from renewable energy sources in the IEA countries vary, development is necessary because these energy sources offer diversification and sustainability of energy supply. Reducing greenhouse gas emissions alone may be sufficient to re-order priorities and justify an aggressive approach to development and deployment of renewable sources.

*Table 7.7*

**Renewable Energy Systems: Government Role in Technology Deployment**

| Technology | Level of Market Activity | Need for Government Support | Possible Government Measures |
|---|---|---|---|
| **Active Solar Systems** | | | |
| • Heating | M | M | Standards; technology transfer |
| • Cooling | L | H | R&D funding; demonstration |
| **Passive Solar Systems** | | | Energy codes and standards; |
| • Heating | M | M | technology transfer |
| • Cooling | L | H | R&D funding; demonstration |
| • Daylighting | M | M | and technology transfer |
| **Solar Thermal Power** | M | M | R&D funding; technology transfer |
| **Photovoltaic** | M | M | R&D funding; demonstration and technology transfer |
| **Biomass Energy** | | | |
| • Fuels | L | H | R&D funding; demonstration; |
| • Power | M | M | market incentives |
| **Wind Power** | H | M | R&D funding; demonstration; environmental studies; technology transfer |
| **Geothermal** | M | M | R&D funding; technology transfer; environmental impact analysis |
| **Small Hydroelectricity** | M | M | Environmental impact studies; regulations; market incentives; technology dissemination; R&D funding |
| **Ocean Wave and Tidal Energy** | L | H | R&D funding; pilot-scale experiments, demonstration; |
| **Ocean Thermal Energy** | L | H | environmental impact analysis |

Note: L, M, H = Low, Medium, High and signify level of market activity and need for government support.

In non-OECD countries however, issues such as economic development, local environment, employment and foreign exchange also provide justification for the use of renewable energy technologies and systems. Such emphasis on renewable energy may be particularly appropriate for these newly industrialising countries, because infrastructure to support conventional energy systems is less widespread than in fully industrialised countries, and because modular systems using indigenous fuels and offering scope for decentralisation may be more applicable.

The action adopted by IEA Member countries to promote the use of renewable energy supply technology in the long term falls into three basic categories, namely: "global strategies", specific programmes and adoption of legislative or administrative measures. Australia has created a general framework for a "global strategy" with a draft Research Strategy for Renewable Energy Sources and Systems, one of its sustainable development and climate change response strategies. Austria's 1993 Energy Concept gives high priority to renewable energy sources, mainly biomass and solar power, with public funding support. The Netherlands has updated its strategy for renewables to 2010. The New Zealand Government has adopted a Renewable Energy Framework Policy statement concerning the potential for further development of renewable energy sources as part of a $CO_2$ emission reduction programme. The United Kingdom's Non-Fossil Fuel Obligation (NFFO) scheme provides output subsidies for renewable electricity from selected sources, backed up by a government R&D programme. The UK's target of 1 500 MW by 2000 amounts to four times current generation from renewable sources of energy. In Germany, the current goal of renewable energy policy is to exploit more fully in the long term the potential of many renewable energy sources. There are a number of measures in place to promote renewable energy, notably the Electricity Feed Law, but no quantified Federal target for renewable energy use. The Electricity Feed Law provides for the payment of between 65 and 90 per cent of consumer electricity prices to renewable energy generators. With this incentive, wind capacity increased from 2 MW in 1990 to 845 MW by mid-1995. Detailed descriptions and analysis of these policies are contained in the IEA's forthcoming *Policy Aspects of Renewable Energy in IEA Countries.*

Various projects and studies have been carried out to stimulate the commercial applications of renewables. Belgium has evaluated renewable inputs in its three regions and developed a method of standardising collection of data on renewables. Finland has approved a wind power programme that aims to develop 100 MWe of installed capacity. In France, an agreement has been signed between the Agency for Environment and Energy Management (Ademe) and the national electric utility for the joint development of renewable energy technology. A new long-term programme for solar thermal conversion, Solar Thermie 2000, is being elaborated in Germany to demonstrate practical applications of solar energy. Ireland's government programme for 1993-1997 includes development of renewables such as small hydropower, wind power and short-rotation forestry. Switzerland, for its part, began a promotion programme in 1993 for renewable-based installations that will be supported by market incentives.

In addition, specific administrative or legislative measures have been adopted by Denmark and Greece to stimulate the application of renewable energy supply technology. In Greece, the Centre for Renewable Energy Sources is focusing on the development of quality certification, the promotion of standardisation of renewable-based devices and investigation of possibilities for eliminating barriers to market penetration.

### *Role of International Co-operation*

As we have seen, renewable resources are capable of making useful contributions to safeguarding future energy supplies in IEA countries. But much work remains to be done before the relevant technologies can achieve their full technical, economic and market potential. While many issues can be addressed effectively at the national level, international collaboration can accelerate the progress of development and deployment by co-ordinating work towards common goals through sharing of tasks and experience. International collaboration stimulates cross-fertilisation through the exchange of ideas among governments, the technology community and industry in participating countries.

During the past fifteen years, international collaboration on renewable energy R&D under several IEA Implementing Agreements has contributed significantly to technology progress. Current agreements deal with Solar Heating and Cooling, Solar Power and Chemical Energy Systems (SolarPACES), Photovoltaic Power Systems, Bioenergy, Alternative Motor Fuels, Wind Energy Conversion, and Hydropower. In addition, a new agreement on Geothermal Energy Systems will cover areas such as the sustainability of geothermal energy utilisation and the environmental impact of geothermal energy development, hot dry rock technology and exploitation of deep geothermal resources, geothermal power generation cycles and engineering of geothermal fluids.

The focus in the existing agreements is on basic investigation, on assessment and R&D relating to critical cost-related issues and on institutional barriers to deployment. In some cases where institutional barriers have been found, collaboration has been directed towards the development of tools for removing them, including design models, handbooks and source books suitable for the dissemination of a technology.

Through these IEA activities, databases and published documents are produced which serve as long-term reference material for international use. Examples are the Production Systems Handbook for biomass growers, and standard procedures for the performance measurement of photovoltaic power systems. Technical collaboration on these projects has reduced the variations between national assessments of costs and effectiveness of specific renewables technologies. For example, the Solar Heating and Cooling project discovered that numerous software programmes are available to simulate energy performance in buildings, but that they produced widely diverging results. Through a collaborative project, a software evaluation and diagnostic tool was developed to certify these programmes, and to assure architects and engineers that a particular simulation programme gives reasonable results.

Benefits could be consolidated by:

- developing increased collaboration that focuses specifically on removing market barriers;
- sharing experience regarding effective technical, economic and regulatory means of increasing synergy between renewable and conventional energy systems during transition periods for market entry for renewables;
- supporting collaborative R&D on methods and data bases to determine the environmental and social costs and benefits of currently available and future renewable energy systems;

- promoting the establishment of a clearinghouse for information transfer, in which countries not belonging to IEA would be invited to participate, and thus facilitating technology deployment in these countries; and,
- identifying innovative approaches towards reducing market barriers and measuring the effectiveness of specific measures in various countries (such as technology demonstrations and financing schemes) which may either assist and inhibit market entry of renewable energy technologies and systems.

## Approach

Renewable energy systems thus have a major role to play in terms of IEA Member countries' concerns about energy security, global environmental issues and the implications of increasing globalisation. As indigenous fuels, they are also well suited for applications in newly industrialising countries. Their ability to be used in modular and decentralised forms within energy systems offers still further advantages. In spite of these advantages, however, they face significant barriers to market entry: a lack of existing infrastructure, relative technical and economic immaturity, inadequately demonstrated reliability and maintainability, and a need for economies of scale associated with component manufacture and deployment techniques.

Investment in new and improved renewable energy systems is currently hampered in several ways. First, there is a much larger experience base for fossil-fuelled energy systems than for renewable energy systems. So investors view renewable technologies as options backed up by less accumulated experience. For their part, energy planners are reluctant to use new technologies when reliability, operating lifetimes, maintenance requirements, and resource availability are not well known. A closely associated factor is the large existing infrastructure for building and operating installations using more conventional energy and power technologies, alongside the infrastructure for new renewable energy sources that is only beginning to develop. Some renewable energy facilities may be comparable to other energy sources in terms of long-term cost, but they initially involve large capital outlays per unit of production. Though these outlays are offset over time by low or nil fuel costs, financial markets prefer the lower risks associated with low-capital-cost facilities.

While competing with conventional energy technologies, renewable energy resources can nonetheless operate in synergy with them and help pave the way towards future energy fuel mixes and systems. Hybrid systems can enhance overall system robustness and flexibility, essential attributes in terms of energy supply for the foreseeable future. Because institutional challenges are involved in facilitating the market entry of new fuel resources, infrastructure and systems, the pace of application of renewable energy resources will be dependent on international co-operation in this strategic technology area. Progress is contingent upon successful policy integration and improvements achieved through R&D in order to lower capital costs and enhance system capability.

The most promising renewable energy options and technologies include the following:

- large-scale hydro and geothermal power, which offer available and mature technologies, although still subject to improvements;
- active and passive solar heating and daylighting, wind power, small-scale hydropower, and power from biomass, which are available and deployed technologies offering substantial opportunities for technical and economic progress as next-generation technologies during the time-frame of this study; and
- photovoltaic systems and fuels from biomass (also, to a somewhat lesser extent, solar thermal power and ocean energy), which are either available or have been demonstrated and have attained varying degrees of technical maturity and economic competitiveness; these renewable energy technologies and systems have the potential to perform well as next-generation technologies and they promise cost improvements, as well as significant large-scale market penetration.

Non-commercial energy uses of biomass are widespread, but cannot readily be extended in their present form to respond to commercial demand. Biofuels obtained from biomass may merit special attention because of their application in the transport sector and their potential as substitutes for conventional hydrocarbons. Wind power and biomass co-firing of electricity generation are economic in specific locations today, and utilisation has increased rapidly. The solar electric technologies are demonstrated technologies and their economics have improved over the last decade at a steady pace that is continuing. For all three resources and technologies, however, the economic potential, and therefore the market potential, is significantly limited by current performance capabilities.

In addition to their generally favourable (although not entirely impact-free) environmental characteristics, the emerging renewable technologies permit access to a large-scale and widely-dispersed resource base. Ultimately, the scale on which the resource base can be exploited depends on the technology and its economics. In the case of each resource, there arise questions of most favourable location and of land use, although technological progress does offer substantial potential for broadening the range of regions for application.

The past decade or so has seen major advances in development of technologies for using renewable energy, and many innovative technologies are heading for successful commercialisation in the energy marketplace. A focused R&D effort must continue. A government-led technology strategy and R&D collaborative programme to incorporate the technology priorities identified in this chapter should consider the measures listed below.

- Selective and continuing R&D effort to reduce costs and improve the performance and efficiency of emerging renewable energy technologies and systems. Specific R&D approaches should focus on active and passive solar thermal and electric systems, photovoltaic power generation, biomass energy production and fuels, wind power and geothermal energy. Equally important is the contribution to fundamental and applied research that fosters progress in renewable technology and prepares further renewable options for the longer term, in such fields as hydrogen fuels, hot dry rocks, ocean energy and other emerging concepts.

- Implementation of cost-shared collaborative R&D ventures at both international and national level, with the involvement of industry and public utilities, to reduce technical risk, to demonstrate new and improved renewable energy technologies and systems, and to bring them to the marketplace, addressing at the same time the requirements of sustainable development and environmental protection.

- Adopting technical standards and stimulating markets to facilitate integration of new and improved renewable energy systems on a competitive basis in conventional energy systems, at the same time removing regulatory and institutional barriers.

- Supporting centres of technology excellence and best practice which inform interested parties and the general public of technological progress and alternatives to conventional energy technologies, and which support technology transfer.

- Assessing the performance, environmental impact and life-cycle cost of renewable energy technologies by preparing guidelines and defining criteria to incorporate the most significant externalities within market prices.

# Chapter 8

## ELECTRICITY PRODUCTION AND DISTRIBUTION

### Goals and Rationale

Demand for electricity is increasing throughout IEA countries, as it is in the rest of the world. The increase is attributable to electricity's versatility, its transportability and the ease with which it can be controlled, as well as to the steady advances in generation and end-use technologies. World final electricity and heat demand are projected to grow at an annual average rate of between 2.4 and 3.1 per cent to 2010. Electricity and heat demand in non-OECD countries is expected to grow more than twice as fast as in OECD countries. In non-OECD countries, annual electricity generation per capita is expected to almost double from around 0.7 MWh to between 1.3 and 1.4 MWh, still less than one sixth of electricity generation per capita in the OECD in 2010. By 2010, annual worldwide electricity generation per capita is expected to increase from 2.3 MWh to 3.0 MWh in the IEA's capacity constraints case and 2.6 MWh in the energy savings case. Electricity's share of total final energy supply grew from 12.2 per cent in 1971 to 19.9 per cent in 1993 and it may increase to as much as 22.2 per cent by 2010, according to the capacity constraints case outlined in the 1996 edition of the IEA *World Energy Outlook.*

The need to meet growing demand for electric energy over the coming decades raises a number of vital questions. How will future electricity be generated? What fuels will be used? Electricity generation, transmission and end-use have benefited from very substantial technology improvements. Governments and the electricity supply industry have a special role in ensuring that safety, efficiency and the reduction of pollutant emissions are overriding attributes to be taken into account when new technologies are being assessed. Fossil fuels (natural gas, oil, coal), nuclear and hydropower are the sources of practically all the electricity produced in the world today. Other renewable energy sources account for only a minor share, although their contributions may be significant at the local level. The growth in their role will depend upon continued technological development. Sustained increases in investments in new power generation will be required to meet the expected growth in electricity demand and the need to replace decommissioned plants. With new demand requirements, future efficiency gains alone will not be sufficient to cope with peak power requirements. Increasing fuel diversification will allow electricity to be produced from a variety of energy sources and so contribute to ensuring greater energy security in the provision of electricity.

Much of the current worldwide debate over environmental concerns tends to focus on the electricity sector, which is a highly visible and relatively easily regulated source of pollutants. Electricity is a clean source of energy at its point of use, and opportunities for mitigating its environmental consequences exist on the supply side, as well as through improved efficiency of fuel consumption, changing the fuel mix, and the introduction of strengthened demand-side management practices. As environmental regulators cope with concerns over urban smog, ozone depletion, acid rain and global climate change, there is increasing pressure to produce power with lower emissions of particulates, nitrogen oxides, sulphur dioxide and carbon dioxide. Governments need to address public opposition to siting of new facilities when that opposition risks limiting the availability of future capacity. All of this is occurring within the context of introducing greater competition in the utility industry.

Against a background of change, the priority technology goals in the domain of electricity production and distribution can be set out as follows:

- to reduce the environmental impact of power generation, including traditional emissions like $SO_2$ and $NO_X$ as well as greenhouse gas emissions;
- to encourage greater energy source diversification and, where feasible, fuel flexibility; and
- to develop and apply advanced load and demand-side management techniques to increase the efficiency of the electric system.

A substantial part of this subject matter overlaps with information on the subject of electricity supply and end-use technologies presented in other chapters of this study. What follows here is less detailed, since fuel-specific and use-specific chapters are viewed as the primary reference. Technology options are considered in the context of the electricity grid, where they compete with each other on cost, environmental emissions, reliability and quality of service. Two further aspects are also discussed, namely: key technologies which can modify the structure of the electric system, its operation and evolution; and the identification and consideration of non-technological factors and requirements affecting the electricity supply industry, since these can have significant effects on the technical characteristics of new technology and the pace of its deployment.

## Technology Description and Assessment

### *Description of Significant Technologies*

Over the coming decades, a diversified technology development and deployment strategy will have to be pursued against the backdrop of more uncertainty in the industry. Both the electric utilities and industry in IEA countries are concerned about environmental protection and pollution abatement. They also recognise the need for constantly improving energy efficiency and conservation as well as the shift towards greater competition in the electricity market.

The traditional approach of seeking to produce plentiful and cheap electricity needs to be reconciled with a heightened awareness of the desirability of safeguarding environmental quality associated with electricity generation. No form of electricity generation is without its environmental effects or safety considerations. Electricity generation accounts for approximately 25 per cent of energy-related carbon dioxide emissions in the IEA region. Growing concerns over the risk of global warming and climate change lend urgency to the need for a technology response. In the short to medium term, electric utilities will find it very difficult to implement large-scale actions to curb carbon dioxide emissions rapidly without incurring high costs and causing market distortions. In the absence of technological breakthroughs that could totally replace fossil fuel use, strategy measures will be necessary. The key elements of that interim technology response strategy will include upgrading existing fossil plants, expanding the use of natural gas in new plants, exploiting available hydropower resources, promoting other renewable energy sources where economically viable, deploying improved and advanced nuclear power plants, and accelerating investment in cost-effective means of enhancing demand management and end-use efficiency. This approach would also include efforts to close the large efficiency gaps between countries and, more particularly, between the industrialised and the developing countries. Such an interim strategy, utilising cost-effective technologies that are generally worth applying irrespective of global environmental benefits, will "buy time" for further R&D on carbon-free and low-carbon technologies. In the very long term, beyond the scope of this study, generating capacity may be dominated by nuclear power plants, renewable energy technologies and innovative fossil fuel technologies with lower emission of greenhouse gases.

Alongside these obligations regarding the environment, utilities also have to meet the more traditional requirements imposed by government regulators to provide reliable and affordable service to customers. How to reconcile and pursue these sometimes conflicting goals will continue to be a significant challenge for utilities in the future. Meeting the challenge will call for even more rigorous application of the range of technology options described above to ensure that the electricity supply industry has the means to respond to changing market conditions and regulations cost-effectively. No single technology will be the best choice for every situation, since cost and availability of energy sources vary between regions and countries.

Several taxonomies can be proposed to classify electricity production and distribution technologies. With a view to meeting the priority technology goals described in this chapter, three main groups of key technologies can be identified as elements in the response to future challenges.

- Electricity production technology for environmental protection: changes in fossil fuel technology for power production will be increasingly driven by the need to reduce the cost of complying with more stringent environmental requirements for both traditional $SO_2$ and $NO_X$, and to reduce greenhouse gas emissions.

- Carbon-free technologies for power generation and diversification: R&D efforts to abate greenhouse gas emissions should focus mainly upon new renewable energy sources and on nuclear power, while augmenting energy source diversification.

- Technologies for efficient electricity distribution: advanced demand-side and load management will constitute an increasingly important part of an integrated resource planning strategy, incorporating efficient electricity end-use technologies into electric grid design and operation.

A selection of key technologies to pursue these three courses of action have been identified. Their technical status, feasibility and other factors are set out in Table 8.1, while R&D needs and opportunities are summarised in Table 8.2.

*Table 8.1*

**Key Electricity Production and Distribution Technologies: Technical Status**

| Technology | Status | Technical Feasibility | Application Issues | Potential for Emissions Reduction |
|---|---|---|---|---|
| **a) Electricity Production Technology for Environmental Protection** | | | | |
| (i) High-temperature gas turbine technology | Commercial/ Demonstrated | • High conversion efficiency in combined cycles<br>• Controlled scaling-up and scaling-down in power generating systems | • Base-load electric utility power generation<br>• Distributed electricity generation, co-generation, peaking and intermediate load-power generation | H |
| (ii) Repowering and retrofitting technology | Commercial/ Demonstrated | • Reduction of environmental impact<br>• Efficiency upgrading and fuel switching | • Responds to need to comply with stricter environmental requirements<br>• Opportunities exist for life extension | H |
| (iii) Co-generation technology | Commercial/ Demonstrated | • Fuel saving, environmental emissions reduction and waste minimisation<br>• Co-generation systems with overall fuel efficiency of 60 to 80 per cent | • Increments of new electricity generating capacity without investing in a large power plant<br>• Application in simple-cycle and combined cycle configurations | H |
| **b) Carbon-free Technologies for Power Generation and Diversification** | | | | |
| (i) Carbon dioxide removal technology | R&D | • Variety of chemical and physical processes<br>• Energy-intensive technology | • Electric utilities may consider option in the very long term<br>• A few industrial plants are in operation for the chemical absorption of $CO_2$ from stack gas | H |

Note: L, M, H represent Low, Medium, High potential for emissions reductions.
Source: *Electric Power Technologies: Environmental Challenges and Opportunities,* IEA (1993).

*Table 8.1 (contined)*

**Key Electricity Production and Distribution Technologies: Technical Status**

| Technology | Status | Technical Feasibility | Application Issues | Potential for Emissions Reduction |
|---|---|---|---|---|
| **b) Carbon-free Technologies for Power Generation and Diversification** *(continued)* | | | | |
| (ii) Carbon dioxide disposal and utilisation | R&D | • Technologies for large-scale $CO_2$ disposal in deep ocean and underground deposits still need assessment and laboratory testing<br>• Industrial use of $CO_2$ is established practice | • Governments may include the problem of $CO_2$ disposal and utilisation in their broad-scope strategies for $CO_2$ abatement in the very long term | M |
| **c) Technologies for Efficient Electricity Distribution and End-Use** | | | | |
| (i) Advanced control and communication technology | Commercial/ Demonstrated | • Progress in general electronics is providing electric utilities and industry with new means for grid control and management | • Advanced sensors and controls to improve electric grid efficiency and reduce losses<br>• Interactive communication between utilities and customers through telemetering | L |
| (ii) Electricity transmission technology | Commercial/ Demonstrated | • High-voltage AC and DC transmission is widely applied technology | • Use in large grid inter-connections and regional systems | M |
| (iii) Electricity storage | Commercial/ R&D | • Systems connected to the utility grid to allow energy to be stored for dispatching when its use would be more economical, strategic or efficient | • Pumped hydro and battery energy storage are available technologies<br>• Opportunities exist for integration of renewable energy sources into the electric system | M |
| (iv) Solid-state power electronics | Commercial/ Demonstrated | • Next-generation solid-state devices for transistors, rectifiers, amplifiers, switching, control and command are available | • Efficient electric grid operation and management | L |

Note: L, M, H represent Low, Medium, High potential for emissions reductions.
Source: *Electric Power Technologies: Environmental Challenges and Opportunities,* IEA (1993).

*Table 8.1 (contined)*
**Key Electricity Production and Distribution Technologies: Technical Status**

| Technology | Status | Technical Feasibility | Application Issues | Potential for Emissions Reduction |
|---|---|---|---|---|
| **c) Technologies for Efficient Electricity Distribution and End-Use** *(continued)* | | | | |
| (v) Super-conductivity technology | R&D | • Design, development and testing of HTS wire and coils in progress<br>• Prototypes of HTS electric generator and motor in progress | • High-efficiency compact electric components and systems | M |

Note: L, M, H represent Low, Medium, High potential for emissions reductions.
Source: *Electric Power Technologies: Environmental Challenges and Opportunities,* IEA (1993).

*Table 8.2*
**Key Electricity Production and Distribution Technologies: R&D Needs and Opportunities**

| Technology | Bottlenecks | Spillovers | R&D Requirements |
|---|---|---|---|
| **a) Electricity Production Technology for Environmental Protection** | | | |
| (i) High-temperature gas turbine technology | • Limited reliability, maintainability and durability | • Electricity generated with significantly lower environ-mental emissions | • New materials and designs for high turbine inlet temperatures<br>• $NO_x$ abatement in higher temperature systems<br>• Cycle architecture to enable high system efficiency |
| (ii) Repowering and retrofitting technology | • Regulatory constraints and limitations | • Advanced clean coal technology<br>• Pre-combustion coal cleaning<br>• New control systems | • Remaining life analysis of components and systems |
| (iii) Co-generation technology | • Changing regulatory framework | • Environmentally friendly power and heat generation | |

*Table 8.2 (continued)*

**Key Electricity Production and Distribution Technologies: R&D Needs and Opportunities**

| Technology | Bottlenecks | Spillovers | R&D Requirements |
|---|---|---|---|
| **b) Carbon-free Technologies for Power Generation and Diversification** | | | |
| (i) Carbon dioxide removal technology | • Cost and energy effectiveness of technologies and systems | • $CO_2$ removal system engineering | • $CO_2$ chemistry<br>• Advanced $CO_2$ separation techniques |
| (ii) Carbon dioxide disposal and utilisation | • Need to establish priorities<br>• High cost of disposal processes | • New $CO_2$ uses in the industrial and energy sector | • $CO_2$ dynamics and diffusion in the oceans<br>• $CO_2$ life cycle and migration in underground deposits |
| **c) Technologies for Efficient Electricity Distribution and End-Use** | | | |
| (i) Advanced control and communication technology | • Lack of compatibility between different utilities' systems<br>• Training of specialised personnel | • Technology transfer to/from other industrial applications, notably chemical processes and large engineered facilities | • Expert systems<br>• Advanced local area networks<br>• On-line sensors for process and environmental control |
| (ii) Electricity transmission technology | • Technology development and operational tests still required<br>• Cost of high-voltage direct-current converter stations | • Incentive to integrate resource planning<br>• Application potential in developing countries and economies in transition | • Environmental impact of UHV transmission<br>• Advanced converter system configurations<br>• Low impedance transformers |
| (iii) Electricity storage | • Limited availability of pumped-hydro systems and access to them<br>• Lack of low-cost, modular, turnkey battery energy systems | • Hybrid power generating systems incorporating battery energy storage and renewable energy sources<br>• Transportable battery systems | • Advanced electric batteries<br>• Superconducting magnetic energy storage (SMES) |
| (iv) Solid-state power electronics | • Inadequate component reliability and durability<br>• Professional training of experts needed | • Increased flexibility and controllability of electric grid | • Advanced multi-purpose components<br>• New materials and physical processes |
| (v) Superconductivity technology | • Component reliability and durability yet to be demonstrated | • Reduced electricity transmission and distribution losses<br>• Industrial applications | • New materials and basic HTS physics<br>• Prototype testing and scaling-up |

a) *Electricity Production Technology for Environmental Protection*

Fossil fuel technologies have the serious drawback of producing substantial amounts of air pollutants. In the case of coal there is a large amount of solid waste. Notable air pollutants are particulates, sulphur dioxide and nitrogen oxides, which contribute to acid rain. While significant improvements have been made in scrubber and other technologies to curb emission of these traditional air pollutants, the need to reduce future greenhouse gas emissions presents enormous challenges since all fossil-fuelled electricity generation emits carbon dioxide. Significant reductions in $CO_2$ emissions can be achieved by switching from high to lower carbon-content fuel. Advanced technologies can help, through improvements in plant conversion efficiency, to decrease generating plant greenhouse gas emissions per unit of electricity delivered (Figure 8.1). New and improved technology for coal-based power systems was discussed in Chapter 2. Most of that technology applies to other fossil-fuelled power plants as well.

*Figure 8.1*

**Indicative Efficiency and Carbon Dioxide Emissions From Fossil-Fuelled Power Plants**

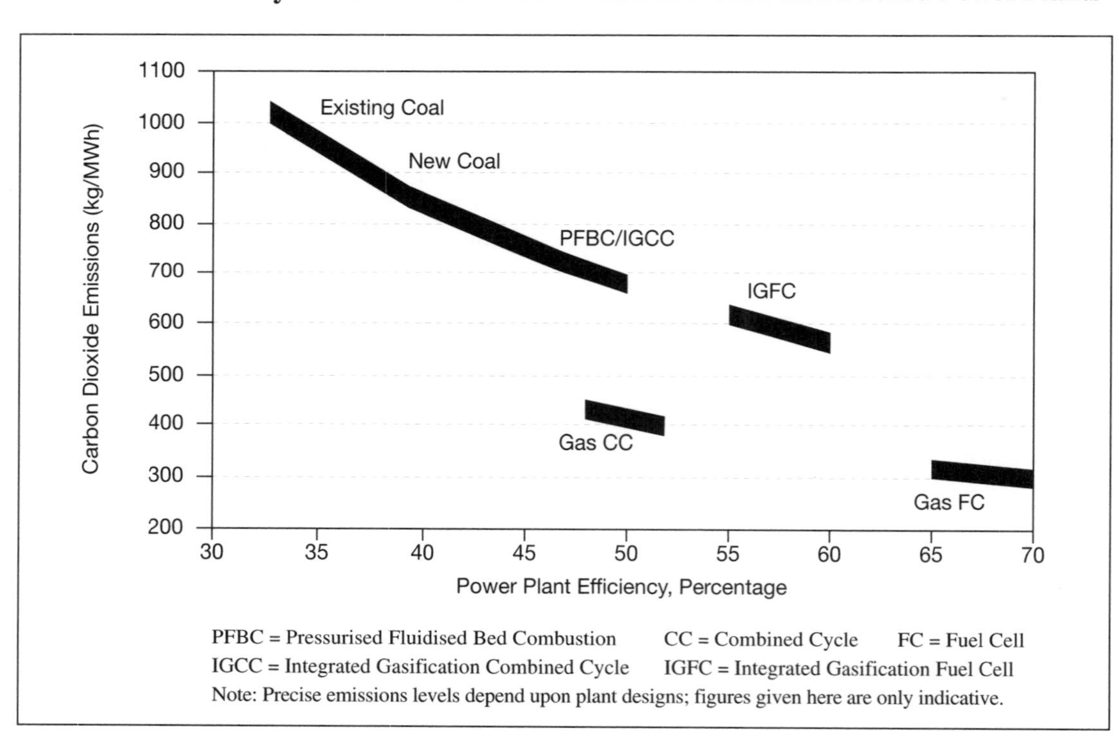


Source: *Electric Power Technologies: Environmental Challenges and Opportunities* (IEA, 1993)

Concern over environmental protection is focusing increasing attention on the entire fuel cycle and life cycle of power plants, with all their environmental impacts. This concern has led to requirements for plants to emit fewer pollutants, either by retrofitting and refurbishing existing power plants, or by developing new combustion technologies. But "add-on" equipment and technology improvements cannot provide an ultimate umbrella solution.

Rather, the trend is towards an integrated approach to total emission control and waste minimisation, aimed at the optimisation of total resource use. At the same time, technology development and deployment are coming under increased public scrutiny, creating greater pressures on governments, which for their part are relying more on market forces to ensure adequate supply, reasonable prices, and manageable demand and to guide technology investments. As a result of strengthened market forces, accelerated progress is expected regarding a few critical power-producing components and systems. These technology developments may considerably change future electricity supply options and affect the structure and operation of the electric grid. Among these key technologies are high-temperature gas-turbine technology, repowering and retrofitting technology and co-generation technology. An added advantage is that they can help realise the benefits of competition among fuels and promote efficient exploitation of the energy resources.

(i) High-temperature gas turbine technology

Evolving gas turbine technology is making the gas turbine an increasingly strong competitor as a power source. Instead of being driven by steam, the turbine is driven by natural gas or other gaseous fuels, such as synthetic natural gas (SNG) and light oil liquid distillates, which are burned in compressed air that is allowed to expand directly through a turbine. The use of air allows higher pressures and temperatures to be used. A distinction is made here between heavy-duty industrial turbines (designed specifically for stationary applications) and the aeroderivative turbines (derived from jet engines). The heavy-duty industrial turbine is quite familiar in the power sector, and it is the technology of choice for the gas turbine and steam turbine combined cycle systems that are coming into much wider use.

By the turn of the century, combined cycle conversion efficiency, based upon the lower heating value of the fuel, is expected to approach 60 per cent, with $NO_x$ emissions less than 10 parts per million by volume without post-combustion cleanup. While combined cycles offer many advantages compared with conventional steam-electric power plants, this class of energy-efficient gas turbine-based power system does not exhaust all existing possibilities. Advanced aeroderivative gas turbines and cycles involving steam injection for power and efficiency augmentation have great promise for some market applications requiring high-power density.

Aeroderivative turbine units are lightweight and compact, with relatively small capacities of 30 MWe to 35 MWe at the upper end of their range, with high compression ratios and further increases in turbine inlet temperatures. Aeroderivative turbines are expected to benefit from continuing advances in jet engine technology and, importantly, from cost-cutting mass production. Conversely, aeroderivative engines would be more costly per kW than industrial turbines, and more difficult to maintain.

The most significant new development relating to stationary power applications of aeroderivative gas turbines is the introduction of small-sized and relatively low-cost steam-injected gas turbines (STIGs) or the equivalent humid air turbine, which will have somewhat lower efficiency. Natural gas (or SNG as a possible alternative) is burned to drive a gas turbine to produce electricity. The exhaust gases from the turbine are then channelled to a boiler to produce steam, not for a second turbine (as in combined cycles) but for injection into the combustion chamber. The steam injection increases the energy output and somewhat decreases efficiency, while also reducing $NO_x$ emissions. An advantage with this system is comparatively lower capital cost and size flexibility. A drawback with STIG cycles is that they release significant quantities of steam into the atmosphere. In fact, STIG cycles require about five times the high-quality water and demineralisation processing capacity that is required by combined cycles.

Further efficiency can be gained if the combustion air, which has to be compressed, is cooled between stages of compression. Efficiency is gained because less power is required to compress cool air. Because such intercooled systems (ISTIGs) can be small and modular, they are suitable for industry as well as utilities and meet the needs of industrialising nations. The chemically-recuperated gas turbine (CRGT) is a proposed variation on the STIG and ISTIG theme and might achieve an enhanced efficiency of more than 55 per cent. The approach involves the pre-combustion catalytic reaction of natural gas with steam to yield hydrogen ($H_2$) and carbon monoxide (CO). The chemical energy of the products would be greater than that of natural gas itself.

(ii) Repowering and retrofitting technology

Refurbishment or rehabilitation of existing fossil fuel-fired power units can, in some cases, overcome regulatory problems, mitigate public opposition and reduce the investments associated with new plant construction. Where fuel prices are low, capital costs high, siting difficult and electricity demand strong, investing in existing plants can be very attractive. Under a refurbishment or rehabilitation strategy, repowering technologies essentially upgrade plant performance, whereas retrofit technologies are introduced to meet new environmental requirements. In the past, repowering and retrofitting were practised less. Demand for electricity was growing rapidly, power plant siting was relatively easy and the industry was a regulated monopoly. Today, new plant siting is increasingly difficult, there are increasing competitive pressures to utilise all assets fully and regulations are making it harder to fully recover the capital costs of new plant.

The term repowering is often used to describe the integration of new technology into an existing power plant site, thereby increasing the available capacity at the site, improving efficiency and lowering the plant's air emissions profile. From a technical standpoint, the power plant has a site, structure and internal components, some of which are retained (such as the steam generating equipment). Repowering replaces part of the old plant with new technology, which may include options such as a natural gas high-temperature turbine, heat-recovery, atmospheric or pressurised fluidised bed combustors or integrated coal gasification combined cycle. Pollution control is inherent in the process, but it is not the only advantage. A repowered plant can produce more power than the original plant (sometimes twice as much or more), as well as extending the plant's lifetime by 20 or 30 years. An example of repowering could be the conversion of an old (near retirement) oil- or natural gas-fired unit into a combined cycle unit, by extending the life of the turbine/generator, replacing the boiler with a new heat-recovery boiler, and installing combustion turbines with a higher rated capability.

Retrofitting can be regarded as an ultimate form of fossil-power plant maintenance, intended to restore or better the original performance, while coping with changing environmental requirements and prolonging plant life. Retrofitting technologies generally consist of pollution control devices that can be installed on older plants without making major changes in the plant design. Available options include: pre-combustion coal cleaning, limestone injection multistage burners, in-duct sorbent injection, gas reburning, and advanced scrubbers. Some retrofit concepts may offer a means of reducing sulphur emissions by 50 per cent or 70 per cent (called for in most legislation to reduce acid rain) at far less cost than using a scrubber. As a result, significant plant-life extension can be obtained for a capital outlay below the cost of a new power station. Since off-site infrastructure requirements already exist (e.g. for delivery of fuel, disposal of ash and delivery of electricity to the grid), there is, again, a saving in capital cost if the life of an existing site can be extended. The added life will depend upon the age of the power plant at the time it is retrofitted, and on the nature of rehabilitation technology. The potential market for power plant retrofitting is very large, since many current plants are reaching the end of their design lives. Very strict environmental regulations, however, might reduce the market for retrofit by setting unattainable standards. On the other hand, this would improve the market for repowering, to meet environmental requirements with more modern technology.

(iii) Co-generation technology

Overall energy efficiency and environmental quality can often be enhanced through more widespread and increasing use of co-generation in industry and use of combined heat and power (CHP) schemes in commercial and residential buildings. In Europe CHP includes industrial co-generation. Co-generation is defined as the simultaneous or sequential production of both electrical or mechanical power and thermal energy, from a single energy source. Fuel is burned first to produce steam that is used to turn a turbine shaft connected to a mechanical device or an electrical generator. The steam leaving the turbine provides process heat or drives machines throughout the host industrial plant and related facilities. From an energy-policy perspective, the appeal of co-generation is its ability to improve fuel efficiency. Co-generation systems achieve overall fuel efficiencies 10 to 30 per cent higher than if power and heat were provided by separate conventional energy conversion systems; that is, they use less energy than if the fossil fuel were burned in an industrial boiler to produce process heat and at an offsite utility power plant to generate electricity to be transmitted to the industrial site.

Industrial co-generation plants will benefit from many of the same efficiency improvements as utility generation because they use the same basic technologies. In addition, better integration of industrial co-generation and utility system operations, through planning and dispatch, offers net improvements in system performance. The best opportunities are concentrated in the chemicals, petroleum refining, pulp and paper, and steel industries. But co-generation may not always produce significant efficiency advantages. Almost the entire output of newer, combined cycle, natural gas-fired co-generation systems is electric power generation, with little steam for process applications. This being the case, there is a much smaller efficiency gain from co-generation and a net shift in primary fuel demand from the utility sector to the industrial sector. Thermal conversion losses in electric utility and industrial combined cycle generating units are similar, but there are some small savings in avoided transmission and distribution losses. If a significant portion of the co-generated power is sold to the local electric utility, these transmission and distribution savings would largely disappear.

Co-generation can also be attractive as a means of quickly adding electric generating capacity at sites where thermal energy is already being used. Combined heat and power (CHP) can be regarded as a special case of co-generation in which the production of electricity is combined with the principal aim of using heat to provide space, process or water heating for domestic or industrial applications. The heat may be supplied through mains for district heating. Reduced technology costs and increased reliability have prompted more interest in CHP systems. Small-scale "packaged" CHP units, fuelled by natural gas, are likely to extend the size range of buildings to which CHP may be applied in the absence of district heating.

The environmental consequences of CHP schemes are the same as for other types of fossil fuel-fired generation, in terms of emissions and their control. An advantage of back pressure CHP plants is that there is no requirement for large cooling towers. There are no health and safety issues associated with heat distribution, but considerable local disruption would occur during the laying of district heating mains, which may influence public acceptance. CHP is an old, well-established technology. Because of the wide variety of options, it is not possible to characterise the technology in a general way. A more detailed analysis is required to provide the necessary information for the design, construction and operation of CHP systems, with special focus on the type of organisation which would run them and on standards, codes of practice and legislative requirements.

b) *Carbon-free Technologies for Power Generation and Diversification*

Both renewable energy technologies and nuclear fission power are fundamental elements in any long-term strategy for energy supply diversification away from fossil fuels. Both renewable energy and nuclear fission are "carbon-free" energy sources that contribute little or nothing to greenhouse gas emissions. Given the current state of technology R&D, nuclear fusion power applications are likely to go beyond the timeframe of consideration in this study. The analysis presented in Chapter 7 suggests that mature renewable technologies such as hydro, geothermal, and use of municipal solid waste will continue their market penetration and improve in performance, although their diffusion may be constrained by public opposition, regulatory requirements and limitations in the resource base. New renewable power production technologies, including solar, wind, biomass, wave, ocean thermal and tidal power, have made significant progress over the past twenty years but, in the absence of further technology advances, these are unlikely to replace other grid-interconnected power supply options in any major way over the coming years. Moreover, for very large-scale deployment, land requirements and operational limitations would be substantial, especially with solar and wind power generation. Conversely, nuclear power is making a substantial contribution to the electricity output in several IEA Member countries and, consequently, to their overall energy supply mix. A number of IEA governments and utilities believe that nuclear fission technologies can provide an important response to environmental challenges and fuel diversification strategies in the electricity sector. To meet these environmental or fuel diversification goals, it appears essential to maintain and further develop the highest available standards of safety, to encourage continued and strengthened international co-operation in approaches to the safe operation of nuclear facilities, to support the development of new reactor systems and to support improved waste management and disposal. Options for introducing entirely "carbon-free" fuels based on fossil energy sources are also possible and deployable in the very long term, should the need arise.

Where the "carbon-free" use of fossil fuels is concerned, carbon dioxide removal and carbon dioxide sequestration would require the development of special technology options for the long term and these approaches are not technologically or economically feasible today. Both renewables and nuclear energy can also offer long-term approaches. Furthermore, due to the timeframe involved in the "carbon-free" approaches discussed below, and the many scientific and technical uncertainties, a thorough evaluation of approaches, processes and end-products should be undertaken before significant effort is committed to any R&D programme in this area. The subject is very important, however, because of the likely impact on the useful life of the fossil fuel resource base. A brief description of carbon dioxide removal technology status and prospects is given below.

(i) Carbon dioxide removal technology

In principle, carbon dioxide can be removed after fossil fuel combustion. In 1992, nearly 0.95 billion tC (or 3.5 billion tonnes of $CO_2$) were released into the atmosphere in the IEA region as a result of fossil fuel use to generate electricity.

Of all known means for sequestering carbon dioxide from the atmosphere the best is biomass. Photosynthesis by plants, algae or synthetic methods can absorb carbon from the ambient air. In view of the large area requirements, massive afforestation does not represent a practical opportunity for removing the large amounts of $CO_2$ emitted, as explained in Chapter 2.

Steam reforming of natural gas into $H_2$ with $CO_2$ removal has been suggested as a means for carbon abatement prior to combustion. The same process can be adopted for coal, provided it is gasified, followed by a shift reaction. In both cases the resulting mixture of gases includes $CO_2$ and $H_2$, making it possible to extract $CO_2$ by an absorption or separation process. The use of solar or nuclear energy as a source of heat would further reduce the quantities of $CO_2$ generated in the process. Many variations of the basic process have been proposed. For example, an integrated gasifier combined cycle (IGCC) plant has the advantage that coal is converted to an intermediate synthesis gas. Subsequently, the carbon is recovered from this synthesis gas in three steps: conversion of CO to $CO_2$, extraction of $CO_2$ by a physical absorption process, and compression of $CO_2$ after drying. Since $CO_2$ would be removed at high pressure, the energy penalty can be reduced by using a physical absorbent such as Selexol. The advantage of removing $CO_2$ from a large, concentrated source such as the flue gas of a power plant, compared with direct removal from the atmosphere, is obvious. $CO_2$ is about 500 times more concentrated in flue gases than is its level of dilution in the ambient atmosphere of about 350 ppmv (parts per million by volume). Conventional, predominantly coal-fired power plants produce flue gas streams with a $CO_2$ concentration of around 15 per cent by volume.

To remove $CO_2$ from the flue gas, four main scrubbing technologies can be considered: cryogenic distillation of $CO_2$ from flue gas; separation by membrane; molecular sieves; and chemical absorption. A few industrial installations use chemical absorption. It can be asked whether $CO_2$ capture technologies should be developed for retrofitting existing plants or solely for use with new power plants. A few industrial installations currently produce $CO_2$ for use as a raw material. Two chemical processes are used for scrubbing on a large scale, the monoethanolamine process and the econamine process, both of which involve chemical absorption of the $CO_2$ and subsequent stripping to the desired degree of purity.

Each of the alternatives has some inherent limitations. For example, in membrane separation, there is a trade-off between the permeability of the polymer membrane used and the purity of $CO_2$ separated. Similarly, chemical absorption is an energy-intensive process. It has been estimated that monoethanolamine capture of $CO_2$, including compression and dehydration for transport, is likely to involve an energy output penalty for a typical coal-fired plant of about 35 per cent, while electricity cost would approximately double. R&D would be needed to optimise the process and improve the economics.

(ii) Carbon dioxide disposal and utilisation

Once the carbon dioxide is captured, the problem of its long-term sequestration remains. The physical amount of $CO_2$ generated by scrubbing alone would grow to be enormous. The removed carbon could be either used as a basic raw material or disposed of. An example of its use is the injection of $CO_2$ in oilfields to obtain enhanced oil recovery. Other possible users are the beverage and chemical industries, but all these requirements of $CO_2$ are minuscule in comparison with the amounts that would be generated. Again, research may expand the productive uses.

With regard to the disposal route, long-term storage or sequestering of $CO_2$ in underground repositories might be a possible option. Approaches could include storage in active or depleted oil and natural gas reservoirs, in deep confined aquifers, or in mined salt or rock caverns. The main problems are the volume available for storage, the long-term integrity of the storage, and the cost associated with $CO_2$ transport to the disposal site and the disposal operation itself.

The deeper layers of the ocean, below about 1 000 m in depth, may be a preferable candidate to serve as a possible sequestering medium for anthropogenic $CO_2$ emissions. The ocean is vast and deep sea is separated from the atmosphere by a surface layer and thermal confinement. There are various possible deep ocean disposal schemes: either to pump $CO_2$ in high-pressure pipes to the ocean floor, or to transfer it from storage tanks into shuttle ships which travel 100-120 km offshore and then inject the $CO_2$ at a sufficient depth underwater. Liquefied $CO_2$ has to be injected to a minimum depth of 3 000 m if it is to stay down, whereas with the gaseous form 300 m will suffice. However, the feasibility of such schemes is today based on speculation and many scientific and technical unknowns are involved, so deep-ocean disposal raises a number of questions. Perhaps most important are the possible ecological effects of $CO_2$ dispersion. In sum, since little is known about diffusion rates, changes in deep ocean acidity and other important ecological questions, further research is needed on this possible sink for anthropogenic sources of carbon.

c) *Technologies for Efficient Electricity Distribution and End-Use*

Efficiency in the distribution, and particularly the use, of electricity are essential parts of any strategy to address energy security concerns, environmental pollution, acid rain and the greenhouse gas issue. Utility technology purchases and customer programmes to encourage improved energy efficiency play an important role in the electricity sector in many IEA Member countries.

Energy conservation and demand-side management (DSM) programmes are organised utility activities (often prompted by government regulation), aimed at modifying the amount and timing of customer electricity use and at improving electric grid productivity and the quality of service. Electric utilities use demand-side management for a number of purposes. Where opportunities exist for cost-effective end-use conservation and technology, as in the use of high-efficiency lights and motors, heat pumps, and heat recovery systems, the purpose may be to reduce demand. By controlling demand for electricity and thereby creating room for expansion without providing additional supply, successful DSM programmes can defer the need to build power plants.

DSM programmes may affect the way electricity-consuming equipment is operated. Where opportunities exist to use the power system more efficiently by making more intensive use of high-cost equipment while reducing use of fuel, the purpose may be to manage loads by shifting demand to another time of day or year, and, in particular, the purpose may be to reduce peak loads. Load management is intended to influence customer demand through technical measures or economic incentives, usually with the objectives of decreasing demand during peak periods, and/or encouraging demand during off-peak periods. At the same time, load management programmes can also be directed at retaining load or customers, and expanding overall electricity consumption.

In pursuit of these goals, DSM is based upon a broad array of technologies and their combinations. Enabling electricity consumers to benefit from time-of-use rates generally requires installation of smart metres that allow measurement of both the quantity and timing of electricity use. Several of the new and improved technologies are discussed in Chapter 10.

In addition to DSM, several new types of technology will have a significant impact on electricity distribution and utilisation in the future. A description is given below of the current status and anticipated future progress in a few important electricity distribution technologies and cross-cutting technologies. A number of technologies are highlighted, namely: advanced control and communication; transmission technology; electricity storage; solid state power electronics; and high-temperature superconductivity.

(i) Advanced control and communication technology

Techniques for DSM and load management take three forms: direct, local and distributed control. Sophisticated communication/computer technology and grid management techniques provide real-time, automatic control of the electric power grid and the integration of various electricity generation sources, including renewable energy systems, so as to achieve increasingly optimised and efficient use of energy resources.

Load control measures differ according to the degree of control and input exercised by the utility and the customer. They range from programmes in which the utility asks customers to reduce load, and the customer decides which appliances or equipment to switch off, to direct load control systems that are highly automated and have no customer input. Direct automated control systems are by far the most common form of load control. They typically consist of a communications system that links the customer's equipment with the utility and a decision logic system (i.e. a computer programme) that dispatches commands to the customer equipment in response to information on utility and/or customer loads. Using direct control, the utility can interrupt the power supply to selected customers or loads, such as machinery, hot water heaters, or air conditioners, at times of peak demand. This is usually done with prior approval of the customer, often in return for reduced rates or rebates. In a residential load-management programme, equipment might be installed to allow the utility to cycle participating home air-conditioners and water heaters off briefly during times of peak load with little or no noticeable disruption to the customer.

Distributed control techniques require that customers be given control over their loads in response to utility signals; they require communication technologies, such as metres, cables or intelligent building controls. Special billing metres may allow each customer to manage his load in response to real-time price signals, based on utility operating costs at any given moment. Smart controllers can be programmed to operate heating, cooling, appliances, and local energy storage devices to the residential or commercial customer's advantage when compared to normal utility time-of-use rates. Many advanced communications technologies for DSM have been demonstrated, but few are widely deployed.

(ii) Electricity transmission technology

The advantages of power use can be reinforced through continued improvements in electric transmission and distribution grids to increase their flexibility, capacity and efficiency. For industrialised countries, power losses between the generating plant and the customer average just 10 per cent, and power from available plants is typically dispatched to minimise the overall cost of power production at any given time. Installation of high-efficiency transformers, expansion of high-voltage transmission lines, and eventually the application of advanced power electronics and devices incorporating superconducting materials, should make it possible to significantly improve the operation of electric grids. All these technologies, with the exception of superconducting transmission, have been demonstrated to be technically feasible. The main outstanding problem is to reduce their costs.

Pressures to reduce future plant reserve margins and to optimise transformer investment in general have made more advanced techniques essential, both to assess the state of transformers in service and to predict likely performance at the design stage. A number of R&D projects are being undertaken by electric utilities and manufacturers, aimed at either understanding the ageing process of transformers or aiding the design of new ones. Longer-term possibilities are the use of spray-formed core steels and amorphous metals in order to reduce transformer core losses significantly, and the use of new fluids to provide greater heat transfer capabilities.

In recent years, there has been increased interest in high-voltage direct current transmission (HVDC), attractive because of the economic, functional and environmental advantages it offers in certain applications. Although requiring relatively expensive converter equipment, DC systems can, in particular circumstances, provide a more economic alternative to AC systems. DC systems possess certain characteristics which cannot be matched by AC alternatives. Such advantages are the direct control of power, no transmission of fault current, and de-coupling of stability problems from one system to another. R&D activity in HVDC is largely directed at reducing the cost and improving the efficiency of the converter equipment, including focus on thyristor stacks, static compensation and harmonic filters.

(iii) Electricity storage

Electricity generation can benefit greatly from next-generation storage technologies. Electrical energy is stored for stationary applications and can be released upon demand. Systems based on these technologies can supply electricity in the form of direct or alternating current over a range of power requirements and time durations. Most commonly, storage shifts loads from plants with high operating costs to those where costs are lower. In addition, storage can increase the potential contribution of intermittent power sources such as wind power and photovoltaics, allowing continuous use of power from a mix of sources. Energy storage systems consist of an energy storage device, a power conversion subsystem, and plant components such as switchgear, controllers and auxiliaries.

Some energy storage systems, such as pumped hydro and secondary batteries, have already been commercialised. Others, such as residential heat and cold storage, or systems using advanced batteries, are still under development or demonstration. Storage is also essential to the operation of electric vehicles, potentially major users of electricity in urban markets. The only bulk storage system in wide commercial use is pumped hydro, in which high-head water turbines are used either to pump from a low reservoir to a higher one during off-peak periods, or to generate electricity by discharging water in the opposite direction during peak periods.

Secondary batteries have several desirable features. Their high energy density means compactness for mobile applications, while their low electrolyte leakage and other factors make them highly efficient. They are made from abundant natural resources and are easily installed close to the electricity demand location, reducing transmission losses. Worldwide R&D in batteries is proceeding, with advances in lead-acid, sodium-sulphur, lithium-aluminium/iron-sulphide, sodium/iron-chloride, zinc-chlorine, and zinc-bromine battery technologies. A wide variety of approaches is being investigated, although sodium-sulphur and zinc-bromine are leading battery candidates because of storage density per weight, efficiency and availability of materials. R&D goals include continuing to improve energy density, reduce recharge time and increase the number of charge-discharge cycles.

Superconducting magnetic energy storage (SMES) is a system consisting of a superconducting coil, a cryostat and a refrigeration apparatus. A 1-MWe, 1-second, commercially available SMES system has been constructed in the United States to prove the feasibility of the design for short-term power quality applications. A 30-MWe, one-minute system is under development to provide critical reserve power at a utility in Alaska. Storage efficiency (the ratio of energy in to energy out) is estimated at 90 per cent using low temperature superconductors, compared to roughly 75 per cent for hydro, the best current alternative.

Compressed air energy storage can provide bulk energy storage and has application in diverse geological conditions. This technology uses off-peak electricity to drive a motor to compress air which is then stored in salt caves, hard rock caves or aquifers. When peak or intermediate power is needed, the stored air is brought to the surface, heated by burning gas or oil, and expanded through a combustion turbine to drive a generator. The motor and generator are combined in one machine.

(iv) Solid-state power electronics

Solid-state power devices are small but versatile units that can perform a great variety of control functions in electric and electronic equipment. Unlike earlier electron devices, which depend for their functioning on the flow of electric charges through a vacuum or a gas, solid-state devices make use of the flow of current in a solid. Available solid-state and next-generation technology is used in transistors, rectifiers, detectors, amplifiers, oscillators, electronic switches and modulators. Other types of devices and combinations of these are employed in solid-state power circuits to perform auxiliary functions, such as bias control, temperature compensation, and circuit triggering.

Solid-state devices have many important advantages over other types of electron or electromechanical devices and apparatus. They are very small and lightweight. They have no filaments or heaters, so they require no heating power or warm-up time and therefore consume very little power. They are also solidly constructed, extremely rugged, free from microphonics, and can be made impervious to severe environmental conditions. The key technology barriers are material preparation, limits in operating conditions, durability and cost.

(v) Superconductivity technology

Superconductivity consists in the property of certain materials to conduct electricity virtually free of resistance or power loss. This technology has been utilised in medical diagnosis (magnetic resonance imaging) and in magnets for high energy physics accelerators and fusion devices. Until recently, superconductivity was observed only in some metals and at temperatures of about -250°C, which called for the cooling capability of liquid helium. This is costly and has limited the application of superconducting technology. Since 1986, researchers have discovered and been developing a class of ceramic materials which superconduct at higher temperatures that can be maintained through cooling using liquid nitrogen, at a cost much lower than in traditional low-temperature superconductors. There is hope that additional breakthroughs can be achieved with as yet unknown materials, which can function at even higher temperatures, and can be used in a very wide range of applications.

High-temperature superconductivity (HTS) enormously increases prospects for augmenting the efficiency of components and thus system efficiency. The possibility of use at higher temperatures opens the way to much broader application of this superconducting property. As observed above, one application is electricity storage. Another application is power transmission; superconducting cable could halve the losses in conventional underground transmission cable systems. Since the system is effective at low voltages, losses due to reactive power could be reduced even more. A third application is in electric generators and motors; superconductivity could raise generator efficiency from 99 to nearly 100 per cent and raise motor efficiency from 98 to roughly 99.5 per cent. This would be a modest, but very significant, increase in efficiency in an enormous number of electrical devices. Superconductors may also expand uses of electricity in process industries or in magnetically levitated trains.

The market for superconducting materials in utility applications is potentially very large, so long as the technical and cost issues are resolved. The development of devices incorporating high-temperature materials will also take a great deal of time. Penetration of such equipment into the market is likely to be gradual, so widespread use by utilities is at least 20 or 30 years away. The possibility of such major advances argues strongly for the vigorous support of related R&D activities and programmes. Perhaps the foremost R&D challenge regarding HTS resides in the basic properties of superconducting ceramic materials, which are not yet fully understood. For superconductors in utility applications, more important issues are limited carrying capacity and the lack of manufacturing techniques for fabricating into useful configurations. When the critical current-carrying capacity or the critical magnetic field strength are exceeded, superconducting material can lose its properties; materials with higher critical values must therefore be found. While the required capacity for feasibility varies according to application, achievement of higher critical values is necessary for all applications. Since substantial experience has been accumulated in making ceramics into flexible fibres, this problem is not entirely new, but until it is solved the design and development of practical utility systems and applications cannot proceed further.

### *Assessment of Technical and Economic Potential*

Progress in electricity production and distribution technology is influenced by several factors, namely the regulatory framework for activities and the energy security, environmental, fiscal and other policies that affect the allocation of R&D resources. In designing R&D programmes that advance technology, while taking account of the national context, governments and utilities should consider the need for:

- ensuring that electricity prices reflect total replacement costs;
- incorporating energy security considerations into resource selection, and encouraging reductions in greenhouse gas emissions;
- promoting efficiency in electricity production and end-use and encouraging DSM activities among utilities and third parties; and
- encouraging and ensuring co-ordination between technology development and investments in new electricity generation, transmission and distribution.

All forms of electricity production have certain drawbacks. Oil-fired generation is viewed as risky in terms of price and import dependence if it represents too large a part of the generating mix and if alternatives do not exist; there are also environmental effects associated with its use. In some countries, nuclear power is not widely accepted by the public, its cost may be high, and acceptable long-term waste disposal and decommissioning procedures have in general yet to be implemented. Coal generation is faced with major environmental restrictions related to its being a source of acid rain, greenhouse gas emissions, air toxins, and solid waste. The main hydroelectric sites in IEA countries have already been developed, and there is substantial public opposition to additional large-scale installations, so further contributions from hydroelectricity are unlikely to be significant in IEA countries. For other renewable energy sources, unit costs remain high (though they are falling in many instances) and they are not likely to make a major contribution to base-load power generation before one or two decades hence. The remaining fuel, natural gas, can be expected to be a major focus for increasing deployment in the near to medium term. Natural gas environmental characteristics, technological performance, and construction lead-time currently make it a competitive source of energy in many IEA countries.

The use of natural gas for electricity generation projected for the next decade has raised some questions regarding available supply, and more difficult questions about the price at which incremental supplies will be available. Technology progress can mitigate these concerns in two ways. First, the natural gas growth trajectory reflects the fact that most current technologies for producing, transporting and converting natural gas into electricity offer opportunities for technology innovation and progress. Improved technologies for natural gas exploration, development and transport could help stabilise prices and offset the effects of increasing demand. Second, the demonstration of coal gasification technology comes at a time when natural gas prices are moderate and many combined cycle units are being built. Possible future increases in gas prices could encourage use of combined cycle units capable of switching from natural gas to gasified coal. The availability of this option may have an important influence on gas prices, while further opportunities may emerge for using a wider range of fuels in oil-fired capacity. One source of interest is heavy oil and extra-heavy oil, which could compete with coal for market share. The development of technology to gasify low-grade residual fuels presents a further opportunity for diversifying use of oil products in existing plant.

The technical and economic potential of electricity production and distribution technologies is primarily determined by the relative cost and environmental acceptance of each technology. From a long-term perspective, exploitation of the potential of any power supply technology will depend upon the costs associated with its fuel-cycle and life-cycle, which means taking account of environmental costs, economic and social benefits, spinoffs and drawbacks. A growing number of studies attempt to combine the environmental effects of power technologies as externalities with the market cost to allow comparisons, on a total-cost or social-cost basis, of different technologies for electricity generation. These analyses assist policy-makers and others in identifying areas critically in need of R&D and technology progress. As explained below, environmental cost analyses involve a large number of assumptions. Changing assumptions can profoundly affect the results, at the same time reflecting widely differing views on the value of the environment.

With regard to electricity end-use, substantial improvements have already been demonstrated for technical and economically cost-competitive efficiency improvements and technology advancement. The potential exists for even greater technical improvements. In the industrial sector, the major users of electricity are electric motors and drives, waste heat recovery systems, electrolytic processing, industrial lighting, and industrial electrotechnologies. The trend towards increasing electrification of industrial processes is expected to continue. There are a variety of electrotechnologies that could boost industrial electricity use over the next several decades and that promise net savings in fossil fuel consumption. Examples of these technologies are plasma beam heating, ultraviolet curing, electron beam heating and laser beam systems. In the residential and commercial sector, demand would be driven by expansion of existing uses (such as space heating and conditioning, lighting, cooking and refrigeration), by new uses and technology advances (more powerful office and home computing, high definition television, advanced heat pump systems, "smart" houses and offices), and the penetration of new end-uses such as electric vehicles.

At present, there remain many regulatory, institutional and market barriers to realising the technical and economic potential of new electricity technologies. In the effort to overcome these and other difficulties, integrated resource planning techniques have proved the best currently available instrument through which government agencies and electric utilities may incorporate the technical and economic potential of new and improved technology into their decision-making processes.

In assessing technology prospects and potential, governments and utilities will turn increasingly to powerful decision-making instruments to confront the complexity of the electricity grid and the variety of options available. Environmental cost analysis and integrated resource planning are two important techniques which are described in this section.

a) *Environmental Cost of Electricity Generating Technology*

A recent study undertaken jointly by the International Energy Agency and the OECD Nuclear Energy Agency (NEA) indicates that the projected direct economic costs for the early 21st century for the three base-load electricity generation technologies – coal-fired, nuclear and natural gas combined cycle generation – are sufficiently close in most countries for their ranking to be very sensitive to required discount rate or rate of return on investment, and to fossil fuel prices. The representative technologies were given a standard profile for the purposes of that study, although site conditions and utility preferences clearly affect power plant design and generation costs. Apart from large-scale hydropower and geothermal energy, other renewable energy sources would have a limited economic potential and would be likely to make only modest contributions to overall base-load generation in the foreseeable future.

Those that prove economically competitive and environmentally acceptable will be adopted, but there is as yet no sign that a dramatic breakthrough, resulting from technological development, is in the offing. Prospects for expanded use of municipal solid waste, biomass and landfill gas are good, driven in part by government policies favouring greater resource recovery. Importantly, electric power plants using these sources pose no special problems for power grids since they have been proven commercially and can supply power at high availability and capacity factors. Such sources could provide a small fraction of electricity supply in industrial countries, but a significant fraction of energy supply in developing countries. Advances in biomass conversion and use would combine with reversing land clearing trends.

Power generation from the more intermittent renewable energy technologies has made great strides. A factor aiding the commercial penetration of renewable energy sources is that much of the initial work of mapping their resource potential has already been undertaken and many suitable locations identified. With successful R&D, new renewable energy technologies may enable competitive electric power to be produced at optimum geographical locations. Peak power could thus be supplied in conjunction with fossil or nuclear base-load plants, or it could displace scarce fuels by providing a secure energy option. In large-scale applications as an alternative to fossil or nuclear plant, these technologies would require energy storage at a level that would significantly decrease their economic potential.

To the extent, however, that governments decide that polluters should pay more for the costs they impose on the rest of the economy, and to the extent that these costs are internalised, the economics of less polluting methods for extracting, converting, and using energy will improve relative to more polluting means. This relative improvement may accelerate the penetration of renewables-based technologies, though further work will be needed to assess their environmental impacts.

Nuclear power generation is already heavily regulated to ensure negligible risks for the workforce and the public. Design criteria require that the risks and potential consequences of accidents be reduced to levels that are in economic terms very small compared with direct generation costs. The external costs associated with residual low-level escape of radioactivity and accident risks are thought to be small relative to the overall costs of electricity. Nuclear power technologies may receive renewed interest in the future.

Electricity environmental cost studies are attracting the attention of decision-makers and regulators in various spheres. While the trend is towards internalisation of environmental costs within the price of energy and electricity tariffs, there is at present no accepted method of evaluating certain environmental costs. Some externalities have been avoided as a result of environmental controls, others have been included in energy prices. Other environmental emissions, such as greenhouse gases, remain largely unregulated.

Many of these problems should be addressed through further research and analysis, though some key disagreements over methodology may mask more fundamental differences of opinion over values, basic policy goals, and the intended role of environmental cost studies. If the assumptions and embedded values used in environmental electricity cost studies are explained carefully, and if the results present both quantitative and qualitative aspects, they can be useful for technology developers, regulators and policy-makers. Quantitative aspects include not only the estimates of final environmental costs, but also disaggregated results showing the relative importance of various factors on the final estimate, as well as sensitivity analyses to show how the results vary when important factors such as technology options are changed. Qualitative aspects include identifying emissions that account for the majority of the effects on specific impact categories and fuel-cycle activities, as well as identifying alternative technologies and R&D that could substantially alter the qualitative results.

The methods for the quantitative analyses vary widely, as do the estimates themselves. The two primary methods for estimating monetary values of environmental externalities are the "damage cost" approach and the "control cost" approach. Damage costs are developed by identifying the amount and type of environmental damage, and then placing a monetary value on that damage. Each step requires data for modelling, and it contains many assumptions that may need special investigation. Damage costs represent the monetary benefit of environmental protection. Control costs, on the other hand, represent how much society has to pay to avoid the environmental impact, that is, the monetary cost of environmental protection. Control costs thus are derived from government emission standards. Such standards are based on the assumption that the value of protecting the environment equals or exceeds the cost of meeting emission standards.

One major unknown is how attitudes towards environmental protection will evolve. Whether measures are implemented through direct regulation of emissions, through the introduction of tradeable emission permits, or through the introduction of fiscal incentives, any such measures would affect the cost of electricity. Clearly, this approach to analysing and presenting environmental electricity cost estimates poses a substantial challenge. Without such approaches, however, any long-term assessment of the comparative advantages and disadvantages of the various electricity production and distribution technologies would be incomplete. The regulatory trend towards quantification and inclusions of externalities in resource planning has nevertheless slowed considerably, and in some cases been reversed, at least in the United States. There are several reasons. One is the current regulatory focus on competitive issues and restructuring. Another is the emphasis within more competitive markets on actually lowering electric prices, based on pressures from customers competing in global markets. Further reasons are the lack of generally accepted estimates of environmental damages for many emissions sources (e.g. $CO_2$) and the internalisation (through environmental laws and regulations) of many important pollutants (e.g. $SO_2$).

b) *Integrated Resource Planning*

Integrated resource planning (IRP) is a technique used by utilities and regulatory agencies to develop flexible plans for providing a reliable and economical electric power supply for customer needs. The technique includes explicit comparison of both supply- and demand-side resource and technology options to meet a range of future electricity demand scenarios. In a consistent manner, utility planners compare the lifetime capital costs and operating costs, the availability and reliability, and the environmental impacts and costs of the various supply- and demand-side alternatives in order to prepare an overall plan to respond to identified future needs at least cost. There are several competing methodologies for defining what resource and technology choices constitute a "least-cost" mix. The IRP process generally takes account of opportunities for public involvement and regulatory review, as well as environmental and other social effects of utility resource alternatives.

Each utility's IRP approach is different, reflecting its regulatory environment, system characteristics and priorities, as well as its corporate culture and organisational structure. However, every IRP process follows a general framework in that it evaluates a broad range of resource and technology options and prepares a long-term resource plan. Using an initial load forecast, planners survey potential supply-side and utility-sponsored demand-side resources to identify measures for inclusion in the integrated resource planning portfolio.

For supply-side options, planners consider existing generation, transmission and distribution investments and technologies, as well as utility information about load, environmental and siting requirements, and capital, fuel, operating and maintenance costs. The result is a supply-side transmission and distribution stack with its development potential.

Demand-side options on the other hand would be identified by looking at existing customer use patterns, availability of energy-efficient technologies, demographic data, and evaluations of existing utility DSM programmes. Planners estimate costs, load impacts and participation rates to produce an initial stack of demand-side resources. The detailed forecast can be used to identify an appropriate mix of generation, transmission, distribution, power purchase, and energy-efficiency technology options to meet system needs under a range of future scenarios.

In some cases, IRP programmes have resulted in uneconomical investments and higher rates to customers, without the expected improvements in environmental protection. In the United States, there has been some movement away from IRP as a regulatory tool to promote demand-side management and renewable resources. From a utility perspective, the cost and rate of impacts of mandatory purchase requirements from co-generators and renewables embodied in the 1978 Public Utility Regulatory Policies Act show the degree to which well-intentioned national programmes affecting local utility regulation can be economically very costly. Other approaches that would move away from central planning, "command and control" regulation, need to be developed that address longer-term social concerns like environmental quality.

## Technology Prospects and Markets

### *Market Trends*

In 1993, the installed electricity generation capacity in IEA countries totalled 1 675 GWe, of which 498 GWe was solid fuel-fired, 367 GWe came from hydropower, 182 GWe from oil-fired plants, 334 GWe from natural gas-fired plant, 268 GWe from nuclear generating plants, 10 GWe from forest biomass, and eight GWe from geothermal, municipal and industrial solid waste, solar and wind energies. The share of fuels used for electricity generation differed greatly among IEA countries.

Coal was the leading source, contributing more than 50 per cent of the fuel input in the following countries (in descending order of proportion contributed): Denmark, Australia, the United Kingdom, Greece, the United States and Germany. Hydropower provided more than 50 per cent of the electricity in several countries, namely New Zealand, Austria, Canada, Switzerland and Sweden. Hydropower provided almost all the electricity generated in Norway. Nuclear power was by far the dominant electricity source in France and Belgium. It also accounted for some 30 per cent or more in Sweden, Switzerland, Spain, Finland and Germany. Only in the Netherlands was natural gas the leading fuel (56 per cent), while Italy depended mainly on oil (52 per cent).

From the IEA perspective, an important change since 1973 has been the diversification in electricity generation away from oil, whose share fell from more than 25 per cent of generation to 9 per cent. In large measure, this diversification was due to the development of nuclear power generation, whose share grew from four per cent in 1971 to 24 per cent in 1992. Now, however, nuclear power development in most IEA countries has come to a standstill, and the nuclear share of total electricity generation is expected to decline slowly to 2010, as demand growth is met by other fuels and older nuclear power plants are taken out of service.

Projections show that coal is expected to remain the primary fuel in electricity generation, its share rising from 39 per cent in 1992 to around 41 per cent in 2010. The major constraint on the use of coal for power generation is the perceived effect of its combustion on the environment. Development of technology to control emissions of $SO_2$, $NO_x$ and particulates has mitigated some of these effects, and further development and deployment of advanced technology that is both clean and efficient would further enhance the role of coal in the generation mix.

During the same period, natural gas will be the fuel with the best growth prospects in electricity generation in the IEA region. The reason for this is the removal of restrictions on natural gas for power generation and the availability of high-efficiency combined cycles. Combined cycle technology make natural gas a more economically competitive base-load fuel and also broadens the economic applications in industry. High-efficiency gas turbines will increasingly become key components in industrial and utility generation systems, which in some cases may include dual- or multi-fired capabilities, as well as in industrial co-generation systems. The trend towards greater use of natural gas would be furthered by the changing institutional and regulatory framework in the electricity industry, and by the increasing importance attached to the environmental advantages of natural gas. Expanding electricity production by independent producers in more deregulated markets is also encouraging this trend. As a result, projections for natural gas use have constantly been revised upwards in recent years.

Renewable energy sources other than hydropower contributed only 0.4 per cent of electricity generation during 1992, though the past 20 years have seen impressive improvements in their performance and cost. Hydropower is expected to remain the most important renewable source of electricity. But the potential for increasing hydro generation in the IEA region is modest, and hydropower's share of IEA countries' electricity consumption is expected to stay relatively stable in the long term. It is planned that nearly 37 GWe of new electricity capacity will have been brought online in the period 1993 to 2010, while a minimal amount would be decommissioned over the same period.

The trend towards improved efficiency in electricity end-use technologies and systems observed in the 1970s and 1980s will likely continue, though the rate of change appears to be slowing in the IEA region as a whole. Price developments could be a partial explanation for the slackening pace, but it may be that the easiest measures to increase efficiency have already been substantially deployed. Nevertheless, electricity savings resulting from efficiency increases will continue to accumulate as capital stock is replaced by more efficient equipment.

Utilities generally see a financial advantage in reducing demand so long as the costs of measures taken do not exceed the difference between the loss in revenue and the avoided costs of not meeting the increased demand. Such an advantage exists where the tariffs allowed by regulatory agencies or set by the utility are below long-run marginal costs. If tariffs are set at or above long-run marginal costs of supply, there is little or no financial advantage in DSM for utilities. Some utilities charge more for peak loads and higher volume usages to reflect the increased costs of providing such service. There has been a great deal of activity involving time-of-use rates for large industrial and commercial customers, but more limited experience with time-of-use rates for residential customers. These trends are expected to expand in the future, with intensified communication between utility and customer, more public awareness campaigns, energy audits, bill enclosures and use of smart metres. Loans may eventually finance energy-saving technology and "guaranteed" energy savings, and allow the customer to repay energy efficiency investments.

With the approval of regulatory bodies, electric utilities may adopt a variety of mechanisms to promote the adoption of efficient electricity technology while changing customers' behaviour. Such mechanisms might include load controls, differential or incentive rates, rebates, loans and grants, shared electricity-savings agreements, energy audits, technical assistance, direct equipment installation and replacement, and comprehensive energy management programmes. Clearly, government decisions in a number of areas could significantly affect the success and cost-effectiveness of utility programmes and investments.

### *Key Players*

The structure, ownership and regulation of the power and electricity distribution system are undergoing a period of dramatic change in many IEA countries. The increasing liberalisation of the energy market, the move towards deregulation, privatisation and unbundling, as well as grid interconnection, all affect the traditional structures of the electricity sector and create the need for new structures and approaches. The extent and the consequences of these changes on development directions and priorities for electricity supply and distribution technology, and on utility-sponsored R&D, remain to be seen. In the past, some IEA governments have required the electric utilities to choose indigenous fuels, even when uneconomic, or they have encouraged choice of a specific technology, in some cases with adverse effects on fuel diversity, or they have rationed or accelerated investments. With a privatised, competitive industry, this type of government intervention becomes inappropriate.

Changing the economic parametres that underlie decision-making will change fuel and investment choices. The liberalising of electricity markets tends to trigger effects such as: lower investment in large generating stations, increased diversity of investors, technology and fuels, and increased development of smaller units, typically closer to load centres.

It is not possible, however, to make a general statement that the changing mix of fuels and investment choices in power generation will have an adverse affect on energy security or environmental protection. Rather, the roles of the different players – electric utilities, power equipment and engineering companies, the electric appliance industry, regulatory agencies and individual customers – are being affected, as is their role in technology development and deployment. In order to take full advantage of the advancing technology frontier, electric utilities may establish new forms of technology collaboration and partnership. Relations between electric utilities and the industry supplying power generating equipment and engineering services would be strengthened, and so would interaction between utilities and electrical appliance producers. In the past there has been considerable activity and technology collaboration associated with the former link (this is where supply technologies are developed), but much less with the latter. Given the new pressures for increased efficiency and environmental protection, electric utilities and appliance and equipment manufacturers in some countries have begun to work together. There are many examples of where this is already happening, particularly through the creation of "golden carrot" programmes to encourage the development and manufacture of more efficient products.

The appliance industry, however, has become increasingly regulated by efficiency standards and is segmented into different technological areas, such as lighting, household appliances, industrial electrotechnologies and consumer electronics. Utility industry DSM programmes may help to establish technological links between utilities and equipment manufacturers. Canada's Power Smart programme is one example where utilities are co-operating with equipment manufacturers to promote efficient technologies. The planning framework envisaged for comparing the cost of the most effective DSM programme and technology in a particular demand category with its next least-cost (marginal) supply alternative is similar to a market-based decision-making process in many respects, and would not require costly regulatory monitoring. The advantages of such a framework, when compared with a highly centralised and integrated planning process, may be substantial.

### *Market Barriers*

Table 8.3 presents information on the market potential of the key electricity production and distribution technologies that are described in this chapter. Power generators and the power industry are facing dynamic market conditions, which will require a variety of technology options. Various features of the market have been addressed, notably: the size of the customer base, the expected rate of growth in electricity demand, the level of competition, the rate of retirement of existing capacities, the need to meet changing load requirements and the ability to obtain adequate capital for capacity expansion.

Markets must ultimately determine the most economic mix of electricity supply options (as well as end-use options). In principle, competitive markets ensure economic efficiency and provide the best context for promoting technological innovation. There should be reform of regulations that unnecessarily impede the development of electricity sources and technologies, and that undermine ability to respond to changing conditions. Public participation and environmental safeguards should be sought, while duplicative, cumbersome or unnecessary regulatory procedures should be eliminated or replaced by more effective and less costly approaches.

It can thus be assumed that, in some industrialised countries, electric utilities will increasingly evolve over the coming decades from being entities oriented solely towards supply, which build and maintain large electricity production facilities, to electricity organisations that are oriented towards supply co-ordination and service, whose cost of expanding or replacing generating capacity is balanced against the cost of increasing the efficiency of both supply and end-use, and whose independent power production and wheeling of power play a more important role. Consequently, the number of technology response options will grow, and technology will play an increasingly important role in ensuring profitability and high quality customer service.

Security of supply is, and will remain, an important factor in the adoption of solutions, but less for electric utilities than for governments and regulators. For utilities, reliability is a great concern. Energy source diversity would decrease supply vulnerability. This strategy of pursuing energy source diversity includes the introduction of energy-efficient power systems such as co-generation and fuel-flexible plants. But local and regional situations exist which may require the use or adaptation of special technologies because of the physical constraints, limits on available investment capital, unique resource endowments, and political or regulatory frameworks.

*Table 8.3*

**Key Electricity Production and Distribution Technologies: Comparative Market Potential**

| Technology | Time-frame | Nature/Size of Market | Market Challenges |
|---|---|---|---|
| **a) Electricity Production Technology for Environmental Protection** | | | |
| (i) High-temperature gas turbine technology | 0-30 years | • Large market potential among electric utilities and independent producers<br>• Natural gas-fired power generation (use of SNG and other gaseous fuels is also feasible) | • New power generation and repowering |
| (ii) Repowering and retrofitting technology | 0-15 years | • Large market potential in aging fossil-fuelled power plants<br>• Fossil fuel-fired power plants in countries with economies in transition | • Responding to changing environmental regulations<br>• Existing power companies facing siting/regulatory limitations |
| (iii) Co-generation technology | 0-20 years | • Co-generation options in chemicals, petroleum refining, pulp and paper processing, steel industry<br>• Combined heat and power production in industrial and commercial facilities | • Responding to strong growth in the industrial sector<br>• Providing low-cost packaged systems for small units (less than 20 MW) |
| **b) Carbon-free Technologies for Power Generation and Diversification** | | | |
| (i) Carbon dioxide removal technology | More than 30 years | • New and existing fossil fuel-fired power plants<br>• Market prospects will be determined by long-term $CO_2$ reduction goals | • High conversion efficiency fossil-fuelled power plants represent an alternative technology option |
| (ii) Carbon dioxide disposal and utilisation | More than 30 years | • Market prospects will be determined by long term $CO_2$ reduction goals | • Deep ocean disposal easier for plants located near the coastline |
| **c) Technologies for Efficient Electricity Distribution and End-Use** | | | |
| (i) Advanced control and communication technology | 0-10 years | • Load management and control<br>• DSM programmes<br>• Telemetering | • Utilities with low grid efficiencies<br>• Utilities needing to improve the quality of service |

*Table 8.3 (continued)*

**Key Electricity Production and Distribution Technologies: Comparative Market Potential**

| Technology | Time-frame | Nature/Size of Market | Market Challenges |
|---|---|---|---|
| **c) Technologies for Efficient Electricity Distribution and End-Use** *(continued)* | | | |
| (ii) Electricity transmission technology | 0-10 years | • National and international markets driven by the need to compete | • Opportunities in large-scale grid interconnections |
| (iii) Electricity storage | 0-20 years | • Electric utilities in grid-connected applications<br>• Stand-alone applications at individual sites | • Supplying peak demand for the customer at individual sites<br>• Storage integration for intermittent renewable energy systems |
| (iv) Solid-state power electronics | 0-10 years | • Utilities needing to improve grid operation etc.<br>• Support to DSM and load-management programmes | |
| (v) Superconducting technology | 10-30 years | • Utility power systems<br>• Market will depend upon the development of cost-effective manufacturing for component fabrication | • High-efficiency electricity use and storage technology |

An area of major uncertainty for most new generation technologies lies in the future stringency of environmental regulations. There is also uncertainty over future costs of technologies, and particularly over the ability of R&D to lower the costs of various technology options. There is further uncertainty regarding factors affecting the pace of technology adoption, even when it is shown to be economical and environmentally beneficial. For example, government regulation of utility rates may bias decisions away from capital-intensive technologies which in the long run might be the cheapest and cleanest. In the United States, ratemaking procedures have tended to favour capital-intensive resources. Greater competition tends to increase risks and shorten planning horizons and cost-recovery schedules; it also tends to favour less capital-intensive options. Conversely, market competition among generating technologies may make financing more difficult for the new technologies that are least familiar to private investors and whose total life-cycle costs are not well known. In increasingly open and competitive electricity markets, government regulation of utility rates is likely to decrease.

## Technology Policy Issues

### *Role of Governments*

It is clear that there are many solutions to the technology and institutional questions and issues involved in electricity production and distribution. In the first place, this is because of the complex relationship between the functioning of the market and the policies of governments. Economic factors have a major influence. Frequently, other factors come into play, such as differences in climate, geography, resource base and level of industrialisation. Many countries have little or no economically viable energy resources and have to import the bulk of their needs. It is not surprising, therefore, that there is no standard electricity policy and technology development strategy in market economies.

But, while there may be differences between IEA countries regarding the role played by government, there are also many similarities. All countries have to find a balance between ensuring adequate, secure energy supplies, economic growth and protection of the environment, at the national and global levels. Government's role in technology progress has focused on R&D support but also reflected the view that investments in electricity conservation and efficiency should be allowed to compete equitably with investments in electricity supply and distribution options. This goal is best achieved by giving consumers and producers incentives to make the right decisions concerning efficient consumption and production, and by fostering competition among providers at the levels of both electricity generation and demand reduction services. Integrated resource planning is a principal tool that policy-makers can adopt to provide a framework for such incentives and foster such competition. Increased attention to system concepts also has relevance in assisting newly industrialising nations and economies in transition.

In general, a wide range of technological options is available for the electric utility sector. Through regulation and other policies, governments have the means to modify the structure of electricity markets and pursue energy and environmental objectives. Governments have also sought to remove hindrances to investment in new and improved technologies among power producers and to increase competition among alternative fuels and systems, also to take the lead in providing information programmes to focus public attention on both the existence of new and improved technologies and the potential benefits of their accelerated deployment.

Many countries have tried to avoid providing financial support to their electricity supply industries or to avoid using barriers to trade to protect primary industries that supply power generating equipment and electrical appliances. In this context, it is clearly important for governments, in concert with the electricity generation and distribution industry, to call for legislative and regulatory action to open the market to greater competition, reduce consumer costs and promote adoption of flexible and efficient technology.

Governments should remove obstacles that artificially restrain participation in the market by competent builders and operators of electric power plants, and they should streamline regulations so as to remedy inadequate access to transmission facilities, difficulty in siting new plants and transmission lines, and conflicts between central and local administrations. Greater access to transmission facilities would increase competition and promote consumer access to electricity supply at the lowest reasonable cost.

The long-standing environmental aspects of electricity production – such as air and water pollution, acid deposition, waste disposal, noise, land use and siting – are currently receiving increased government attention. Substantial progress has been made by most IEA countries in controlling air pollutants from the combustion of fossil fuels and in reducing the other environmental effects, both locally and regionally. On the climate change issue, IEA governments are now called upon to formulate sectoral policies to deal with the reduction of greenhouse gas emissions. As a means of balancing the complex and sometimes conflicting goals of policies in the economic, energy, trade and environmental domains, governments could place increasing emphasis on the development of economic instruments that enable markets to seek the most efficient combined approaches that promise the greatest efficiency.

The IEA has indicated the political and economic scale of measures that would be needed to stabilise $CO_2$ emissions in its Member countries alone, and in their electricity sectors. Given the size of the problem in its global dimension, improving fossil-fuelled power plants in developing and transitional economies would appear to be a highly cost-effective means of reducing emissions of sulphur dioxide, nitrogen oxide, and carbon dioxide worldwide. Yet obtaining financing for the necessary environmental retrofitting and plant repowering is difficult, since such economies have many pressing priorities competing for scarce funding. If appropriate clean-coal technologies are to be introduced on a timely basis, concerted action will be required, involving commercial joint ventures and jointly implemented projects for power plant construction and operation, as well as the exchange of technical personnel and support by major international financial institutions. Governments can play a catalytic role in providing the technological know-how, capital and training expertise of industrialised countries to match the needs of Economies in Transition and developing countries that have coal resources.

### *Role of International Co-operation*

A sustained upward trend in worldwide demand for electric power stems from higher standards of living and from the great versatility of electricity. Yet no single country has sufficient technology or expertise to single-handedly satisfy all its needs in an effective, technologically advanced fashion. No single technology, moreover, is the best solution for the entire range of national circumstances. Therefore, the combined and well planned application of alternative power generation technologies in a co-operative international context will be increasingly important in the future. There are many opportunities, indeed, for governments and electric utilities to establish new international collaboration, to promote the development of next-generation electricity supply and distribution technology, and to assist newly industrialising nations and Economies in Transition.

Governments and regulators need to implement creative measures that will remove some of the barriers to deployment and so ease the introduction of new, environmentally friendly generating technologies. A regulatory framework should be designed to give utilities better signals about where to invest and to measure the total-cycle costs as well as the social costs of the facilities. To meet both short- and long-term objectives, there should be converging strategies for R&D, demonstration and deployment. This is essential, both to ensure application of new and improved electricity generating systems, and to enhance their prospects for commercialisation. Co-operation among utilities, engineering and equipment industries, regulatory agencies and research centres is a key element. This includes more interaction among utilities themselves and between utilities and governments, suppliers and consumers.

Enhanced international co-operation in R&D and technology transfer is needed to facilitate application of the most efficient electricity generation and distribution technology. The need for international co-operation is becoming more acute, in fact, because of the global character of many of the problems, the wider dimension of the opportunities facing the electric sector and the internationalisation of technology markets. Because adoption of new technologies promises global as well as regional benefits, it is in the interest of all the industrialised world to assist this process, in whatever form it deems most appropriate. Ad hoc international mechanisms for information exchange and technology transfer should be established to fill technical information gaps, especially in the fossil fuel and renewable energy areas. It should be stressed that there are no "low-grade" or second class technologies designed especially for developing countries. Rather, effective technology transfer, equity investments and adherence to free market principles should provide developing countries with more opportunities for deploying more environmentally acceptable technologies from the outset, or modifying and retrofitting existing plants.

The rapid growth, however, in demand for electricity in developing countries requires special action. Rapid growth, combined with lack of access to adequate capital, may lead to implementation of technologies with far less than optimum performance. The gap must be closed between the state-of-the-art technologies in industrialised countries and technologies currently being employed in developing countries and in the Economies in Transition.

A vehicle for international collaboration is provided by the IEA's Implementing Agreements in the electricity production and distribution area. In the Implementing Agreement on Assessing the Impact of High-Temperature Superconductivity on the Electric Power Sector, fifteen parties from fourteen countries undertook to facilitate contacts between key experts in different countries, to make available the results of assessments on the subject and to highlight specific issues on which a common approach would aid further progress. The IEA Implementing Agreement on Demand-Side Management provides participants with a forum to exchange information and knowledge on how utility demand-side programmes are operated and the means to promote adoption and development of efficient electricity end-use technology. Other possible proposals have included an Electric Power Technology Information Network and the East-West Electric Technology Centre to link together databases, disseminate information on best electric technology practice and share fossil-fired power plant operating experience with interested parties from central and eastern Europe and the Newly Independent States.

As a result of institutional and regulatory action (or governmental control) over past decades, the electric utility industry has become much more averse to risk and capital expenditure, adopting a more technologically conservative approach. While the degree of conservatism does differ from country to country, it certainly impedes rapid adoption of technological advances and innovations which may be important to IEA Member countries in addressing key objectives motivating this assessment. Collaboration to identify, address and remove such hindrances on an international scale thus merit a substantial joint effort, in which IEA institutional leadership would appear to be particularly appropriate. Collaborative international efforts to demonstrate certain priority technologies could equally be envisaged. For example, two or more electric utilities might share the costs of a large-scale demonstration project on photovoltaics, which would evaluate the difficulties and potential benefits of incorporating photovoltaics into an electric grid. Cost-sharing for demonstration projects in other priority areas, such as fuel cells and passively safe, standardised nuclear power plants, might also offer significant benefits to participants. Such collaboration would involve positive joint action aimed at establishing an international marketplace and standardised environment, thus fostering increased industrial investment by users, manufacturers and suppliers, and speeding the pace of technological development and increasing the scale and rapidity of deployment.

## Approach

Generation, distribution, and use of electricity sustains economic productivity in IEA countries. It is conducive to technological innovation and can have a positive effect on the quality of the environment. Electricity is a clean energy source, convenient and flexible at its point of use. These benefits are gained at the expense of concentrated environmental impact, complex technology and high-cost investment in fixed facilities at the point of production. Consequently, the pace of deployment of new technology in the electricity supply industry depends upon the shared interests of utilities, governments and regulators, the engineering and electric equipment industries and the public, and their mutual awareness that technology progress is needed to address significant objectives for society like energy security, environmental sustainability and economic growth, and therefore should be encouraged.

Over the next few decades, electric utilities throughout the IEA region, and in the developing world, will face a number of common problems: heavy capital cost requirements, rising fuel prices and increasingly stringent environmental regulations. Solutions to these problems will require improved power system efficiency, increased unit modularity and standardisation, diversification of fuels, careful management of energy demand and better pollution control. Opportunities for technology improvement exist in every area, now and in the long term. Changes in patterns of demand growth, combined with increased application of demand-side management, market deregulation and growing competition, could continue to make forecasting of load and financing of large new capacity units more difficult. Changing economic and environmental requirements place greater emphasis on investment decisions for new technology and the upgrading of existing aging power plants. Meeting electricity needs in a world of uncertainty will call for the development of a wide variety of technologies. Only a broad technology base will equip utilities with the flexibility to respond in a cost-effective manner to dynamic market conditions and to regulations. No single technology will be the best choice for every situation; market forces will ultimately determine the most viable options on a regional and national basis. IEA Member countries and their governments face a challenge to collaborate in the transition to a new era of electric technologies, and to assist each other and newly industrialising nations and transition economies in minimising pitfalls and maximising benefits.

To meet the technology priority goals identified in this chapter, IEA Member countries may therefore wish to consider contributing to and co-operating in a technology strategy and collaborative R&D programme that includes the measures listed below.

- Supporting R&D efforts in the field of new and improved system and component technology for power production, transmission and distribution in order to increase security of electricity supply and address shared regional and global environmental concerns, which also means promoting inter-utility and inter-industry R&D co-operation.

- Fostering energy source diversification, efficient fuel conversion and fuel switching as a key element in an interim technology strategy for curbing greenhouse gas emissions.

- Facilitating advances in electricity distribution and end-use technology by promoting a range of approaches including: DSM and load management programmes, minimum efficiency standards for new electrical equipment and appliances, development of next-generation control and communication systems, superconducting materials and electricity storage technology.

- Supporting regulatory frameworks and tariff structures that promote greater market competitiveness and that encourage the integration of supply technology and end-use efficiency and conservation decision-making.

- Encouraging the adoption of total-fuel and life-cycle concepts to help optimise resource use.

- Providing leadership and focus for the electricity supply industry in technology partnerships and jointly implemented projects.

- Encouraging the environmental upgrading of power generation plants in developing countries and the Economies in Transition.

# Chapter 9

## TRANSPORT TECHNOLOGY AND FUELS

### Goals and Rationale

The efficient transportation of people and goods is an essential factor in relation to the IEA countries' concerns regarding energy security, environmental protection and economic growth. The transport sector accounted for about 32 per cent of total final energy consumption in the IEA region in 1993 and it represents about 60 per cent of oil consumption. Air and road transport combined account for about 95 per cent of total transportation demand. Changes in demand have varied considerably by region. In North America transport demand has increased 21 per cent since 1973, compared with 90 per cent in the IEA Pacific countries and 65 per cent in IEA Europe. In the United States, fuel consumption per car-kilometre was nearly double that in IEA Europe and Japan through most of the 1970s, and was reduced by about one-third during the 1980s, in part due to higher fuel prices and the adoption of fuel economy standards in 1979. Transport energy use in the IEA region has increased by 39 per cent since 1973. Transportation worldwide has grown rapidly in the past and this growth is expected to continue through the next decades. Since modern ground transportation is almost solely based on internal combustion engines for power, its energy source has historically depended upon petroleum. Increasing use of petroleum in transport dominates future growth projections[1]. While some ground fuel modes, such as subways, intercity rail, trolley buses, and a limited number of cars and trucks, use electricity for their power source, they account for under 1 per cent of total ground transportation energy demand in the IEA countries. In addition, a significant number of vehicles use propane or petroleum gas, as well as natural gas in both developed and developing countries.

The focus of this chapter will be on road vehicles. Throughout this century, the relative cost of travel has been falling; at the same time, wealth per capita has been increasing. This trend has contributed to a rapid growth in transportation demand and a commensurate increase in energy demand and vehicle emissions. A comparison between travel demand and per capita gross national product appears to show little sign of market saturation. Growing travel demand is compounded by population increases worldwide, contributing further to the dramatic growth in road transport. In 1950, there were about 53 million cars on the world's roads. Only four decades

1. For an analysis of transportation energy demand see IEA *World Energy Outlook,* 1995 Edition, pp. 245-246.

later, the global automobile fleet was over 470 million, with an additional 144 million commercial vehicles. On average, the fleet has grown by about 10 million automobiles per year over this period. This growth in five selected IEA Member countries is illustrated in Figure 9.1. At the same time, as illustrated in Figure 9.2, the truck and bus fleet has been recently growing by about three million vehicles per year. The growth of motorisation has over the past 40 years exceeded the growth of population.

Figure 9.3 illustrates the likelihood of continued dramatic growth in vehicle populations and growth in energy requirements due to increasing motorisation in developing nations. While the economic growth rate has slowed in the highly industrialised countries, population growth and increased urbanisation and industrialisation are accelerating the use of motor vehicles elsewhere. Projections of the future vehicle population have to be made taking into account population growth and economic development, which are the major factors influencing vehicle growth. In making estimates of future growth of vehicle populations and vehicle use, vehicle saturation, increased congestion and increasing policy intervention by governments may restrain future growth, especially in highly industrialised areas. However, by early next century, based on current trends, the rapidly developing areas of the world (especially Asia, central and eastern Europe and Latin America) and the IEA Pacific will have as many vehicles as North America and IEA Europe, although per capita rates will remain substantially lower.

*Figure 9.1*
**Automobile Registrations for Selected Countries**
(1950-1992)

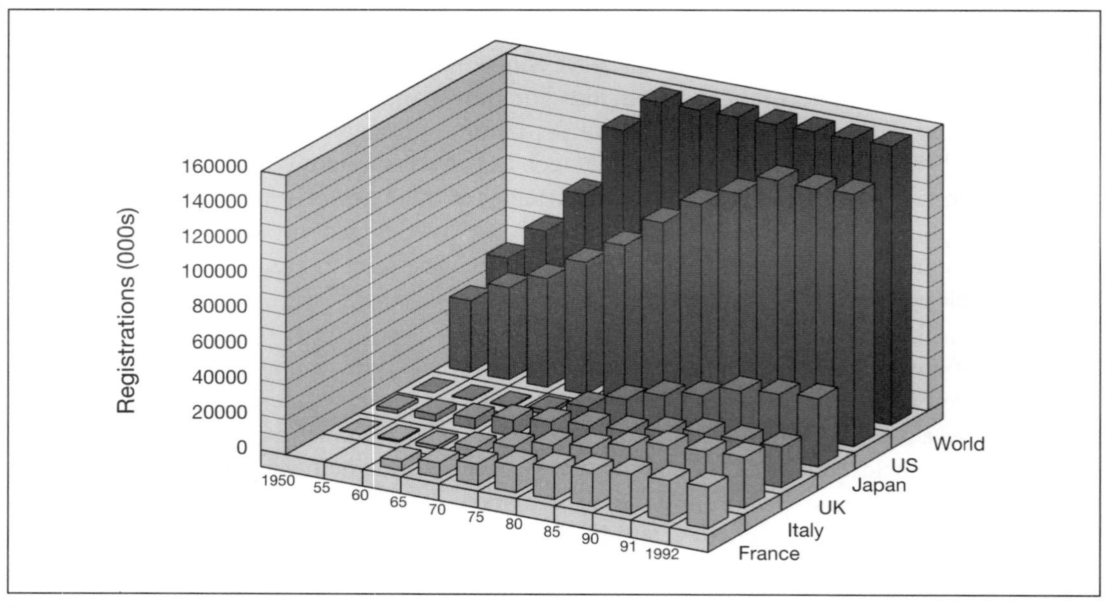


Source: American Automobile Manufacturers Association, *World Motor Vehicle Data, 1994 Edition,* Detroit, MI, 1994, pp 26-28, 163.

*Figure 9.2*
**Truck and Bus Registrations for Selected Countries**
(1950-1992)

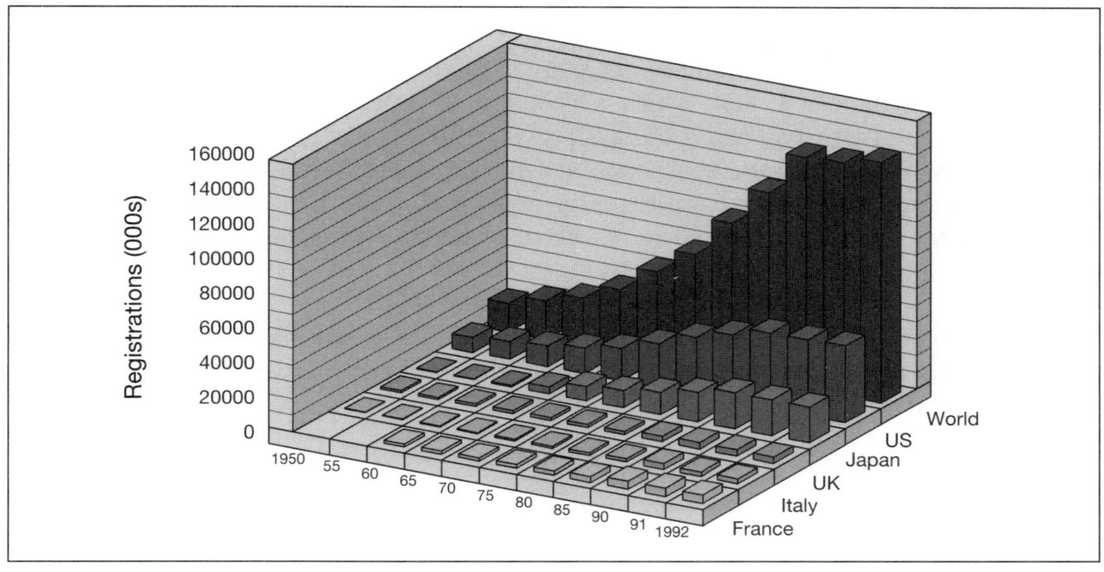


Source: American Automobile Manufacturers Association, *World Motor Vehicle Data, 1994 Edition,* Detroit, MI, 1994, pp 26-28, 77, and annual.

*Figure 9.3*
**Motor Vehicle Registrations**
(population per car)

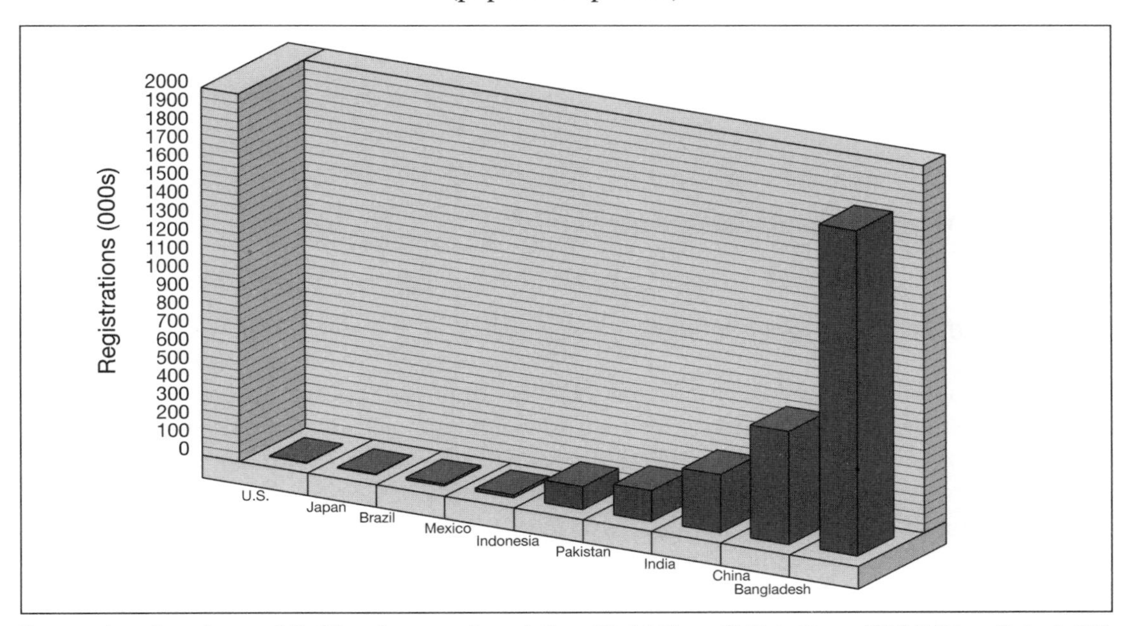


Source: American Automobile Manufacturers Association, *World Motor Vehicle Data, 1994 Edition,* Detroit, MI, 1994, pp 26-28, 77, and annual.

The transportation manufacturing industry is global in scale, but each operating entity is a key component of the local economy. Frequently, individual countries or blocks of countries develop policies and vehicle regulations which effectively become non-tariff barriers. This is true for new product standards (in particular, emissions and safety regulations) and fuel pricing (as it affects efficiency), which can have significant consequences for trade and technology collaboration. For instance, there are apparent discrepancies between the United States and the European Union, which have imposed different environmental emissions standards. This is also true among individual provinces, states, and cities which have imposed specific policy measures in the transportation field. Decisions have to be taken concerning land-use planning, highway and mass transit construction and fuel characteristics. These choices will be strongly influenced by expected technology progress over the next 20 to 30 years.

Increasing consumption of oil-based transportation fuels has been a major contributor to both greenhouse gas emissions and urban pollution. Priority goals for road transport and fuels technology are to:

- increase the efficiency and flexibility of transport fuel use; and
- continue development of environmentally sustainable substitute fuels and facilitate their increased use.

In the context of these goals, the emphasis is on the private automobile (other vehicles are also important) as the primary factor in energy utilisation and environmental impact. Until more sustainable options, such as alternative fuels, become economically practical on a large scale, reducing the specific fuel consumption of conventional vehicles appears to be a key means to lowering $CO_2$ emissions from transport. As part of a more general goal to reduce demand and dependency on fossil fuels, steady improvements in the fuel efficiency of conventional vehicles could buy time for the gradual implementation of more advanced technologies or other approaches.

## Technology Description and Assessment

### *Description of Significant Technologies*

Research on automobile and truck efficiency covers improved engines, more efficient drive trains, and vehicle design characteristics such as weight and aerodynamic drag, which affect fuel economy. Advanced propulsion technologies and alternative fuels have the potential to significantly increase efficiency and reduce pollution without sacrificing safety and comfort. A very wide range of technology options exists in this sector, but experience has demonstrated that in-use fuel and emissions performance depends upon proper vehicle maintenance. Effective inspection and maintenance programmes encourage vehicle owners to maintain their vehicles, the service industry to ensure proper maintenance and vehicle manufacturers to improve product serviceability and durability.

A summary of key transport and fuel technologies, the main reasons for their selection, and their current technical status is shown in Tables 9.1 and 9.2. Short descriptions are given in the following sections.

a) *Internal Combustion Engine (ICE) Control*

Essentially all road vehicles are powered by internal combustion engines (ICE) using spark (gasoline-fuelled) or compression (diesel-fuelled) ignition cycles. Progress in fuel efficiency has continued in spite of declining real fuel prices in most countries and slackened consumer interest in high-efficiency vehicles because the same technologies that can offer increased fuel efficiency can also provide other emissions reduction benefits. At present, the spark ignition engine is cheaper and offers good performance but at the expense of fuel economy. Compression ignition engines offer better fuel consumption, particularly at part load, but at a higher capital cost and with more noise, vibration, bulk and weight. Because of massive capital and technology investment in the ICE, it is likely that it will remain the basic powertrain for automobiles and trucks for the foreseeable future. Changes in engines are typically evolutionary as opposed to revolutionary in nature since completely new engines have historically taken a relatively long time to develop and produce.

(i) Improved exhaust treatment

Significant progress has occurred over the past two decades in the development of a wide variety of emissions-reduction technologies for petrol-fuelled vehicles. Before controls were required, engine crankcases were vented directly to the atmosphere. Improvement in engine emissions and energy performance over the last two decades has resulted from introduction of in-engine emissions control and the use of catalytic converters to eliminate pollutants from the engine exhaust, as well as significant improvements in manufacturing techniques. These techniques have provided closer tolerances, with resulting decreases in frictional losses, blow-by gases and size of coolant channels.

The technical potential for further improvements in automotive fuel efficiency and emissions is substantial. Exhaust emissions of unburnt hydrocarbons (HC), volatile organic compounds (VOC), carbon monoxide (CO), and nitrogen oxide ($NO_X$) are related to the air/fuel mixture injected, the peak temperatures and pressures in each cylinder, the use of either leaded or unleaded petrol, combustion chamber geometry and other engine design parameters. Variations in these parameters are therefore capable of causing significant increases or decreases in these emissions. The most important parameters are probably air/fuel ratio and mixture preparation, ignition timing and combustion chamber design. Dilution of the incoming charge has been shown to reduce peak cycle temperature by slowing flame speed and absorbing some heat of combustion. Recirculating a portion of the exhaust gas back into the incoming air/fuel mixture (EGR), thereby lowering peak cycle temperature, is therefore used to lower $NO_X$. Improvements in mixture preparation, injection systems and ignition systems can increase dilution tolerance. This can also be achieved by increasing the burn rate or flame speed of the air-fuel charge. Techniques to do this include increased swirl and squish, shorter flame paths and multiple ignition sources.

*Table 9.1*

**Main Reasons for Selection of Transport Technology and Fuels**

| Technology | Examples | Reasons for Selection |
|---|---|---|
| **a) ICE Control** | | |
| (i) Improved Exhaust Treatment | • Catalyst traps, exhaust gas recirculation (EGR)<br>• Intake and exhaust systems<br>• Advanced emissions abatement in heavy-duty vehicles | • Effective for HC, CO, $NO_x$ emission reduction<br>• Continuation of current technology does not change basic powertrain<br>• Technology allows for use of other cycles with higher efficiency |
| (ii) Improved Combustion | • Ceramic components<br>• Ignition systems<br>• Flow dynamics variable valves<br>• Turbine engine | • Efficiency gains<br>• Modifications to current powertrain<br>• Wide variety of new technologies |
| (iii) Fast Warm-up | • Thin wall engines<br>• Start/stop with flywheel storage | • 20-40% of commute trip affected<br>• Especially in cold weather, increases time in steady state engine temperature conditions |
| **b) Fuel Substitution** | | |
| (i) Improved Gasoline and Diesel Fuel | • Reformulated gasoline<br>• Reduced Reid vapour pressure (RVP) | • Builds on current refinery and distribution structure<br>• Can produce fleet-wide effects quickly |
| (ii) Natural Gas and LPG | • On-board storage<br>• System integration | • Substantial supply<br>• Reduced HC, CO emissions<br>• Eliminates refining losses |
| (iii) Alcohol Fuels (in an ICE) | • Neat methanol<br>• Neat ethanol M85 | • Multiple sources of feedstocks<br>• Possible emissions reduction<br>• Liquid fuel at atmospheric pressure |
| (iv) Hydrogen (in an ICE) | • Neat $H_2$ in ICE storage systems | • Very low emissions<br>• Multiple sources of feedstocks and process energy |
| **c) Energy Regeneration** | • Hydraulic and kinetic storage<br>• Engine management and electric storage | • Potential for significant energy demand reduction<br>• Base technologies available |
| **d) Electric and Hybrid Vehicles** | • Electric batteries<br>• Fuel cells<br>• Solar photovoltaic cells<br>• Hybrid systems | • Multiple source of electrical generation<br>• Multiple technologies for on-board storage/generation<br>• Significant decrease in local emissions<br>• Base technologies available |
| **e) Vehicle Improvements** | | |
| (i) Drag and Rolling Resistance Reduction | • Drag coefficient reduction<br>• Reduced rolling resistance<br>• Reduced bearings friction | • Increased energy efficiency<br>• Air/marine material forming<br>• Computer-aided designs (CAD) potential for "smooth" designs |

*Table 9.1 (continued)*

**Main Reasons for Selection of Transport Technology and Fuels**

| Technology | Examples | Reasons for Selection |
|---|---|---|
| **e) Vehicle Improvements** *(continued)* | | |
| (ii) Structural Weight | • Light structures<br>• Bonded/composite structures<br>• Light powertrains | • Increased weight-efficiency of vehicle |
| (iii) Transmission | • Electronic shift<br>• Multistep lock-up<br>• Continuously variable transmission (CVT) electric drives<br>• Drivelines and suspensions | • Reduced transmission losses<br>• Optimised engine speeds with CVT/IVT (intermittently variable transmission) technologies<br>• Increased hybrid powertrain possibility |
| (iv) Accessories | • On-board electronic controls<br>• Constant speed drives<br>• Efficient components | • Containment of parasitic losses<br>• Decreased loads through current or near term designs |
| **f) Transport Productivity** | | |
| (i) Traffic Control | • Electronic tolls<br>• Road information systems<br>• High occupancy vehicles | • Increased road capacity<br>• Optimised speeds for optimum fuel use<br>• Cost-effective capital investment and vehicle costs |
| (ii) Travel Substitution | • Telecommunications<br>• Software development | • Reduced energy-intensive travel<br>• Shifting to energy-efficient use of communications<br>• Electronics as major technology support |
| (iii) Route Planning | • On-board navigation systems<br>• Electronic displays and interactive warning | • Reduced distance travelled per trip<br>• Optimised route and increased average speed<br>• Avoidance of congestion delays and costs |

Techniques for exhaust gas after treatment include catalytic converters, particulate traps and various devices for reducing $NO_X$ to oxygen and nitrogen gases. Oxidation catalysts are devices which are placed on the tailpipe of a vehicle to remove unburned HC and CO in the exhaust stream through oxidation. If the vehicle is properly maintained and fuelled with unleaded gasoline, these reductions can be considerable. Three-way catalysts, so called for their ability to lower HC, CO and $NO_X$ emissions simultaneously, were first introduced in the United States. For three-way catalysts to work effectively, it is necessary to control air/fuel mixtures much more precisely than is needed for oxidation catalyst systems. Trap-oxidisers are frequently proposed in the context of diesel emission control. A trap-oxidiser system consists of a durable particulate filter (the "trap") positioned in the engine exhaust stream, along with some means for cleaning the filter by burning off ("oxidising") the collected particulate matter.

*Table 9.2*

**Technical Status of Transport Technology and Fuels**

| Technology | Status | Technical Feasibility | Conversion Efficiency | Application Issues | Emissions Reduction | | |
|---|---|---|---|---|---|---|---|
| | | | | | $CO_2$ | Acid Rain | Other |
| **a) ICE Control** | | | | | | | |
| (i) Improved Exhaust Treatment | • Deployed in autos<br>• Limited diesel application | • Continuing after treatment improvement<br>• Allows continued use of ICE | • Slight decrease for significant $NO_X$ reduction<br>• Increased back pressure reduces efficiency in diesels | • Precious metal-dependent component cost<br>• High durability of ceramics | • Minimal, unless used with higher conversion efficiency vehicle | • $NO_X$ reduction | • HC and CO reduction |
| (ii) Improved Combustion | • Incremental improvements | • Good variety of technology<br>• Available technology must integrate with current ICE | • 5-10% engine efficiency gains | • High temperature materials<br>• Low heat transfer injection<br>• Variable diagnostics | • Lower than 10% | • Feasibility of $NO_X$ control | • HC and CO reduction |
| (iii) Fast Warm-up | • Incremental improvements | • Transient time decreased by 50% | • Average efficiency gains of <5% | • Complexity of system | • <5% lower | • Minimal | • HC and CO emissions reduction at start-up |
| **b) Fuel Substitution** | | | | | | | |
| (i) Improved Gasoline and Diesel fuel | • Within current refining techniques | • Chemistry available<br>• Refinery balance and the need to produce more light ends | • <2% gain for vehicles<br>• Increase in refinery energy efficiency | • Refinery operation and cost optimisation | • <1% or lower | • Minimal | • $SO_X$, $NO_X$ and VOC reduction |

Note: Fuel conversion efficiency improvement relative to similar conventional vehicle.

*Table 9.2 (continued)*

**Technical Status of Transport Technology and Fuels**

| Technology | Status | Technical Feasibility | Conversion Efficiency | Application Issues | Emissions Reduction | | |
|---|---|---|---|---|---|---|---|
| | | | | | $CO_2$ | Acid Rain | Other |
| **b) Fuel Substitution** *(continued)* | | | | | | | |
| (ii) Natural Gas and LPG | • Demonstration fleets<br>• Field trials<br>• Fuels commercially available | • Range extension needed<br>• System cost abatement | • Close to gasoline with engine adaptation | • Availability of supply<br>• Containment/safety<br>• Availability of stations<br>• Methane transmission leakage | • 10-20% lower<br>• Reduction of evapora-tive losses<br>• Reduction of reactive HCs | • Possible $NO_X$ control | • $SO_X$, $NO_X$, CO and VOC reduction |
| (iii) Alcohol Fuels (in an ICE) | • Demonstration fleets<br>• Field trials in large vehicles<br>• Commercial availability of blends | • Supply limitation and cost needs<br>• Change in OEM design<br>• Low-cost emissions control option<br>• Multiple feedstocks | • <15% improvement | • Availability of supply<br>• Availability of stations<br>• Aldehyde emissions | • Feedstock dependent | • Minimal | • SOx, NOx, HC and particulate reduction |
| (iv) Hydrogen (in an ICE) | • R&D and prototypes | • Infinite source of supply<br>• Distillation & production hurdles | • Dependent on feedstock and storage system | • Highly variable production costs<br>• Safety issues concerning storage and fuelling systems | • Feedstock dependent | • Feedstock dependent | • Eliminat-ion of essentially all vehicles emissions |

Note: Fuel conversion efficiency improvement relative to similar conventional vehicle.

*Table 9.2 (continued)*

**Technical Status of Transport Technology and Fuels**

| Technology | Status | Technical Feasibility | Conversion Efficiency | Application Issues | Emissions Reduction | | |
|---|---|---|---|---|---|---|---|
| | | | | | $CO_2$ | Acid Rain | Other |
| **c) Energy Regeneration** | • R&D and prototypes<br>• Large vehicles with electric trains<br>• Demonstration bus fleets | • Energy storage systems<br>• Transmission of power requires availability of CVT to blend power | • Dependent on mission profile but 15-20% improvement possible | • System costs and space claim | • Direct reduction of fuel used<br>• Transient load emissions | • $NO_x$ and particulates reduction | • CO and HC reduction |
| **d) Electric and Hybrid Vehicles** | • Demonstration fleets<br>• Field trials in niche markets | • Range and cost limitations may limit market<br>• Adopting hybrid drives may increase use options | • Dependent on base fuel with 20-40% gain possible | • Load levelling source of electricity<br>• Shifting of emissions point sources | • Power source dependent | • Power source dependent | • Minor vehicle-based recharging emissions |
| **e) Vehicle Improvements** | | | | | | | |
| (i) Drag and Rolling Resistance Reduction | • Commercial potential for improvement in low- friction bearings and lubrications<br>• Low-friction tyres to be tested | • Continuation of improvements dependent on material properties & cost of manufacture<br>• Study on basic physics | • Speed sensitive benefits<br>• Gains of 1-5% possible | • Possible to retrofit better tyres | • $CO_2$ reduction due to decreased power demand | • $NO_x$ reduction | • CO and HC reduction |

Note: Fuel conversion efficiency improvement relative to similar conventional vehicle.

*Table 9.2 (continued)*

**Technical Status of Transport Technology and Fuels**

| Technology | Status | Technical Feasibility | Conversion Efficiency | Application Issues | Emissions Reduction | | |
|---|---|---|---|---|---|---|---|
| | | | | | $CO_2$ | Acid Rain | Other |
| **e) Vehicle Improvements** *(continued)* | | | | | | | |
| (ii) Structural Weight | • Commercial/ demonstrated<br>• Bonded structures in limited use<br>• Composite materials in most vehicles | • Continuation of improvements<br>• Limited by material properties and relative cost of manufacture | • 0.2 to 0.4% gain for every 1% weight reduction | • Increases relative cost of manufacturing<br>• Recyclability | • Direct percentage reduction | • $NO_x$ reduction (by decreasing power demands on accelerations and increasing total useful work) | • CO, HC and particulate reduction |
| (iii) Transmission | • Commercial/ demonstrated technology<br>• CVT available<br>• High power CVT in prototype<br>• Lock-up and electronic control | • CVT/IVT in widespread use in next decade<br>• Hybrid powertrains feasible with CVT/IVT | • 10-15% gain over manual with CVT or IVT<br>• Electronic drives could further increase this conversion efficiency | | • Direct percentage reduction | • $NO_x$ reduction | • CO, HC and particulate reduction |
| (iv) Accessories | • Demand responsive systems gaining preference<br>• Constant speed systems in demonstrations | • Highly feasible for constant speed<br>• High-efficiency accessory systems | • <5% efficiency gain | • High accessory load vehicles such as buses and trucks | • Direct percentage reduction | • $NO_x$ reduction | • CO, HC and particulate reduction |

Note: Fuel conversion efficiency improvement relative to similar conventional vehicle.

*Table 9.2 (continued)*

**Technical Status of Transport Technology and Fuels**

| Technology | Status | Technical Feasibility | Conversion Efficiency | Application Issues | Emissions Reduction | | |
|---|---|---|---|---|---|---|---|
| | | | | | $CO_2$ | Acid Rain | Other |
| **f) Transport Productivity** | | | | | | | |
| (i) Traffic Control | • Commercial/ demonstrated<br>• Interactive signals and controls deployed | • Interactive signals and controls feasible<br>• Intervehicle controls<br>• High occupancy vehicle | • Significant local gains with the elimination of stop & go traffic (>10%)<br>• Increased capacity of highways | • High volume roads or restricted access roads | • Direct percentage reduction | • $NO_x$ reduction | • CO, HC and particulate reduction |
| (ii) Travel Substitution | • Commercial/ demonstrated<br>• Telecommuting in trials<br>• High occupancy vehicle programmes<br>• Electronics use expanding rapidly | • Dependent on modal shift of transport market and flexibility of work arrangements | • Move to more efficient energy conversion modes<br>• Higher overall transport productivity (10-30% possible) | • Commuting trip changes<br>• Reduced need for business travel<br>• Modal shifts to lower energy options | • Direct reduction | • $NO_x$ reduction | • CO, HC and particulates reduction |
| (iii) Route Planning | • Commercial/ demonstrated<br>• Satellite-based communication positioning systems in marine/air use<br>• Demonstration on highway<br>• On-board maps & interactive reporting | • Anti-congestion measures feasible<br>• Advanced communication technology<br>• Staggered work hours | • Gains depend upon interaction between vehicle and overall road transport system | • Education programmes for high-efficiency driving | • Direct reduction | • $NO_x$ reduction | • CO, HC and particulate reduction |

Note: Fuel conversion efficiency improvement relative to similar conventional vehicle.

(ii) Improved combustion

Promising new engine technologies under development include the gas turbine and various low-heat-rejection engines. The gas turbine promises high efficiency with expectations for low emissions and multifuel capability, but it will require ceramic components which can operate reliably at very high temperatures.

Low-heat-rejection (LHR) reciprocating engines offer improved efficiency through minimisation of heat losses and reduction of the parasitic losses of fans and water pumps. Reduction in size or elimination of radiators can permit additional improvement in vehicle aerodynamics as well. High-temperature materials, thermal barriers and compatible high-temperature lubrication systems are the critical requirements for LHR engines. In addition, combustion systems must be optimised and, if necessary, reconfigured for LHR engines to ensure compliance with emissions regulations. Turbo-compounding and bottoming cycles are demonstrated fuel-saving technologies and are very effective when combined with LHR engines, but they are more practical for heavy trucks than for light trucks and passenger cars.

(iii) Fast warm-up

With continued progress in combustion control and enhancement (e.g. catalytic surfaces), unthrottled engines, with their inherent efficiency advantage, may achieve larger penetration into the transportation sector. Ignition-enhancing technology in unthrottled engines may allow fuel flexibility and use of gasolines and methanol instead of only diesel fuel. Direct injection versions are typically the most efficient, thus falling under the definition of the widely recognised direct-injection stratified-charge engine.

Two-stroke (or even rotary) versions of these engines, which offer better power-to-weight ratios and lower internal friction losses than the more common four-stroke versions, may yield additional fuel economy gains, but again combustion enhancement (with consideration of fuel flexibility) and emission control will be the keys to the success of these technologies.

b) *Fuel Substitution*

Eventually, alternative fuels will have to be used for transportation to mitigate increasing dependence on petroleum-based gasoline and diesel while reducing atmospheric emissions. Alcohols from biomass, compressed natural gas, electricity, liquids from coal, and hydrogen have been proposed for use in automobiles. Table 9.3 presents the main properties of various alternative and conventional fuels. The major constraint on the use of these fuels for the next several decades is likely to be their ease of use, performance and, importantly, cost. Earlier penetration of methanol and other oxygenated fuels could occur and would support environmental goals. These fuels result in less ozone (a prime cause of smog) and less carbon monoxide than does gasoline. Many alternative fuels offer potential environmental benefits. Flexible-fuel vehicles could bridge the gap between the introduction of a new fuel and the development of the necessary infrastructure.

Automobile engines can be readily adapted to methanol using available technology, so they are not included on the list of most promising technology developments. However, research on the integration of the issues of fuel supply (production and distribution) and engine fuel requirements may point the way to productive lines of development.

*Table 9.3*

**Characteristics of Alternative and Conventional Fuels**

| | Diesel | Gasoline | Methanol | Ethanol | LPG | CNG | Biodiesel |
|---|---|---|---|---|---|---|---|
| Energy Content (hhv Mj/kg) | 45.15 | 43.65 | 23.86 | 29.73 | 50.37 | 55.53 | 37.02-37.2 |
| Liquid Density (kg/litre) | 0.843-0.848 | 0.735 | 0.7914 | 0.7843 | 0.5077 | 0.4225 | 0.83 |
| Energy Density of Liquid (MJ/litre) | 38.16 | 32.1 | 18.9 | 23.32 | 25.6 | 23.46 | 32.43-33.11 |
| Normal Boiling Point °C | 140-360 | 37-205 | 65 | 79 | -42.15 | -161.6 | |
| Research Octane No. | -25 | 91-97 | 112 | 111 | 125 | 130 | |
| Cetane No. | 45-55 | 0-5 | 5 | 5 | -2 | 0 | 45-59 |

Source: OECD (1995)
Notes: hhv signifies higher heating value
Biodiesel is made of rapeseed methylester
Energy density of gas at standard temperature and pressure, 0.036 MJ/litre

Analysis indicates that, while benefits can be achieved by alternative fuels, a large number of important and sometimes costly tradeoffs must be considered prior to fuel changes. These include:

- extraction, refining, environmental impacts and costs;
- distribution complexity, evaporative emissions and leaks; and
- emissions, energy efficiency, safety and relative costs of changing fuel usage in vehicles.

(i) Improved gasoline and diesel fuel

Gasoline and diesel fuels are complex mixtures of several hundred types of hydrocarbons. Conventional, oxygenated and reformulated gasolines and diesel fuels have most of the same component hydrocarbons, but differ in the relative quantities of the various hydrocarbons and oxygenates they contain. Chemical reformulation provides a means to decrease ozone-forming pollutants and carbon monoxide vehicle emissions per kilometre. Improvements in gasoline and diesel chemical characteristics have the most impact on non-catalyst controlled vehicles. These improvements would be substantially less for catalyst-controlled vehicles, and no decrease in energy consumption (and thus $CO_2$ emission) has been documented.

Performance criteria that conventional, oxygenated and reformulated gasolines must address include driving range, cold-start ability, smooth running after warm-up and avoidance of vapour lock. The fuel should also prevent spark plug fouling, filter plugging and excessive engine wear. While performance criteria are being met, evaporative and exhaust emission requirements cannot be exceeded. Gasoline volatility is characterised by the Reid vapour pressure (RVP) index and the distillation range is measured by per cent of gasoline evaporated over the full gasoline boiling temperature range. These parameters are adjusted seasonally and geographically to meet different performance criteria and regulatory requirements.

(ii) Natural gas and petroleum gas

Using natural gas and petroleum gas directly as an automotive fuel can decrease emissions further since they are cleaner than gasoline and diesel and do not have the disadvantage of chemical-reforming costs. Natural gas can be used as a motor vehicle fuel either compressed in cylinders as compressed natural gas (CNG) or as liquefied natural gas (LNG). In practice, LNG is rarely considered, since it is more expensive and more difficult to handle than CNG.

Liquefied petroleum gas (LPG) is a by-product of refining and natural gas processing, and consists mainly of butane and propane. As this fuel represents only a small proportion of oil and gas production, its potential as an alternative fuel appears to be limited in the longer term, but it offers some advantages over natural gas (such as higher energy density, easier transport). LPG vehicles are most suitable in centralised fleets where refuelling is most convenient. For decentralised fleets, new refuelling infrastructures have to be put in place to support a transition to dedicated LPG vehicles.

Natural gas is a relatively well-tested alternative fuel: around half a million vehicles currently use CNG in IEA countries. In Italy, the Netherlands, Canada, New Zealand and the United States, CNG fleets and private car conversions have been introduced and markets have been developed in limited-range target populations. Because of costs and market risks, no lightweight natural gas vehicle has yet been commercially developed. This situation could change in North America where new CNG vehicles are likely to be manufactured in response to environmental and energy security requirements.

CNG vehicles emit much less carbon monoxide (CO) than gasoline or methanol vehicles, because CNG mixes better with air than do liquid fuels and it requires less enrichment for engine start-up, but the extent of the reduction in pollutants will depend upon the emission control system. Natural gas vehicles (NGVs) will emit similar or possibly higher levels of nitrogen oxides than gasoline or methanol vehicles. Because natural gas is mostly methane, NGVs will emit fewer non-methane hydrocarbons than gasoline and methanol vehicles. NGVs will emit essentially no unregulated pollutants (e.g., benzene), smoke or sulphur oxides, and slightly less formaldehyde than gasoline vehicles, and their use would be expected to lower ozone levels in comparison with use of gasoline vehicles. Greenhouse gas emissions from CNG could be a potential problem if fuel-cycle methane emissions are significant.

(iii) Alcohol fuels (in an ICE)

Alcohol-based fuels (oxygenated fuels), typically methanol and ethanol, are available alternatives to gasoline and diesel. Brazil, the United States and Canada are among countries that have commercially introduced ethanol in blends with gasoline (such as gasohol) on a large scale, using existing retail systems and with minor vehicle modifications. Comparable results are achievable through alcohol-containing compounds. Examples of these compounds are methyl-tertiary-butyl ether (MTBE) and ethyl-tertiary-butyl ether (ETBE). Biodiesel or vegetable oils have been promoted as possible diesel fuel substitutes due to their good ignition quality. But their high viscosity, which results in poor fuel atomisation, fuel injector blockage and contamination of lubricating oil, makes them best used as blends with diesel fuels in mixes of up to 50 per cent. Vegetable oil esters, as reaction products of vegetable oils and alcohol, offer greater potential, since they have lower viscosities and higher cetane numbers. Flexible-fuelled vehicles are generally considered transition vehicles, until the supply of alternative fuels is sufficient for dedicated-fuelled vehicles. Change to neat (100 per cent) ethanol or methanol will require investments by fuel producers, automotive manufacturers and consumers.

Methanol can be produced from natural gas, coal (see Chapters 2 and 4), crude oil, biomass or organic waste (Chapter 7). Ethanol is similar to methanol, but is less toxic and less corrosive. Ethanol, or grain alcohol, can be produced by processing agricultural crops such as sugar cane or corn. However, it is more expensive to produce and requires large harvests of these crops and large amounts of energy for its production, which leads to other environmental problems, in particular soil degradation.

IEA investigations of emissions and system energy impacts of methanol and ethanol indicate that a significant decrease in greenhouse gas emissions would occur with a straight substitution of methanol for gasoline in a standard car, even with natural gas as the feedstock. The decrease would be even larger if hydrogen produced in either nuclear or solar photovoltaic systems were used. Conversely, coal use as the feedstock would increase $CO_2$ emissions, although production efficiencies (and costs) could be further improved. Production of alcohol fuels from biomass has the demonstrated potential to significantly reduce $CO_2$ emissions, but production efficiencies and costs must be further improved. Also, the importance of ethanol for improving air quality has been reassessed since it was found that ethanol blended with gasoline actually increases evaporative losses from the fuel and is thus responsible for a greater contribution to the formation of photochemical smog. $NO_X$ emissions are also somewhat higher than for methanol, but still considerably lower than for conventional gasoline and diesel engines. On the other hand, as with methanol engines, particulate emissions are very low. One area of possible concern with ethanol and methanol vehicles could be the emission of formaldehyde, a first oxidation product of alcohol fuels. Very high emissions of formaldehyde could result in harmful local effects.

(iv) Hydrogen (in an ICE)

Hydrogen is considered by many analysts to be the fuel option for the long term with the lowest emissions. Apart from $NO_X$ emissions, hydrogen combustion is virtually non-polluting. The main combustion product is water vapour. Hydrogen vehicles do not produce significant amounts of CO or hydrocarbons (only small amounts from the combustion of lubricating oil), particulates or other greenhouse gases. Properly functioning, advanced ultra lean-burn hydrogen engines will produce nominal amounts of $NO_X$, but little else. The use of hydrogen would provide significant reductions in transportation-related ozone and CO. If hydrogen were used in a fuel cell, system efficiency of energy conversion could surpass

60 per cent and emissions would be virtually eliminated. Development time for a large-scale demonstration of hydrogen-fuelled vehicles is at least 20 years, with another decade for commercialisation, assuming fuel and vehicle economics and regulations support hydrogen use.

Key issues remain regarding the production path best suited for hydrogen, its distribution and storage. Production and distribution could be essentially pollution-free if hydrogen were made from water, using a clean, renewable power source. If hydrogen were produced from fossil fuel feedstocks, on the other hand, significant emissions would result. The distribution of hydrogen may be the other major barrier to its widespread use. The cost of cryogenic transport of the fuel to retail fuelling stations, as well as storage costs (infrastructure, refrigeration costs), could be relatively high. On-board storage of hydrogen also poses even more of a technical barrier than for other gaseous fuels due to hydrogen's relatively low energy density. Alternatives, such as using a hydrogen carrier, which is a more conveniently handled liquid (methanol or ammonia) and which could be dissociated from gaseous hydrogen on board the vehicle, have been tested and show technical potential.

c) *Energy Regeneration*

Between 30 and 50 per cent (depending on duty cycle) of all automotive energy accelerates the vehicle to the desired speed; most of this is subsequently dissipated in braking the vehicle. Regeneration of this energy could significantly improve fuel efficiency and emissions. Energy and emissions benefits from regeneration can be quite significant, as the acceleration portion of the driving cycle power can be supplied by zero-emissions energy, i.e., by stored potential or kinetic energy. Stop-start systems conserve fuel, shutting off the engine during long idles, and can result in significant energy savings, particularly in heavy traffic. In transit bus applications, systems have achieved 25 to 35 per cent fuel consumption reductions, with similar reductions in HC, CO, and $CO_2$, and 60 to 70 per cent reductions in particulate emissions from diesel engines. In automotive applications, fuel and emission benefits will probably be lower, in the 20 to 30 per cent range, because of the high average speeds of the vehicle mission profile.

A principal hurdle to regeneration is in the conversion of the energy, without excessive losses, into and out of the energy storage media. Increased availability of high-efficiency hydraulic pumps and motors, mechanical continuously variable transmissions and high torque electric motors improve the economics of regeneration. It is also possible to store this retrieved energy within electrical systems, using either capacitive or battery storage.

d) *Electric and Hybrid Vehicles*

The main attraction of electric vehicles (EVs) is zero emissions from the vehicle, and consequently the promise of improved urban air quality. Using electricity to power vehicles allows greater flexibility in the source of prime energy supply. If renewable energy sources like solar, wind or hydroelectric power are used to generate the electricity, then EVs will essentially be non-polluting. Use of nuclear power may entail other environmental problems. Generally, the effect of EV use on pollutant emissions will be country-specific, depending largely on the fuel mix used for power generation. Use of coal-fired plants would generally cause the highest levels of pollution.

Present technologies for on-board storage or generation of electrical energy rely upon batteries. Fuel cells and solar cells have been tested as technology options for the long term. The cost and limited energy density of storage media restrict the useful range and consumer attractiveness of electric vehicles. Significant efforts in R&D have been undertaken to improve energy density, durability and unit costs of electric batteries.

Recent studies indicate niche markets where electric vehicles are closing the gap (on a life-cycle cost basis) in competition with gasoline or diesel vehicles in range-limited applications. In the United States both Chrysler Corporation and General Motors Corporation have announced new electric vehicles. The GM EV-1 is a sporty two-seat passenger car developed specifically as an electric vehicle. The majority of current R&D on electric drives centres on energy storage in electrochemical form. The principal objectives in developing storage technology are to reduce system cost, increase battery and fuel cell life, increase power densities, and to reduce weight of battery containment and control systems. New infrastructural requirements to provide recharging and servicing of electric vehicles are also important. Recharging needs, for non-fleet vehicles in particular, have yet to be adequately addressed.

Electric vehicles will be recharged primarily during off-peak hours, thereby providing new revenues to utilities, without significant demand for new generating capacity. Additional revenues accruing from increased use of electric vehicles should lower long-term average electricity rates. Regeneration technology coupled with electric battery storage can transform the vehicle drive-train into a hybrid drive concept in which there is more than one power source. Typically, hybrid drives have two sources, one to provide or recover transient power (acceleration and deceleration) and the other which operates at a near steady power level. Hybrid drives can also be designed to operate in series, rather than in parallel, and can be used, in this mode, to increase range assurance. Major improvements in system thermal efficiencies have been demonstrated with hybrid drives. Current market impediments to high efficiency hybrid drives are cost and, in some cases, system weight and size.

e) *Vehicle Improvements*

Computer-optimised control of the engine and transmission coupling with current automatic transmissions may prove to be a more practical way to achieve similar objectives. Lighter materials, improved aerodynamics, and tyres with lower rolling resistance, as well as a multitude of specific design innovations, may be important in improving vehicle mileage.

(i) Drag and rolling resistance reduction

A major technological approach is to minimise the energy required to move vehicles. At speeds over approximately 40 kilometres per hour, the largest power demand from the engine is to overcome aerodynamic drag. According to estimates, a 10 per cent reduction in the drag coefficient results in a reduction in fuel consumption that ranges from about 2.5 per cent for city driving to 7 per cent at 140 kilometres per hour. Aerodynamic styling leading to a reduction in air friction is a focus for manufacturers' R&D. Significant gains have been achieved in the last decade but further reductions may provide smaller economic advantages. For lower rolling resistance and higher fuel efficiency, tyres need to be narrow and inflated to high pressure, but this tends to make them noisier. During the

1980s, tyres tended to become wider, but advances in car technology, such as four-wheel drive and steering, as well as active suspension systems, should make it possible to reduce their width.

(ii) Structural weight

Since fuel consumption is strongly related to overall vehicle mass, reducing vehicle weight can yield perhaps the most significant improvements in energy efficiency. Estimates show a 5 to 6 per cent reduction in fuel consumption for every 10 per cent reduction in weight. Decreasing vehicle weight can be achieved through size reduction, material substitution or component redesign. Increases in the structural efficiency are essential for high-efficiency vehicles. Changes in the types of material used in vehicles will continue as they have over the last decade. The potential for further improvements is large but so are the industrial impediments. The entire drive-cycle can be affected by weight-conscious vehicle designs which maximise interior space, load/power relationships and structural integrity while minimising use of materials, or by substituting plastics, aluminium or other lightweight metals for heavier conventional structural elements. The principal barriers to producing lighter bodies are product costs and availability of material that physically performs as well or better than current materials (crush strength, paint finish quality), manufacturing problems of some materials (forming and curing times, assembly time) and bonding processes, and the possible recyclability or disposal of materials.

The weight and size of the main powertrain is important in determining overall vehicle weight. Thus, research in such areas as lightweight two-stroke engines, or adiabatic engines (weight reduction because little or no cooling is needed), has a potential multiplier effect, since nearly an equal amount of body weight can be removed for each kilogram of engine weight reduction.

(iii) Transmission

Advanced transmission designs are already playing an important role in increasing vehicle efficiency. Advanced clutch designs and increases in the number of gears and ratio range can minimise the pumping and frictional energy losses associated with automatic transmissions. With intermittently variable transmissions (IVT), engines should operate most efficiently only with small ranges of combined speeds and powers, and maximum efficiency is attained only when the engine runs slowly under high loads. Part-load performance can be improved by selecting appropriate gearing to increase the load for the performance required. Electronic controlling transmission shift points and lock-up range can help optimise transmission efficiency by adjusting gear ratios according to instantaneously detected, rather than average, driving conditions. The fuel-saving capabilities of manual transmissions, which have the potential to be very efficient, if used correctly, can also be heightened by using electronics that indicate ideal shift points in response to real driving conditions. The most promising innovation in transmission technology is offered by the continuously variable transmission (CVT) which enables the engine to be matched more closely to vehicle load. These systems are estimated to provide up to a 20 per cent improvement in consumption compared with a four-speed gearbox when fitted to a conventional gasoline-fuelled car.

(iv) Accessories

Due to the many inter-related design and operating variables, engine control systems have become increasingly important. Modifications in one variable must be co-ordinated with all others to achieve optimum performance. Controls that can precisely adjust the various operating variables to driving conditions can help reduce vehicle maintenance and improve vehicle durability when compared to traditional mechanical systems. Design of engine management systems has reached a high level of sophistication and complexity, but full implementation of this type of equipment is dependent on the development of reliable communications networks and improved sensors. The motor industry generally views this technology as essential for meeting emission standards while maintaining driving comfort and low fuel consumption. A further attraction is that microprocessor-based electronic systems can be used for sophisticated control functions in the vehicle and this has customer appeal, particularly in the high-performance and luxury parts of the market.

f) *Transport Productivity*

Changing the energy intensity of transportation can decrease fuel consumption and atmospheric emissions more quickly than changes in vehicle technology, because measures affect the whole vehicle population. Measures include improving the useful work ratio or load factor (by inducing shifts to more efficient transport modes, by shifting time of peak travel demand, by reducing travel demand) and improving roadways, roadway construction and maintenance.

The potential for reducing transportation demand by such measures is great, and reductions of up to 40 per cent have been documented between different urban forms. However, substantial savings generally require substantial lead-times to implement and call for local government action and the co-operation of individual users. The effectiveness of the above measures can be significantly enhanced by using available technology. For example, future growth in demand for road transport may be moderated by application of electronics and telecommunications to allow variable road use charges. Options include varying charges by time of day and/or vehicle type, through the use of active or smart license plates and electronic sensing. The most significant measures in use today are described below.

(i) Traffic control

These measures attempt to increase vehicle load factors (passenger kilometres per seat kilometre). Incentives include carpool matching and information programmes, vanpool and commuter bus programmes, dial-a-ride or shuttle and jitney services. Other measures act to facilitate the use of more efficient transport systems. Incentives proposed include transit fare reductions and service improvements, such as extending coverage, reducing headways, improving travel time and reliability of on-time service, co-ordinating transfers, and construction of park-and-ride facilities. Disincentives usually fall on the private automobile in the form of increased parking charges and surcharges on motor fuel. Transport telematics offers significant energy efficiency potential to improve traffic flow and promote modal shifts. For example, public transport passenger information systems can encourage modal shifts by increasing the attractiveness of public transport.

(ii) Travel substitution

With advances in communications, trip substitution may offer the greatest potential for significant reduction without any perception of interference or restraint on the part of the user. While not commonly considered an inherent element of transportation technology development, telecommuting or trip substitution, for both work and shopping, merits evaluation, with new technology options providing increasingly interesting and economically competitive alternatives to travel in a growing number of situations. International collaborative action could support growing worldwide interest in this area. At present, and in the short term, telecommuting is an attractive alternative for workers in the information and service sectors who can work via computers. Research and development on faster, easier-to-use networks and software could make telecommuting more widespread. Telecommuting not only saves fuel but also reduces congestion. In addition, changes in modal split (e.g. public transportation) could be encouraged.

(iii) Route planning

These measures work to decrease fuel use and transportation emissions per seat kilometre for all modes by spreading congested peak traffic loads over a broader time-frame to improve use patterns of existing transportation capacity, thereby improving vehicle operating efficiency. Included among these policies are freeway ramp metering programmes, four-day work weeks, staggered work hours, and general traffic circulation improvements such as synchronised signals. Intelligent vehicle-highway systems incorporate advanced communication and computer technologies, electronic displays and warning devices, as well as vehicle and traffic-control systems, to allow two-way communication between the road system and the vehicle. In concert with urban transportation policies, such systems could significantly increase transportation efficiency. In the long term, an advanced intelligent vehicle-highway system could incorporate automated vehicle control systems that would also provide power to vehicles. Advanced logistics for road freight transport can help improve load factors and improve transport efficiency.

### *Assessment of Technical and Economic Potential*

IEA and OECD analysis shows that it would be technically possible, by reducing car size and performance, to reduce the energy consumption of gasoline cars, and hence greenhouse gas emissions, by a factor of three. However, the resulting vehicles would not achieve much market share under current market conditions. Estimates of technical and economic potential of new and improved transport technology and fuels are presented in Tables 9.4 and 9.5 respectively.

Alternative fuels can provide IEA countries with opportunities for increasing energy security and reducing pollutant emissions. In particular, greenhouse gas emissions from cars could be reduced by amounts ranging from 20 per cent for CNG vehicles to 80 per cent for methanol vehicles, or even more for hydrogen vehicles. Electric vehicles operating on power generated from renewable sources or nuclear energy could represent an attractive solution since their comparative contribution to atmospheric pollution and greenhouse gas production is potentially negligible. All these alternative options are relatively expensive and are likely to require compromises in vehicle performance and range. They are therefore unlikely to be put to use on any significant scale without intervention in the market. The alternative to market intervention is further technology progress to reduce costs and improve the performance of all these new options.

In relation to next-generation ICE vehicles, there is scope for higher fuel efficiency in passenger and goods road transport without sacrifice of vehicle operating efficiency. An enhanced R&D effort is expected to accelerate the development of new, efficient, fuel-diverse automobile technologies. With regard to alternative fuels, more basic R&D on optimised engines and fuel storage systems is needed. Engine tests should be performed to provide a coherent basis for evaluating emissions, power, efficiency and cost. To date, no vehicle engine has been optimised in all respects for hydrogen, natural gas or even methanol. In view of the expected transition period, light-duty automotive industry research is now devoted to multi-fuel alcohol-gasoline engines, not optimised engines. Engines optimised to meet various performance and emission parameters, for given engine costs, should be developed and tested for each fuel type.

Consumer reactions to large batteries and fuel storage tanks, longer refuelling times, reduced vehicle range, and cryogenic boil-off should be studied carefully. These are important aspects of the attractiveness of hydrogen, electric and fuel-cell vehicles, and to a lesser extent natural gas of alcohol vehicles. To respond to pressing needs, more R&D should address the cost and high density storage performance of adsorbents for natural gas, further development of reliable, cost-effective control of gases boiled off from cryogenic fuels improvements in the mass energy density, and desorption temperatures of metal hydrides. Cold-start problems of engines fuelled by pure alcohol should also be addressed.

Natural gas vehicles are most suitable for areas with potential pipeline access, abundant natural gas supplies and where vehicle users are willing to accept some limitations in driving range and/or performance. As dual-fuel natural gas vehicles involve design compromises, this would entail a willingness to put new refuelling infrastructure quickly in place to support a rapid transition to dedicated vehicles.

Methanol would be obtained from natural gas, but in view of the importance of coal energy security in some IEA countries, development of clean processes for converting coal into liquid and gaseous fuels should continue to be monitored, with particular attention to emissions in the production cycle. In addition, more effort should be devoted to improving thermochemical and hydrolysis processes for converting cellulosic biomass into alcohol fuel. Biomass-based transportation fuels will probably cost about the same as, or perhaps less than, coal-based fuels, they would produce less greenhouse gases, and would be permanently available if sustainably managed. Special emphasis should be placed upon impacts on soils and their long-term protection.

Electric vehicles would be most suitable for areas with significant urban air quality problems, where coal is a minor part of the electricity resource mix, and where some vehicle users (commuters and fleets) are willing to accept cost, driving-range or performance penalties. The net benefits are very dependent on base energy sources. The key target areas for technological improvement in EVs are the life and recharging time of batteries, reductions in the cost and size of high-power fuel cells, vehicle controls and drives.

*Table 9.4*

**Comparative Technical Potential of New and Improved Transport Technology and Fuels**

| Technology | Conversion Efficiency | Environmental Impact | Acceptance Issues |
|---|---|---|---|
| **a) ICE Control** | | | |
| (i) Improved Exhaust Treatment | • <5% gain | • Up to 97% control for HC and CO<br>• Up to 85% control for $NO_X$<br>• Up to 85% control for particulates | • Requires higher grade fuels<br>• Catalyst disposal and recycling |
| (ii) Improved Combustion | • <10% gain | • $NO_X$, particulates and $CO_2$ reduction | • Engine manufacturing cost<br>• In-use durability and maintenance |
| (iii) Fast Warm-up | • <5% gain | • <10% average reduction<br>• <30% reduction in first 60-120 seconds | • Most effect on urban vehicles |
| **b) Fuel Substitution** | | | |
| (i) Improved Gasoline and Diesel Fuel | • Increased refinery energy consumption<br>• Minor vehicle efficiency gain | • Significant VOC reduction<br>• Limitations on fuel additives | • Introduction of improved fuel can immediately affect all vehicles<br>• Differentiated fuel pricing, favouring clean fuels |
| (ii) Natural Gas and LPG | • Nil | • VOC, $CO_2$ and particulate reduction | • Supply security improved<br>• Diversity of fuel supply |
| (iii) Alcohol Fuels (in an ICE) | • <15% gain<br>• Efficiency increase to be gauged against overall fuel cycle | • VOC and $CO_2$ reductions | • Supply security improved<br>• Biomass feedstocks availability |
| (iv) Hydrogen (in an ICE) | • Dependent on feedstock | • Substantial reductions in all pollutants | • Progress required in technology and economics of hydrogen sources<br>• Unlikely to have infrastructure and vehicles in place before 30 years<br>• New fuel storage and transmission systems needed |
| **c) Energy Regeneration** | • 25-30% gain | • Reduction of all emissions in proportion to efficiency gain | • Reduced noise<br>• Increased range |

Note: Fuel conversion efficiency improvement relative to similar conventional vehicle.

*Table 9.4 (continued)*

**Comparative Technical Potential of New and Improved Transport Technology and Fuels**

| Technology | Conversion Efficiency | Environmental Impact | Acceptance Issues |
|---|---|---|---|
| **d) Electric and Hybrid Vehicles** | • Power source and powertrain dependent | • Reduction to zero of all vehicle emissions<br>• Environmental benefit to be gauged against overall fuel cycle | • Allows electrical utility load levelling<br>• Possible integration of braking regeneration<br>• Battery recycling and disposal required<br>• Noise reduction<br>• Vehicle range |
| **e) Vehicle Improvements** | | | |
| (i) Drag and Rolling Resistance Reduction | • <5% gain | • Reduction of all emissions in proportion to efficiency gains | • Increased vehicle performance for smaller engines<br>• Handling and safety impacts |
| (ii) Structural Weight | • <10% gain | • Reduction of all emissions in proportion to efficiency gains<br>• Greater effect on acceleration emissions (urban traffic) as vehicle inertia is diminished | • Increased vehicle performance for smaller engines<br>• Decreased total material usage per vehicle<br>• Vehicle safety impacts |
| (iii) Transmission | • <15% gain | • Reduction of all emissions in proportion to efficiency gains<br>• Engine operation optimised, decreasing emissions even more than efficiency improvement | • Regeneration systems as a possible option |
| (iv) Accessories | • <5% gain | • Emissions reduction facilitated by on-board electronic controls and sensors | • Reduced maintenance and improved durability compared with mechanical controls |
| **f) Transport Productivity** | | | |
| (i) Traffic Control | • 5-10% gain | • Major pollutant reduction (30-50%) at local sites<br>• Reduction of emissions in proportion to efficiency gains | • Safety improvement<br>• Lower operating costs<br>• Decreased land requirements for rights-of-way |

Note: Fuel conversion efficiency improvement relative to similar conventional vehicle.

*Table 9.4 (continued)*

**Comparative Technical Potential of New and Improved Transport Technology and Fuels**

| Technology | Conversion Efficiency | Environmental Impact | Acceptance Issues |
|---|---|---|---|
| **f) Transport Productivity** *(continued)* | | | |
| (ii) Travel Substitution | • 20-30% gain | • Reduction of emissions and change of emission sources<br>• Reduction potential is approximately the same as fuel reductions | • Decreased land requirements for rights-of-way |
| (iii) Route Planning | • 5-10% gain | • Reduction of emissions and change of emission sources<br>• Reduction potential is approximately the same as energy reductions | • Direct restrictions on vehicle use<br>• Parking control measures<br>• Changing modal split between private and public transport |

Note: Fuel conversion efficiency improvement relative to similar conventional vehicle.

*Table 9.5*

**Comparative Economic Potential of New and Improved Transport Technology and Fuels**

(Changes in Cost Relative to Conventional Gasoline-fuelled Road Vehicles)

| Technology | Change in Road Transport Cost Per Passenger | | | Change in Road Transport Cost Per Freight Unit | | |
|---|---|---|---|---|---|---|
| | **Capital cost** (Vehicle) | **Operating cost** (Fuel, Maintenance) | **Total cost** | **Capital cost** (Vehicle) | **Operating cost** (Maintenance, etc.) | **Total cost** |
| **a) ICE Control** | | | | | | |
| (i) Improved Exhaust Treatment | <5% | nil to minor | <3% higher | <5% | nil to minor | <3% higher |
| (ii) Improved Combustion | <5% | <10% lower | slightly lower | <3% higher | <10% lower | slightly lower |
| (iii) Fast Warm-up | <1% higher | <5% lower | <5% lower | <1% higher | <3% lower | <3% lower |

Note: n.a. signifies not available or not applicable.

*Table 9.5 (continued)*

**Comparative Economic Potential of New and Improved Transport Technology and Fuels**

(Changes in Cost Relative to Conventional Gasoline-fuelled Road Vehicles)

| Technology | Change in Road Transport Cost Per Passenger | | | Change in Road Transport Cost Per Freight Unit | | |
|---|---|---|---|---|---|---|
| | **Capital cost** (Vehicle) | **Operating cost** (Fuel, Maintenance) | **Total cost** | **Capital cost** (Vehicle) | **Operating cost** (Maintenance, etc.) | **Total cost** |
| **b) Fuel Substitution** | | | | | | |
| (i) Improved Gasoline and Diesel fuel | minimal | <1% higher | <1% higher | minimal | <1% higher | <1% higher |
| (ii) Natural Gas and LPG | 10-15% higher | 15-25% lower (untaxed and with low pressure system) | 15% lower | 10-15% higher | 10-15% lower (untaxed and with low pressure system) | 10% lower |
| (iii) Alcohol Fuels (in an ICE) | <5% higher | methanol equal to ethanol >20% higher | methanol equal to ethanol >20% higher | <1% higher | methanol <10% higher ethanol >20% higher | <10% higher with methanol >20% higher with ethanol |
| (iv) Hydrogen (in an ICE) | n.a. | n.a. | n.a. | n.a. | n.a. | n.a. |
| **c) Energy Regeneration** | 10-15% higher | 10-15% lower | 5-10% lower | 10% higher | 10-15% lower | 5-10% lower |
| **d) Electric and Hybrid Vehicles** | 20-40% higher | <20% higher (location dependent) | >20-30% higher (location dependent) | n.a. | n.a. | n.a. |
| **e) Vehicle Improvements** | | | | | | |
| (i) Drag and Rolling Resistance Reduction | 5-10% higher | <5% lower | <3-5% lower | <5% higher | <5% lower | <3-5% lower |
| (ii) Structural Weight | <10-20% higher | <10-20% lower | <10-15% lower | <10% higher | <10% lower | <10% lower |

Note: n.a. signifies not available or not applicable.

*Table 9.5 (continued)*

**Comparative Economic Potential of New and Improved Transport Technology and Fuels**

(Changes in Cost Relative to Conventional Gasoline-fuelled Road Vehicles)

| Technology | Change in Road Transport Cost Per Passenger | | | Change in Road Transport Cost Per Freight Unit | | |
|---|---|---|---|---|---|---|
| | **Capital cost** (Vehicle) | **Operating cost** (Fuel, Maintenance) | **Total cost** | **Capital cost** (Vehicle) | **Operating cost** (Maintenance, etc.) | **Total cost** |
| **e) Vehicle Improvements** *(continued)* | | | | | | |
| (iii) Transmissions | <5% higher | 10-15% lower | 10-15% lower | <3% higher | <10% lower | <5-10% lower |
| (iv) Accessories | <3% higher | <5% lower | <5% lower | <1% higher | <5% lower | <5% lower |
| **f) Transport Productivity** | | | | | | |
| (i) Traffic Control | <10% higher | <5% lower | <5% lower | n.a. | n.a. | n.a. |
| (ii) Travel Substitution | n.a. | n.a. | n.a. | n.a. | n.a. | n.a. |
| (iii) Route Planning | <10% higher | <5% lower | <5% lower | <5-10% higher | <5% lower | <5% lower |

Note: n.a. signifies not available or not applicable.

Based on this analysis, R&D needs and opportunities for new and improved transport technologies and fuels are shown in Table 9.6.

## Technology Prospects and Markets

### *Market Trends*

The eventual market penetration of new technology depends on the rate at which older vehicles are scrapped, but the speed of the major car manufacturers in identifying a market need and reacting to it is also crucial. The adoption of both more efficient transport technologies and alternative fuels can be encouraged either by regulation or by raising the price of conventional fuels. Alternative fuels are already being encouraged by lower levels of tax on them than on conventional fuels. The transport market is sensitive to relative fuel prices and relatively insensitive to absolute fuel prices. Individual perceptions of the utility of transportation services range from very important to essential, and thus only major price shifts result in significant changes in vehicle ownership and demand. Vehicles with the lowest fuel consumption are often the least expensive, because these vehicles are equipped with very low-power engines. This inevitably leads to difficulties in selling such low-performance vehicles to a public more concerned with car image and performance than with economy.

The introduction and penetration of alternative fuels must initially be cost-competitive with local low-cost fuel (gasoline); and supplies must be available and sufficient to assure a follow-on market for the vehicle after the first owner. For this reason, alternative fuels should be introduced in the marginal niche market first and then expanded as market forces allow.

Time-series and cross-sector studies of vehicle populations reveal that product life-cycles are lengthening, due to improved designs and materials and better maintenance. So, despite industry progress in product development and a shortened design and building production cycle of five to ten years, rapid change in fleet technical performance is unlikely. Clearly, vehicle performance will change as quickly as new vehicles penetrate the market. Since the average life of existing vehicles in most geographical areas is approaching ten years, cutting the basic technical energy intensity of the vehicle fleet by half will take up to 20 years after the new technology vehicle model is introduced (assuming the average new vehicle has 50 per cent lower energy intensity).

Faster change can occur with shifts in vehicle size, fleet-wide retrofit, ownership and other use factors. Also, there are incremental technological innovations that are simple and relatively cheap, and will require about five years on average to achieve a similar level of penetration (as shown, for instance, by the introduction of the five-speed gearbox as a standard item for new cars).

Due to the high cost of developing consumer-ready automotive products, industry requires long-term indications of market conditions to make investment decisions. However, compared with the lifetime of buildings, industrial plants and equipment, the life cycle of an automobile is relatively short, so decisions to increase the efficiency of the stock take a shorter time to realise fully than in other economic sectors. An example is offered by EVs. Since several major world manufacturers are developing EVs for large-scale commercial deployment within a decade, there is enough certainty within current market forecasts for continued innovation.

The comparative market potential of selected new and improved transport technologies and fuels is summarised in Table 9.7.

### *Key Players*

The automotive manufacturing industry is a major actor in all IEA countries and the possible effects of changes to the marketplace must be carefully assessed. The original equipment manufacturers (OEMs), who provide the original design and materials for assembly and manufacture of their product, are primarily concerned with maintaining market shares. OEMs are directly responsible for manufacturing and modifying vehicles, making the vehicles commercially available and providing a warranty for the finished product.

*Table 9.6*

**New and Improved Transport Technologies and Fuels: R&D Needs and Opportunities**

| Technology | Bottlenecks | Spillovers | R&D Requirements |
|---|---|---|---|
| **a) ICE Control** | | | |
| (i) Improved Exhaust Treatment | • Catalyst durability<br>• Exhaust flow control<br>• Contamination<br>• Sensor accuracy | • Industrial control systems<br>• Electronic sensors<br>• Vehicle driveability | • Catalyst technology<br>• Accurate/inexpensive sensors |
| (ii) Improved Combustion | • Ignition chemistry and physics<br>• High-temperature materials | • Stationary source applications<br>• Advanced process control technology | • Better characterisation of ignition processes<br>• Variable ignition and injection |
| (iii) Fast Warm-up | • System costs<br>• Manufacturing tolerances | • Vehicle driveability | • Thin wall engine designs<br>• Segmented fluids systems<br>• Control systems |
| **b) Fuel Substitution** | | | |
| (i) Improved Gasoline and Diesel Fuel | • Market competition<br>• Increased refining costs and refining processes | • Reduced vehicle maintenance costs<br>• Fuel quality standards | • Basic combustion research<br>• Air pollutant reactivity |
| (ii) Natural Gas and LPG | • Pressure vessel storage<br>• Safety system | • Non-seasonal NG market<br>• Lower-cost fuel in OEM designed vehicles | • High storage efficiency tanks in OEM vehicles<br>• Fast/low pressure refuelling<br>• Low-cost home refuelling |
| (iii) Alcohol Fuels (in an ICE) | • OEM designed vehicles<br>• Engine durability/ lubrication<br>• Biomass conversion technology<br>• Aldehyde control<br>• Fuel costs | • Biomass industry<br>• Use of remote NG resources | • OEM vehicles<br>• Low-cost biomass production<br>• Specifications for fuels and lubricants |
| (iv) Hydrogen (in an ICE) | • $H_2$ production costs<br>• Fuel handling and cryogenics<br>• Fuel safety | • Energy security<br>• Material embrittlement<br>• On-board storage systems | • Low-cost $H_2$ production<br>• $H_2$ distribution systems |
| **c) Energy Regeneration** | • Cost and reliability, continuously variable transmission efficiency<br>• Weight and space requirements<br>• System controls | • Drive-by-wire powertrain<br>• Flexibility of prime mover | • Development and demonstration<br>• Use in sensitive areas<br>• Large-volume production designs<br>• Storage component suppliers |

*Table 9.6 (continued)*

**New and Improved Transport Technologies and Fuels: R&D Needs and Opportunities**

| Technology | Bottlenecks | Spillovers | R&D Requirements |
|---|---|---|---|
| **d) Electric and Hybrid Vehicles** | • Vehicle range limitations<br>• Cost and availability of charging systems and infrastructure<br>• Battery efficiency and cost | • Electrical load levelling<br>• Reduced vehicle complexity | • Battery performance increases (higher charging capability)<br>• Fuel cell development<br>• High power and high efficiency motors |
| **e) Vehicle Improvements** | | | |
| (i) Drag and Rolling Resistance Reduction | • Manufacturing tolerances<br>• High-volume part manufacturing<br>• Material formability and finish<br>• Low resistance tyres and bearings | • Improved modelling of fluid dynamics applicable in other design areas<br>• Material forming | • New tyre design and testing<br>• Aerodynamic drag research |
| (ii) Structural Weight | • Material bonding and testing<br>• Material formability and finish<br>• Safety demands | • New high-strength materials<br>• Faster manufacturing processes<br>• Non-mechanical bonding | • Production moulding process improvement<br>• Requirement for very light-weight vehicles<br>• Improved non-destructive testing |
| (iii) Transmission | • Power limitations of CVT<br>• Manufacturing costs<br>• Reliability and durability testing | • Hybrid powertrain possible<br>• Size and weight reduction | • CVT prototypes and performance upgrading<br>• New powertrains |
| (iv) Accessories | • Component system costs<br>• Coolant chemicals<br>• System complexity | • More compact accessories<br>• System size and weight reduction | • Integration of advanced electronics and communication technology into vehicle systems<br>• Sensor reliability and durability |
| **f) Transport Productivity** | | | |
| (i) Traffic Control | • Multi-jurisdictional control<br>• Infrastructure costs<br>• Communication systems development | • Interactive traffic control | • Prototype systems design and demonstration |

*Table 9.6 (continued)*

**New and Improved Transport Technologies and Fuels: R&D Needs and Opportunities**

| Technology | Bottlenecks | Spillovers | R&D Requirements |
|---|---|---|---|
| **f) Transport Productivity** *(continued)* | | | |
| (ii) Travel Substitution | • Multi-jurisdictional control<br>• Low-cost video and 3D communication<br>• Availability of alternative travel modes (frequency and capacity) | • Reduction in infrastructure requirements<br>• Supports information transfer as opposed to physical travel<br>• Mobile communication technology | • Introduction of integrated voice/data/video systems<br>• Low-cost video and 3D communication |
| (iii) Route Planning | • Availability of cost-effective communication system with interactive data capabilities<br>• Flexible working hours and remote work centres | • Mobile communication systems<br>• Real-time information on activities and traffic demand | • Affordable mobile positioning system |

*Table 9.7*

**Comparative Market Potential of New and Improved Transport Technologies and Fuels**

| Technology | Time-frame | Nature/ Size of the Market | Regional Aspects | Marketability |
|---|---|---|---|---|
| **a) ICE Control** | | | | |
| (i) Improved Exhaust Treatment | • 0-5 years | • New vehicles only | • Dependent on fuel quality<br>• Restricted source of catalyst metal | • Well-established technology, will be enhanced with further in-vehicle electronics<br>• Engine durability and competitive prices are prime issues |
| (ii) Improved Combustion | • 0-10 years | • New vehicles only | | • Good consumer demand |
| (iii) Fast Warm-up | • 0-10 years | • New vehicles only | • Urban vehicle<br>• Cold climates | • Mandated in some IEA countries |

*Table 9.7 (continued)*
**Comparative Market Potential of New and Improved Transport Technologies and Fuels**

| Technology | Time-frame | Nature/ Size of the Market | Regional Aspects | Marketability |
|---|---|---|---|---|
| **b) Fuel Substitution** | | | | |
| (i) Improved Gasoline and Diesel fuel | • 0-10 years | • All vehicles | • Can be implemented regionally | • Price sensitive<br>• Market supply can be regulated |
| (ii) Natural Gas and LPG | • 0-15 years | • New vehicles and fleets | • Fuel tax policies or pricing to provide cost pull<br>• NG supply and distribution<br>• Propane availability | • System complexity<br>• Range limitation |
| (iii) Alcohol Fuels (in an ICE) | • 0-20 years | • New vehicles and fleets | • Mandated installation of refuelling, distribution infrastructure<br>• High air pollution areas | • Tax differentiation favouring low $CO_2$ fuels<br>• OEM design changes needed<br>• Marketable emission credits |
| (iv) Hydrogen (in an ICE) | • 30 years | • New vehicles and fleets | • Hydrogen fuel supply | • Same as above<br>• Vehicle safety and performance |
| **c) Energy Regeneration** | • 10-20 years | • New vehicles only<br>• Niche markets | • Can be regionally implemented<br>• No change in infrastructure | • Cost principal hurdle<br>• Powertrain design and control systems |
| **d) Electric and Hybrid Vehicles** | • 10 years | • New vehicles and fleet fuel supply | • Power supply availability<br>• Areas with environmental concerns | • Range limitation<br>• Battery replacement costs<br>• Low noise benefit |
| **e) Vehicle Improvements** | | | | |
| (i) Drag and Rolling Resistance Reduction | • 0-10 years | • New vehicles only | • Regional implementation likely | • Cost sensitive<br>• Linked to styling |
| (ii) Structural Weight | • 0-10 years | • New vehicles only | • High-value vehicle markets | • Safety issues<br>• Durability issues<br>• Cost barriers |

*Table 9.7 (contined)*

**Comparative Market Potential of New and Improved Transport Technologies and Fuels**

| Technology | Time-frame | Nature/ Size of the Market | Regional Aspects | Marketability |
|---|---|---|---|---|
| **e) Vehicle Improvements** *(continued)* | | | | |
| (iii) Transmission | • 0-10 years | • New vehicles only | • Regional implementation likely | • Cost barriers<br>• Market share in manual transmissions<br>• Integration of powertrain |
| (iv) Accessories | • 0-10 years | • New vehicles only | • Regional implementation likely | • Integration with powertrain design |
| **f) Transport Productivity** | | | | |
| (i) Traffic Control | • 0-20 years | • Major urban areas | • Privileges for high-occupancy vehicles<br>• Road-pricing or distance charges<br>• Land-use planning investments | • Jurisdictional issues<br>• Mechanisms to internalise social costs of transport<br>• Significant capital investments in more efficient transport modes and road infrastructure |
| (ii) Travel Substitution | • 0-20 years | • Intercity trips<br>• Urban commuters | • Car use restrictions | • Based on new data and video communications technologies being introduced into the market<br>• Time benefits are principal gains |
| (iii) Route Planning | • 0-10 years | • Urban road modes<br>• Intercity freight | • Parking control measures<br>• Improvement of public transport | • Public information campaigns |

Outside influences causing shifts in the cost of basic vehicles and the relative competitiveness of companies are often resisted. Product technology is defined by a small number of OEMs consisting of 10 to 15 corporations. Thus, it is not unreasonable to suggest that a joint industry-government co-operative approach could lead to agreements on a common baseline for a competitive market and future transportation goals over the next 20 to 30 years.

Factors to be taken into account include trade sensitivities, industrial locations, various fiscal and regulatory policies between countries and regions, as well as the multinational nature of the vehicle manufacturing and fuel supply industries. There are also benefits to be gained from co-ordinated, consistent and harmonised policies on a regional, national and international basis. Establishing long-range multinational regulatory and economic regimes will also reduce uncertainty over the future, and guide vehicle producers more effectively than in the past. Recent analysis supports the need for long-term non-political support structures for R&D aimed at energy efficiency.

Like the auto industry, the fuel supply and petroleum industries are often multinational and highly globalised in their operations, as well as influential both politically and economically. Since it is unlikely that a single alternative fuel market will develop, market share by fuel type will be determined by retail price, producer profitability and possible regulations (typically by restrictions on total fuel sales by type).

Profitability is an industry goal, while implementation of production technologies and processes requires significant investments and lead times. As a result, a long-term fuels strategy in a trading region, or on a larger scale, can offer the best chance of making new technology options available for the future. Supporting long-term policies and R&D funding decreases the risks of significant economic dislocations during a fuel or efficiency technology transition. Fuel and vehicle markets must be closely co-ordinated to ensure balance of supply and demand (with fuel availability leading vehicle sales).

### *Market Barriers*

In transportation, consumers are the ultimate facilitator of change. It is the vehicle buyer, either private or commercial, who chiefly influences the size and characteristics of the vehicle fleet, although government regulations have played an important role in some countries. There are examples of low-emission car and fuel incentives in OECD Europe and Pacific. Development of environmental labelling similar to the fuel economy programme in the United States and Canada, as well as in some other IEA countries, can inform consumers and encourage shifts in the market

In the United States, pollution costs are addressed indirectly by institutionalised rules for improving air quality. In the near term, four specific requirements will be the driving force for the introduction of clean-burning transportation fuels in the United States:

- stringent new emission standards for diesel vehicles;
- attainment of existing ambient air quality standards for ozone and carbon monoxide, the two pollutants coming primarily from transportation;
- the clean fuels requirements of the Clean Air Act (the Clean Fuel Pilot Program in California, and the nationwide Clean Fuels Fleet Program); and
- the low-emission and zero-emission vehicle approaches adopted in California from 2003 onwards.

It remains to be seen whether these requirements will result in the introduction of significant numbers of alternative transportation vehicles in the United States.

Whatever the mechanism driving change, the real cost of using the private automobile must increase in the consumers' perception before markets will change in IEA countries. For change to happen, programmes must not only change the perceived costs of certain transport modes and attributes, but fuel-efficient cars or high-quality mass public transportation must actually be available.

## Technology Policy Issues

### *Role of Governments*

Governments have several types of policy tools at their disposal to reshape the energy and emission intensity of transportation and to indirectly influence technology advancement. Policy tools include emissions standards, road construction and maintenance, production mandates, market incentives (such as subsidies and fuel or vehicle taxes), as well as voluntary agreements between governments and industry, and combinations of market and command-and-control approaches (Table 9.8). In addition, governments can invest in alternative transportation modes, including public transport and advanced telemeters.

In most IEA countries, the traditional approach for increasing fuel efficiency and reducing air pollution from automobiles has been to introduce or tighten prescriptive and uniform emission performance standards. This command-and-control approach is a common and direct way to address vehicle emissions. Car manufacturers in IEA countries are already subject to the testing, enforcement and administrative mechanisms in place. These measures are familiar to regulators, politicians and the public. Indeed, tightening the standards is generally preferable to mandating the introduction of alternative fuels and vehicles, not only because the standard is a familiar means of control, but also because it allows manufacturers the flexibility, not provided by a production mandate, to search for the most cost-effective solutions.

Incentives, not necessarily financial, may be offered to vehicle manufacturers as inducements to manufacture and market non-petroleum vehicles. Similarly, it may be necessary, at least in the beginning, to offer financial subsidies to retail fuel stations and consumers, possibly combined with taxes placed on conventional fuels, to overcome the cost disadvantage of new vehicles or alternative fuels. A straightforward approach is to raise the tax on petroleum fuels to reflect the best estimates of the value of the damage caused by vehicle pollution (or, alternatively, to raise the price of gasoline high enough to make alternatives competitive). The primary drawbacks of this approach are that raising taxes is politically difficult in many countries and that higher gasoline prices alone may not stimulate R&D and the introduction of transport alternatives (even if the alternatives are cheaper than gasoline), due to industry inertia, the start-up problem and the lingering fact that tax increases may be viewed as temporary.

*Table 9.8*

**Transport Technology and Fuels: Government Role in Technology Deployment**

| Technology | Level of Market Activity | Need for Government Support | Possible Government Measures |
|---|---|---|---|
| a) ICE Control | • Moderate to high depending on standards or goals proposed by IEA governments | • Market environment to support investment in lower emission systems | • Continued push for more stringent controls with adequate lead times<br>• In-use vehicle inspections and financial encouragement to scrap old cars<br>• Possible retrofit for some vehicles (e.g. buses) |
| b) Fuel Substitution | • High activity on improved gasoline and diesel fuel<br>• Moderate activity on alternative fuels depending upon availability of indigenous resources | • Need to develop more acceptable product (range, convenience, etc)<br>• Need to expand availability of fuel<br>• Demonstration in public fleets | • Support product R&D for vehicle application of fuel<br>• Support R&D in energy storage technologies<br>• Investment incentives for vehicle and infrastructure conversion |
| c) Energy Regeneration | • Moderate activity aimed at new vehicle design and testing | • Market environment to support investment | • R&D incentives (direct funding, tax credits) |
| d) Electric and Hybrid Vehicles | • Significant activity aimed at regional and niche markets | • Market environment to support investment<br>• Demonstrations in public fleets | • R&D incentives (direct funding, tax credits) |
| e) Vehicle Improvements | • Moderate activity aimed at cost reduction and new product design | • Incentives required to incorporate energy-efficient technologies into products faster, as the marketplace does not now provide strong signals for fuel efficiency | • International fuel efficiency standards<br>• Incentives for low emissions or energy-efficient vehicles |
| f) Transport Productivity | • High in urban areas and congested regions | • Setting up objectives for improved efficiency<br>• Preferred support for common transport modes<br>• R&D on effectiveness in modal shift and operating efficiency benefits<br>• Expansion of communication networks | • Regulation and pricing policy to encourage development of energy-efficient technologies (e.g. policies to encourage common modes)<br>• Public information campaigns on route planning and mobility options<br>• Promotion of public transport, ride-sharing, etc.<br>• Land-use instruments and fiscal incentives |

***Role of International Co-operation***

A number of international co-operative measures could promote preparation and adoption of energy-efficient and emissions-reducing technologies in the transportation sector. A summary of these measures is provided in Table 9.9. There is a great need to share information on transportation energy and emissions issues and opportunities, with the IEA countries potentially playing a lead role. In particular, technical information on the performance of transportation technologies and the results of demonstration and market initiatives can be shared. The IEA has played a key role in sharing technical information through the existing Implementing Agreements on Alternative Motor Fuels, Production and Utilisation of Hydrogen, Electric Vehicle Technology, Advanced Fuel Cells, Energy Conservation through Energy Storage, and Energy Conservation in Combustion.

Information on the state of new technologies and their energy-efficiency and emission characteristics, under a variety of operating conditions, is important for urban planning. Options for energy-efficient transportation and more effective models to assess energy and environmental impacts of urban transport decisions will assist local administrators and communities. Discussion of issues and solutions should be broadened to include decision-makers who shape the direction of urban planning and transportation systems. Part of the task depends on the ability of existing networks of government agencies, industry associations and educational institutions to incorporate new opportunities into their activities. This process can be facilitated by dissemination of publications discussing energy and emissions aspects of urban transportation and the sometimes conflicting objectives facing urban planners.

At present, the automobile industry regards energy-efficiency and emission constraints as relatively minor issues compared with production economics and transport productivity losses due to traffic congestion. Establishing long-term goals for vehicle emissions and energy-efficiency allows industry to recognise future design requirements and to invest in long-term product development. International co-operation can contribute to raising the priority level of energy-efficiency and emission reductions in product design, selection and use, and to sharing limited financial and human resources. Continuing international discussion of long-term goals for transportation efficiency and environmental protection, particularly motor vehicle technology, would be beneficial. The IEA can play a significant role in this, together with other international organisations.

The main emphasis for governments in transport technology continues to be policy and regulation, based upon technology assessments and transportation system analysis. In addition, governments can participate in the demonstration of new vehicle concepts and technologies, for instance, by using public fleets to assist in creating more favourable market conditions and regulatory frameworks, as well as technology transfer.

Comparability and possible harmonisation of standards and test procedures for energy and environmentally-friendly vehicles would also be beneficial for a number of reasons:

- likely reduction in industrial testing and product development costs and promulgation of improved standards from trade negotiations;

*Table 9.9*

**Transport Technology and Fuels: The Role of International Co-operation in Technology Progress**

| Technology | Prospects for International Co-operation | Modes of Co-operation | Technology Transfer Issues |
|---|---|---|---|
| a) ICE Control | • R&D in combustion<br>• Science and technology<br>• R&D in long-term advanced engine concepts<br>• Catalyst processes and materials | • Collaborative R&D<br>• Information sharing | • Industry involvement and co-funding<br>• Maximum emissions standards |
| b) Fuel Substitution | • R&D, demonstration on alternative fuel technologies<br>• Large-scale use of NGVs and electric and hybrid vehicles | • Collaborative R&D and information sharing | • Industry involvement and co-funding<br>• Supportive policy and regulation framework - fiscal incentives for development of refuelling and distribution infrastructure |
| c) Energy Regeneration | • Demonstrations of vehicles with regeneration systems | • Joint demonstrations<br>• Information sharing | • Industry involvement and co-funding<br>• Supportive policy and regulation framework |
| d) Electric and Hybrid Vehicles | • R&D on electro-chemistry<br>• Demonstration of electric and hybrid vehicles | • Collaborative R&D and information sharing<br>• Joint demonstrations | • Industry involvement and co-funding<br>• Supportive policy and regulation framework |
| e) Vehicle Improvements | • R&D on lightweight materials development, testing, recovery and recycling | • Government support for R&D on high- strength and light-weight materials<br>• Information sharing | • Possible industry involvement and co-funding |
| f) Transport Productivity | • R&D on intelligent vehicle and highway systems<br>• Traffic management and control<br>• Telecommunications applications | • Collaborative R&D<br>• Joint demonstrations<br>• Reporting of trends and progress | • Industry involvement and co-funding<br>• Supportive policy and regulation framework - mechanisms to internalise social cost of transport |

- minimisation of undue economic and trade barriers by inviting all industrialised countries to adopt similar requirements and environmental limits on the same time schedule; and
- establishment of uniform certification for developing countries as the benchmark for new vehicle imports.

Newly industrialising countries have some of the highest growth rates for transportation demand but limited technical or financial resources to influence vehicle technology. The IEA governments could assist in the transfer of information and in planning for future growth in industrialising countries so as to take advantage of prior experience in helping them to reduce future transportation fuel use and emissions. The creation of voluntary vehicle and refinery industry performance targets and goals for products exported to, or manufactured in, non-regulated countries could help ensure that vehicle energy and emissions intensity does not multiply concerns about energy security and the global environment.

## Approach

The transportation sector is still almost entirely dependent on liquid fuels derived from oil. The cost of developing alternative solutions to transportation problems is high. The enormous size of industrial investments in vehicle technology development and the presence of a competitive industry limit government's role.

Identification and understanding of some basic physical constraints to improving engines, fuels, combustion processes, materials and components can greatly enhance the potential for developing better vehicle products.

IEA's basic goals in promoting the development of transportation technology emphasise the need for increased efficiency and flexibility of fuels and for the continued development and expanded market contribution of substitute fuels. Reducing the basic energy intensity of vehicles through advanced materials, structural improvements and new vehicle and engine design offer one way to attain these objectives. Further improvements of ICE combustion and emissions control could also contribute to meeting these goals by increasing engine efficiencies. Introduction of alternative fuels, such as alcohols and CNG, will contribute toward overall sector goals. Progress in all-electric and hybrid electric vehicles offers an opportunity to reduce emissions and increase diversity by employing off-peak power-generation capacity.

Increased collaboration can accelerate technology progress in an internationally focused and competitive vehicle industry. Proprietary interests may limit information sharing to longer-term areas of interest, but regional market opportunities may induce closer inter-government and government/industry interaction and co-operation. Technology collaboration and information exchange tend to be easier in the field trial and demonstration phase.

There is little doubt that improved and more efficient road transport technology and, eventually, a transition to alternative transportation fuels will become necessary, as a result of some combination of environmental pressures (urban, regional and global) and energy and oil security motivations. To meet technology goals identified in this chapter IEA Member countries may therefore wish to contribute to and co-operate in a technology strategy and collaborative R&D programme that includes the measures listed below.

- Focusing on fuel efficiency and environmental benefits that would result from near-term market opportunities and technology advances in fuel quality and ICE control, improved combustion, transport productivity, vehicle design and energy regeneration.

- Supporting next-generation very-low-emission ICE development and demonstration incorporating natural gas, LPG and alternative fuels technology, to contribute to a faster cost-effective transition towards a more sustainable and diversified transport system.

- Increasing R&D and testing efforts to bring electric vehicles and hybrids from niche market use to large-scale application; with a view to the long term, hydrogen R&D would also be maintained.

- Improving voluntary co-operation involving the car manufacturing and fuel industries and their associations to define priorities for applied transportation research and promote vehicle and fuel efficiency and environmental standards, and their harmonisation.

- Continuing balanced integration into the transportation technology programmes and planning process of the multiple goals relating to fuel cycle security, environmental protection, passenger and freight mobility, urban and regional change.

- Prioritising technology and policy goals by analysing energy, environmental and economic impacts and by developing and using life-cycle approaches.

- Increasing transport and fuel technology information dissemination to non-Member countries and assistance to help manage fuel use and environmental pollution problems.

# Chapter 10

## INDUSTRIAL, RESIDENTIAL AND COMMERCIAL ENERGY USE

### Goals and Rationale

Interest in energy efficiency has been rekindled in IEA Member countries in recent years. Improving energy efficiency or energy conservation is being seen increasingly as a promising strategy for achieving simultaneously the goals of energy security, environmental protection and economic growth. The IEA countries reduced their energy intensity (i.e. final energy consumption per unit of GDP) by some 34 per cent between 1973 and 1993 as a result of changes in energy efficiency and changes in the economy's output, as well as fuel substitution. Over this period, the pace of change in energy intensity varied. A particularly marked improvement was seen between 1979 and 1983, while in recent years it has remained slightly below the average level for the two decades. An examination of intensity changes by energy fuel type also indicates that the change was not uniform among energy sources. Oil intensity decreased the most, reflecting the importance the IEA Member countries have attached simultaneously to improvements in end-use efficiency, to energy saving and to substitution of other energy sources for oil. Natural gas intensity also diminished, but electricity intensity increased, in part due to the larger share of electricity in total final consumption.

While there is a vast potential, technically, for increased energy efficiency, there exist significant barriers to its realisation. Market forces alone are unlikely to bring about the level of efficiency improvement implicit in most environment-oriented energy policies seeking to stabilise and reduce greenhouse gas emissions. Past improvements in energy efficiency have played a significant part in limiting greenhouse gas emissions, along with reductions in the carbon intensity of the energy sector of IEA countries. It has been estimated that, without the decline in energy intensity that has occurred since 1973, IEA countries would have been emitting about 25 per cent more $CO_2$ than they were in 1993. IEA governments considering targets for reducing greenhouse gas emissions place emphasis on accelerating gains in energy efficiency to generate the required emissions reductions, especially of carbon dioxide. These countries have therefore strengthened their energy-efficiency programmes.

Although the realistic (i.e. cost-effective) potential for new and improved energy end-use technologies appears to be promising in many end-use applications, the relationship between improvements in energy efficiency, on the one hand, and energy demand and $CO_2$ emission levels on the other, is not straightforward. The future role of energy-efficient technology and R&D in emissions reduction strategies depends on the extent to which efficiency improvements are translated into consumer behaviour that reduces energy demand and environmental emissions. For example, financial incentives may encourage energy saving and fuel switching. Industrial co-generation has become increasingly common, helping to reduce energy intensity in this sector. Energy-efficiency standards have been widely implemented in IEA countries in a variety of applications, notably in minimum performance standards on appliances such as refrigerators, washing machines, lighting systems and motors, and on buildings, including homes, offices, commercial premises and factories. Voluntary agreements and co-operation between government and industry have been established. More attention has been focused on consumer information activities. In the electric utility industry, energy efficiency, and particularly demand-side management programmes, have been more widely pursued. While these policies are encouraging, much more attention should be directed towards ways of increasing the use of efficient energy end-use technologies. Innovative and bold approaches to promote energy end-use technology progress are required if the full technical and economic potential of increased energy efficiency is to be realised.

The analysis in this chapter focuses on energy use in the industrial, residential and commercial sectors. Energy end-use in transport is covered in Chapter 9. Analysis shows impressive technical opportunities to use energy more efficiently and effectively in the industrial, residential and commercial consuming sectors. Technology priority goals are to:

- enhance the demonstration and market deployment of existing technologies for improving the efficiency, economics and flexibility of energy use; and
- encourage further development and application of next-generation technologies, with a view to maximising the potential environmental benefits they offer, including reduction of greenhouse gas emissions.

Due to dissimilar demand growth rates, the sectoral distribution of energy demand in IEA Member countries has changed significantly since the early 1970s. In 1973, industrial use accounted for 39 per cent of total final energy consumption, and residential and commercial sectors used 18 per cent and 10 per cent respectively. By 1993, industrial use had fallen six percentage points and the residential and service sectors combined had risen two percentage points.

The industrial sector is generally more energy-intensive than the residential and service sectors, and reductions in energy-intensive industrial production and significant technology improvements, responding both to past higher energy prices and competitive pressures, have fostered overall reductions in energy requirements. It is important to note that structural changes in these IEA Member countries have often been caused by exporting primary materials, for processing and refining elsewhere. The consequent reduction in the energy intensity of industry hides the change from direct use of primary energy to indirect use. Semi-finished products imported from non-Member countries have involved the use of energy by the basic industries now located there. This fact, combined with global environmental concerns, is highlighting the need to extend the dissemination of technology information and foster technology co-operation with non-Member countries, and thus contribute to realising the shared goals of energy security and global environment protection.

## Technology Description and Assessment

### *Description of Significant Technologies*

Energy end-use technologies cover a vast and diversified area, the nature of which depends very much upon the energy context and the country. Table 10.1 shows the main reasons for selecting specific energy end-use technologies in the three sectors of interest: industrial, residential and commercial (including public) buildings. The technical status of the various technologies and their R&D needs and opportunities are described in Tables 10.2 and 10.3 respectively. Major gains in energy conservation have resulted, and will continue to result, from more efficient energy conversion and end-use technologies, and from improvements in energy management. Many new technologies have been developed and are either ready for the market or for large-scale demonstration as an option for the next generation.

(a) *Industrial Energy End-Use*

For the purposes of this analysis, the industrial sector includes both manufacturing and non-manufacturing enterprises, thus also covering agriculture, forestry, fishing, as well as construction, mining, and oil and natural gas production. The industrial sector is characterised by the diversity of energy uses, equipment and processes. Seven energy-intensive industries account for most of the end-use demand in the IEA region: chemical industries, including petroleum refining; aluminium production; iron and steel; pulp and paper; cement; glass and ceramics; and food processing. There are also cross-cutting technological factors and technology advances that influence the rate at which energy intensity may change.

(i) Chemical industry

Most basic organic and inorganic chemicals are intermediate in the production of other chemicals and involve two major steps, reaction and separation. Overall energy efficiency may be quite low, even though each intermediate product is produced with reasonable efficiency. Each step may be interdependent from an energy point of view, so that changing the energy requirement for one step may alter the energy balance for the entire process. Any fundamental process change that reduces or shortens the steps needed to produce a given chemical may have a significant impact on the energy requirements for producing a particular product. Such process change might arise through improvements in catalysts and reagents, photochemistry or the application of biotechnology. Improvements in reactor design and/or in reaction time could also improve efficiency.

(ii) Aluminium production

The Hall-Héroult process is the basic reduction process for aluminium. Alternative processes promise lower electricity consumption, but none is commercially feasible. Carbo-thermic reduction uses a process similar to a blast furnace in iron-making by directly reducing aluminium in an electric arc furnace. Other changes offering potential for efficiency improvements in aluminium production include permanent anodes and wetted cathodes.

*Table 10.1*

**Main Reasons for Selection of Energy End-Use Technology: Industrial, Residential and Commercial Sectors**

| Technology Area | Opportunity Areas: Examples | Reasons for Selection |
|---|---|---|
| **a) Industrial Energy End-Use** | | |
| Chemical industry | • Biotechnology<br>• Catalysis<br>• Sensors and controls<br>• Separation systems<br>• Waste heat recovery | • Reducing reaction times with lower temperature and pressure<br>• Improvement in product selectivity<br>• Advances in process control and energy management<br>• Major contribution to energy use in chemical processes<br>• Optimal energy management and heat cascading |
| Aluminium production | • Carbothermic reduction<br>• Permanent anodes and wetted cathodes | • Direct reduction of aluminium<br>• Energy and material saving |
| Iron and steel | • Iron-making: alternative processes<br>• Steel-making: alternative processes<br>• Direct casting | • Direct reduction of iron to replace blast furnace<br>• Direct steel-making from ore<br>• Continuous casting with no ingot reheat |
| Pulp and paper processing | • Improvements in pulping processes<br>• Recycled pulp<br>• Improvements in paper-making processes | • Chemical pulping, mechanical pulping, heat recovery<br>• Use of enzymes, fibre separation<br>• Process control and greater speed on the process line |
| Cement production | • Process change<br>• Blending of secondary materials<br>• Kiln insulation | • Conversion from wet to dry processes<br>• Use of waste heat and waste materials<br>• Better insulation and control |
| Glass and ceramics | • Monitoring and control<br>• Regeneration and melting technology | • Improved housekeeping, monitoring and control<br>• Oxygen enrichment, batch preheating, improved refractories |
| Food processing | • Process changes in separation and sterilisation<br>• Use of waste heat | • Biotechnical means of reducing moisture content in raw materials, improved sterilisation and separation processes<br>• Heat recovery from hot water and steam |

See for example IEA (1991); L. Schipper et al (1992).

*Table 10.1 (continued)*

**Main Reasons for Selection of Energy End-Use Technology: Industrial, Residential and Commercial Sectors**

| Technology Area | Opportunity Areas: Examples | Reasons for Selection |
|---|---|---|
| **a) Industrial Energy End-Use** *(continued)* | | |
| Cross-cutting technologies | • Separation processes<br>• Heat exchange<br>• Combined heat and power generation (CHP)<br>• Heat upgrading with heat pumps<br>• Combustion<br>• Electricity use | • Membrane separation, supercritical fluids extraction<br>• Heat cascading and heat storage<br>• Improved overall energy efficiency<br>• Open-vapour recompression cycle, closed-vapour compression cycle, absorption heat pumps<br>• Turbulence enhancement, catalytic injection, oxygen enrichment<br>• New electrolytic processes and electric motors |
| **b) Residential Energy End-Use** | | |
| Space heating and cooling | • Improved building shell and envelope<br>• Efficient space-heating systems<br>• Efficient electric air conditioning | • Improved insulation and windows characteristics, control of air infiltration<br>• Improved boiler and furnace design, reduction in distribution losses, improved controls<br>• Better design of equipment, heat exchangers, fans and controls |
| Water heating | • Back-up systems in central heating<br>• Insulation | • Electric resistance heaters, capacity adaptation to actual load requirements<br>• Reduction of heat losses, improved heat storage |
| Lighting | • Fluorescent bulbs and compact fluorescent bulbs<br>• Use of efficient reflectors and ballasts for fluorescent tubes | • Replacing incandescent bulbs, improved efficiency<br>• Improved design and better control technology |
| Refrigeration | • Efficient compressors and fans<br>• Insulation and CFC alternatives | • Reduced electricity use<br>• Improved consumer service and respect for environmental concerns |

See for example IEA (1991); L. Schipper et al (1992).

*Table 10.1 (continued)*

**Main Reasons for Selection of Energy End-Use Technology: Industrial, Residential and Commercial Sectors**

| Technology Area | Opportunity Areas: Examples | Reasons for Selection |
|---|---|---|
| **b) Residential Energy End-Use** *(continued)* | | |
| Cooking | • Improved electric and gas stoves and cookers<br>• Microwave ovens | • Higher energy efficiency and better cooking service<br>• Changing consumer habits |
| Washing machines | • Reduction in washing temperature<br>• Improved dryers | • Possible because of improved detergents<br>• Possible because of better design of washing machines, use of tumble dryers |
| **c) Commercial Energy End-Use** | | |
| Space heating and cooling | • Building shell and envelope<br>• Space conditioning | • Improved indoor air quality and higher energy efficiency<br>• Improved boiler systems and room heaters, air-conditioning and controls |
| Lighting | • Fluorescent and compact fluorescent bulbs<br>• Adaptation of light levels to the function served and use of efficient reflectors and ballasts for fluorescent tubes | • Replacing incandescent bulbs, improved efficiency<br>• Improved design and better control technology |
| Office equipment | • New generation of microprocessors | • Improved service |

See for example IEA (1991); L. Schipper et al (1992).

*Table 10.2*

**Technical Status of Energy End-Use Technologies: Industrial, Residential and Commercial Sectors**

| Technology | Status | Technical Feasibility | Application Issues | Potential for Emissions Reduction |
|---|---|---|---|---|
| **a) Industrial Energy End-Use** | | | | |
| Chemical industry | Demonstrated | • Improvements in the reaction and separation steps<br>• Heat cascading and optimal energy management | • Need to reassess the energy balance for the entire process<br>• Long-term payback of major process modifications<br>• Options for co-generation | H |
| Aluminium production | R&D and Demonstrated | • Improvements in the Hall-Héroult process<br>• Secondary fusion and recycling | • Search for alternative energy-efficient processes (carbo-thermic reduction) | M |
| Iron and steel | Demonstrated | • Direct reduction of iron<br>• Continuous casting of steel | • Direct steel-making from ore<br>• Scrap beneficiation affects energy intensity | M |
| Pulp and paper processing | R&D and Demonstrated | • Greater reliance on continuous digesters<br>• Spent liquor concentration and gasification<br>• Use of recycled pulp | • Need for fundamental process change<br>• Options for co-generation | L |
| Cement production | Demonstrated | • Use of waste fuels and blending with secondary materials | • Improved grinding technology<br>• Opportunities for plant upgrading and environmental retrofitting | L |
| Glass and ceramics | Demonstrated | • Improved housekeeping, monitoring and process control | • Large potential for efficiency gains<br>• Opportunities for plant upgrading and environmental retrofitting | L |
| Food processing | Demonstrated | • New and improved separation and sterilisation processes | • Options are plant- and process-dependent<br>• Lack of knowledge of energy-efficient technologies | L |

Note: L, M, H represent Low, Medium, High.

*Table 10.2 (continued)*

**Technical Status of Energy End-Use Technologies: Industrial, Residential and Commercial Sectors**

| Technology | Status | Technical Feasibility | Application Issues | Potential for Emissions Reduction |
|---|---|---|---|---|
| **a) Industrial Energy End-Use** *(continued)* | | | | |
| Cross-cutting technologies | Commercial | • Productivity gains are driving change and improvements in energy efficiency | • Higher cost of alternative energy end-use systems<br>• Lack of knowledge of new components, information technology and advanced controls | M |
| **b) Residential Energy End-Use** | | | | |
| Space heating and cooling | Demonstrated and Commercial | • Focus on shell efficiency in new buildings<br>• Integration of heating and cooling components<br>• Improved indoor air quality | • Retrofitting depends upon state of existing buildings, insulation, climate and occupants' behaviour<br>• Building codes may inhibit technology innovation | H |
| Water heating | Demonstrated and Commercial | • Introduction of back-up systems<br>• Use of larger central storage tanks | • Need for better insulation and control | M |
| Lighting | Commercial | • Improved design and better controls | • Higher initial cost of energy-efficient lighting | M |
| Refrigeration | Commercial | • Improved insulation and better controls<br>• Increased quality of the service | • Higher initial cost of energy-efficient units<br>• Consumer response | M |
| Cooking | Commercial | • Increased equipment efficiency | • Increased microwave cooking by consumers | M |
| Washing machines | Demonstrated | • Improvements in the energy efficiency of the washing cycle<br>• Introduction of new detergents | • Consumer response | M |

Note: L, M, H represent Low, Medium, High.

*Table 10.2*

**Technical Status of Energy End-Use Technologies: Industrial, Residential and Commercial Sectors**

| Technology | Status | Technical Feasibility | Application Issues | Potential for Emissions Reduction |
|---|---|---|---|---|
| **c) Commercial Energy End-Use** | | | | |
| Space heating and cooling | Demonstrated and Commercial | • Integrated energy and environmental design<br>• Improved indoor air quality | • Opportunities for retrofitting and upgrading existing buildings and facilities<br>• Priorities are office buildings, trade facilities, schools, hotels, hospitals and public services | H |
| Lighting | Commercial | • Significant opportunities for immediate energy savings | • Higher capital requirements may limit cost-effective replacements in existing buildings | M |
| Office equipment | Demonstrated and Commercial | • Use of new more powerful microprocessors and computer applications | • Information and energy-efficiency labelling to alert users | L |

Note: L, M, H represent Low, Medium, High.

*Table 10.3*

**R&D Needs and Opportunities for Energy End-Use Technologies: Industrial, Residential and Commercial Sectors**

| Technology | Bottlenecks | R&D Requirements |
|---|---|---|
| **a) Industrial Energy End-Use** | | |
| • Chemical industry<br>• Aluminium production<br>• Iron and steel<br>• Pulp and paper processing<br>• Cement production<br>• Glass and ceramics<br>• Food processing<br>• Cross-cutting technologies | • Insufficient demonstration experience<br>• Industry fragmentation<br>• Process flexibility of existing and conventional technology<br>• Immediate need to focus on end-of-the-pipe technology to reduce waste and environment impact<br>• Scarcity of trained operators<br>• Imprecise data on new technology costs | • Aggressive, cost-shared government-industry R&D programmes aimed at industrial processes in energy-intensive production<br>• Manufacturing plant energy audits to accelerate adoption of available cost-effective measures and follow up advice and guidance<br>• R&D on technology and techniques to reduce the rate of waste generation and to allow waste to be used as a resource |
| **b) Residential Energy End-Use** | | |
| • Space heating and cooling<br>• Water heating<br>• Lighting<br>• Refrigeration<br>• Cooking<br>• Washing machines | • Traditions in building practice<br>• Lack of consumer incentives<br>• Low or subsidised energy prices<br>• Absence of reliable sources of technical data<br>• Insufficient number of marketable technologies to increase energy efficiency<br>• Only limited full-scale demonstrations to show benefits of energy-efficient and renewable energy technology integration | • R&D to reduce costs and improve performance of new technologies<br>• Provision of technical information and assistance to industry, utilities, local administrations and the public<br>• Enforcing of energy-efficiency standards by means of national and local building codes<br>• Updating of residential appliance efficiency standards to keep pace with new technology<br>• Demonstration of exemplary energy technologies in public housing and intelligent buildings concepts |
| **c) Commercial Energy End-Use** | | |
| • Space heating and cooling<br>• Lighting<br>• Office equipment | • Existing building and construction practice<br>• Slow capital stock turnover<br>• Lack of technical know-how<br>• Higher investment cost of new technologies<br>• Need to define new practices for integration of energy-efficient technology into conventional systems<br>• Energy costs are passed through to tenants | • R&D to reduce costs and improve performance of commercial-building energy technologies, including lighting systems, windows, heating and cooling equipment, and design techniques<br>• Methods and technologies to improve indoor comfort and environmental quality<br>• Demonstration of exemplary energy technologies in public building design, operation and procurement |

(iii) Iron and steel

There are two major routes to the production of steel: the integrated process, which first converts ore to iron in a blast furnace, then decarburises the melt in a basic oxygen furnace; the alternative, which relies almost exclusively on scrap, melting and purifying it in an electric arc furnace. Two major technological advances, the electric arc furnace and continuous casting, account for the largest part of energy savings in recent years. The use of electric arc furnaces, which are charged mostly with scrap, reduces energy requirements to about half of requirements in the case of integrated steel production. With increasing use of electric arc furnaces, however, scrap beneficiation is needed to remove residual elements. Several approaches hold promise: magnetic separation of shredded materials, vacuum processing, hydrometallurgical techniques, pyrometallurgical treatment using reactants, and improved physical separation. Major savings can also be achieved through improvements in the reshaping process to reduce reheating requirements.

(iv) Pulp and paper processing

Technologies and processes introduced more than fifty years ago continue to dominate the pulp and paper industry. Years of incremental improvements have made these processes reasonably energy-efficient but major efficiency improvements cannot be expected without fundamental process changes. Minor technological improvements, however, offer significant energy efficiency improvements, in both the pulping process and the paper-making process. The three most promising advanced processes are biopulping, chemical pulping with fermentation and ethanol oganosolv (organic solvent) pulping. All involve integrating a fermentation process into a conventional pulping process and derive much of their energy improvement from process integration and use of waste heat. None is yet near commercial development.

(v) Cement production

In cement production, energy consumption ranges from 3.2 to 7.0 GJ/tonne of clinker produced. A representative value for an old plant using the wet process is 6.5 GJ/metric tonne, while a new plant using the same process is likely to produce a metric tonne with only 5.0 GJ. An old plant using the dry process will use 4.2 GJ/tonne, a newer plant 3.2 GJ. The fossil energy content of cement production can be reduced further by using waste fuels and blending the cement with secondary materials.

(vi) Glass and ceramics

Efficiency improvements in the glass and ceramics industry reduced energy intensity considerably during the last two decades. It has been estimated that further efficiency improvements using the best available technology could range from 17 to 33 per cent, while advanced technology available by 2000 could reduce energy intensity a further 37 per cent. Energy intensity could decline by up to 50 per cent if technology that will become available after 2000 is adopted. Since most of the energy used occurs in melting silica and other ingredients, most of the savings would occur here, through oxygen enrichment, batch preheating, improved refractories, process controls, new plasma melting techniques and ultrasonic refining. Use of microwaves in firing of ceramics could also generate more important savings.

(vii) Food processing

Energy accounts for less than 10 per cent of total costs in food processing, where it is used mainly for production of hot water and steam, motor power including refrigeration, fabrication processes and space conditioning and lighting. Raw materials are the most significant cost factor in this branch, so they can be considered as higher on the scale of importance than energy savings. Major process changes in food processing include biotechnical means of reducing high moisture content in raw materials, improved separation processes (membranes, absorbing surfaces, freeze crystallisation) and improved sterilisation (ultraviolet, ionisation).

(viii) Cross-cutting technologies

All industries use energy, even though the fraction of costs devoted to energy consumption may be quite small in some cases. Waste heat recovery and combustion efficiency improvements are two major ways of improving the efficiency of energy use in most industrial activities. Separation technology accounts for a large share of energy consumption in industry, and improvements in this area have applicability across a wide range of industry branches. Similarly, motors and lighting account for much of the electricity use in industry, so improvements in these areas could also contribute to improved efficiency.

The three major techniques for capturing waste heat are heat exchange, combined heat and power generation (CHP), and heat upgrading using heat pumps. High-temperature waste heat recovery is usually carried out with heat exchangers, using thermal storage to overcome the mismatch between time of need and availability. This energy cascading is usually cost-effective and the utility of the heat is magnified as it is cascaded to lower-temperature processes. A heat pump is an effective method for upgrading low-temperature waste heat. The most widely used types involve the open-vapour recompression cycle. They are applied in food processing, which uses large quantities of hot water, in industries that generate steam but do not recycle the feed water, and in a variety of others.

In industries with high demand for both steam and electricity, namely the iron and steel, pulp and paper and chemicals industries, there are various alternatives (depending on the type of energy required) and ample opportunities for CHP technologies, such as cascading heat from combustion. Two examples of this approach are topping and bottoming cycle co-generation. In the former, a combustion turbine generates electricity directly and the waste heat raises low-pressure steam that is used in processing. In the latter, high-pressure steam is raised and used in processing, then waste heat is captured downstream to generate electricity. Often, the remaining low-temperature waste heat may be used for industrial space heating and/or district heating.

(b) *Residential Energy End-Use*

The residential sector consists essentially of all private residences, including single and multi-family homes, apartments, and mobile homes. Institutional residences such as student accomodation, nursing homes, military barracks, schools and hospitals are included in the commercial sector. To assess the scope for efficient energy end-use technology in the residential sector, it is useful to distinguish between energy used for space conditioning (heating and cooling) and that used for appliances. The second category, household appliances, covers diverse technologies, ranging from light bulbs to stoves and television sets, for which technological improvements can be translated much faster into energy demand reductions because the rate of stock turnover is rapid. The average lifetime of household appliances ranges from one year (or less in the case of incandescent bulbs) to as long as 15 years or more for refrigerators, washing machines and other large appliances. The room for improvement in each category is influenced by significantly differing factors that affect the extent to which efficiency improvements can be achieved, as well as the realistic time-frame for achieving them.

(i) Space heating and cooling

Efficiency improvements in space conditioning are generally made possible through changes in the building shell, such as better insulation, for which technology is readily available. However, the turnover of the building stock takes place over a period of decades. In Europe, new buildings are often additions to the existing stock rather than replacements of old stock. Improvements in building shells are usually made in new buildings when constructed rather than in existing ones, where adding better wall insulation or windows with low heat-transmission co-efficients can be extremely costly. Though the technical potential for energy efficiency improvements in heating and cooling end-uses might be substantial, savings are thus limited by the slow turnover of the building stock.

Central heating systems constitute the major share of residential heating. If the best technology available were applied, the efficiency of oil-fuelled systems could be improved by about 20 per cent, and that of natural gas systems, which are already more efficient than oil-based heating installations, by 10 to 15 per cent. Technological developments such as improvements in the design of burners and distribution systems have already contributed to increasing the efficiency of these heating systems. Wider use of control systems would also make a valuable contribution. With regard to electric heating, the conversion efficiency of the heating equipment reaches almost 100 per cent. The overall efficiency is reduced if the full cycle is taken into account. If the full fuel cycle is assessed, the best available gas or oil-fired heating systems can achieve higher overall conversion efficiency than electricity. In air conditioning, opportunities to improve efficiency include better design of the various components of the system, notably heat exchangers and fans, and better controls. In addition, more than 50 million reversible air conditioners (with heat-pump mode for space heating) and a substantial number of heating-only heat pumps are in operation in IEA countries. Moreover, chlorofluorocarbons should be replaced by non-radiative, environmentally acceptable gases.

(ii) Water heating

Natural gas is the main energy source for water heating in IEA countries, providing more than 50 per cent of total residential requirements. Electricity accounts for about 22 per cent and oil for about 19 per cent. Country-specific characteristics, such as price levels and stability, climate and personal income, have a strong influence on fuel choice. The efficiency of water-heating units can be increased by reducing heating losses. Better insulation of tanks and distribution pipes, better controls or more accurate matching of equipment capacity to actual load requirements are commonly used approaches. Efficiency of water heating can also be increased through measures to enhance efficiency at the point of delivery by introducing low-flow shower heads, or reducing the amount of hot water and the temperature required by appliances supplied by central tanks, such as washing machines, also through use of solar energy.

(iii) Lighting

The basic technologies for lighting are incandescent bulbs and fluorescent light bulbs, the latter being substantially more efficient. Lighting efficiency can thus be improved by replacing incandescent bulbs with fluorescent and compact fluorescent bulbs. Further options for reducing electricity requirements include improved design and better control of daylight and artificial light (for example, by varying the light level according to function), more efficient reflectors and ballasts for fluorescent tubes or behavioural changes by consumers, such as switching off lights when they are not needed.

(iv) Refrigeration

Although almost all households in Member countries own refrigerators, there have been substantial shifts in the types of model used. Reflecting changes in consumer behaviour, the market penetration of freezers and combined units (refrigerators and freezers) has increased over the last 15 years. The basic technology for refrigerators and freezers is much the same across Member countries, i.e. electrically powered compressors and fans, and chlorofluorocarbon/hydro-fluorocarbon refrigerants, all of which cool insulated containers. Significant improvements have been made in insulating systems, and technologies such as vacuum insulation may result in further improvements. However, beyond these technological similarities lies a wide range of differences in type, size and the range of possible improvements. Energy-efficient alternatives to the use of CFCs are needed. The cost of the best available technology can raise the price to between 20 per cent and 100 per cent above that of the average appliance sold today, though there is no strict correlation between efficiency and price. Technological improvements to increase efficiency also influence the quality of the service provided, as extra insulation usually reduces the food storage-capacity or increases the size of the appliance. Given the standardised size of many residential appliances, changes in the size could reduce market penetration because of additional installation costs.

(v) Cooking

Energy for cooking, which represents 6 per cent of residential-building energy demand in IEA countries, takes the form of electricity and natural gas. There is a significant potential for energy-efficiency improvements through shifts between technologies. For example, microwaves use about 50 per cent less electricity than conventional ovens. If they were used as a main cooking appliance rather than a supplementary one, the energy savings could be substantial. Other technologies not yet commonly used, such as electromagnetic induction cookers, could considerably reduce electricity demand. Technological improvements can further increase the efficiency of conventional electric ovens as well.

(vi) Washing machines

Washing machines, together with spin and tumble dryers, account for less than 10 per cent of residential electricity requirements in IEA countries. They usually comprise three energy-consuming elements: a water heater, an electric drive for rotation and a waste-water pump. The water heater is the dominant consumer of electricity. Technological efficiency improvements, new detergents, and different washing cycles and load factors have major effects on energy consumption. Reductions in washing temperature can substantially reduce electricity consumption. Such behavioural changes are independent from technology and can be achieved in addition to hardware improvements. Reductions in water requirements reduce energy requirements for water heating and also reduce the amount of waste water to be pumped out of the machine. Lower water and temperature requirements can be achieved through improved, less environmentally harmful, detergents. The design of washing machines can also reduce the amount of energy needed for drying. Higher spin speeds, for example, do not improve the efficiency of the washing machine but they can eliminate more liquid so that less energy is needed if tumble dryers are used.

(c) *Commercial Energy End-Use*

The commercial and service sector covers businesses that are not engaged in transportation or industrial activity. Examples are: offices, retail stores, wholesalers, warehouses, hotels and restaurants, religious and educational institutions, hospitals and government buildings. Energy requirements in the commercial sector were about 10 per cent of total final energy consumption in IEA countries in 1993 and these requirements are rising. Three end-use categories dominate this sector: space heating and cooling, lighting and office equipment. Energy use related to space heating and cooling can be reduced by increasing the efficiency of the building shell and improving heating and air conditioning systems. Furthermore, commercial electricity use has been growing rapidly and electricity efficiency measures in the commercial sector can help to reduce future energy requirements. For example, conservation programmes that concentrate on lighting in commercial buildings can be very cost-effective and achieve considerable reductions in electricity demand.

(i) Space heating and cooling

The technical potential for greater energy efficiency through improvements in the building shell is similar to that in the case of residential buildings. The function of a commercial building largely defines its location and energy requirements for ventilation and cooling. These factors encouarge the use of certain designs that are incompatible with high energy-efficiency construction. The efficiency of the heating and cooling system can be increased by improving boiler systems and room heaters, control systems, air conditioning, heat recovery, cooling systems for night cooling and utilisation of building mass. However, potential savings cannot be easily quantified because they are interrelated and individual savings may not be additive. For instance, sophisticated heating systems that can reduce energy consumption by between 30 and 40 per cent are usually equipped with state-of-the-art control devices.

(ii) Lighting

From a technical point of view, substantial improvements can be made either by replacing incandescent lights with fluorescent bulbs or by using electronic ballasts rather than conventional and high-efficiency bulbs. Major savings can also be obtained through better lighting system design and controls, through more efficient reflectors, through varying light levels according to function, through using natural light because of better building design, and through controls that turn off lights when not needed. Improved efficiency or reduced artificial lighting also reduce the amount of heat released in air-conditioned buildings.

(iii) Office equipment

Office equipment, such as personal computers, photocopiers and other machines, constitutes one of the fastest growing areas of commercial energy consumption. Although there have been rapid technological developments and efficiency improvements, the increased energy consumption generated by the rate of market penetration of such devices has by far outweighed energy savings achieved through steadily improving design. Further efficiency improvements are likely, however, driven by requirements for improved service rather than by energy-cost considerations. Surveys have found that most personal computers remain on when not in use during the day, overnight and during weekends. Desktop computers typically have been designed with little consideration for energy efficiency, unlike portable or laptop models that incorporate a number of energy-saving measures to save battery power. It has been estimated that if desktop units were equipped with technologies that allowed them to shut down when not in use and return quickly to full power capability when needed, they would save up to 50 per cent of the energy currently used to run them.

### *Assessment of Technical and Economic Potential*

A significant conclusion of the analysis presented here is that in virtually all sectors and for all the major energy end-uses involved, improvements in energy efficiency observed over the last 20 years will continue because the energy-efficiency of new equipment and processes available on the market is usually better than that of the average existing stock.

There is great potential for further improvement in available technologies, but such technologies are as yet little used for a variety of reasons, most of which relate to market conditions and consumer behaviour. The benefits of current improvements in the efficiency of energy-using equipment and processes, from industrial systems to domestic appliances, have yet to be fully felt, and the faster the stock turnover the better. Economic growth and the health of the economies of IEA countries can play a major part, not only in accelerating the rate of turnover of existing equipment, but also in sustaining the technological creativity of industry that fuels the development of energy efficiency. Table 10.4 summarises potential offered by the best available technology when adopted in a range of end-use sectors, including transportation (passenger cars and goods vehicles). The estimates of total possible energy savings are based on a comparison between the average efficiency of existing capital stocks and the efficiency of the best available new technology. These estimates include the savings likely to be achieved in response to current market forces and government policies, as well as the proportion of those potential savings not likely to be achieved through current efforts.

More analysis is needed to assess the cost-effectiveness of these energy-efficiency options. In cases where cost data is available and estimates have been provided, the cost-benefit analysis presented is country-specific because energy prices vary markedly from one IEA country to the next. Further gains in energy efficiency are likely to be achieved during the next two or three decades. Continued R&D, leading to technology options for the long term, shows significant promise for yet more efficient processes and components.

*Table 10.4*
**Technical and Economic Potential of New and Improved Energy End-Use Technologies**

| | Estimated Share of Total Final Consumption | Estimated Share of Total $CO_2$ Emissions | Possible Total Energy Savings | Existing Market and Institutional Barriers | Potential Energy Savings (not likely to be achieved) |
|---|---|---|---|---|---|
| Residential space heating and cooling | 11.4% | 11% | 10-50% | Some/Many | Mixed |
| Residential water heating | 3.4% | 3.6% | Mixed | Some/Many | Mixed |
| Residential lighting | 0.6% | 1.2% | Over 50% | Many | 30-50% |
| Residential refrigeration | 1.1% | 2.1% | 30-50% | Many | 10-30% |
| Commercial space heating and cooling | 6.1% | 6.8% | Mixed | Some/Many | Mixed |
| Commercial lighting | 1.5% | 3.4% | 10-30% | Some/Many | Mixed |
| Industrial motors | 4.5% | 9.0% | 10-30% | Few/Some | 0-10% |
| Steel | 4.1% | 4.6% | 15-25% | Few/Some | 0-15% |
| Chemicals | 8.4% | 5.9% | 10-25% | Few/Some | 0-20% |
| Pulp and paper | 2.9% | 1.2% | 10-30% | Few/Some | 0-10% |
| Cement | 0.1% | 0.9% | 10-40% | Few/Some | 0-10% |
| Passenger cars | 15.2% | 13.7% | 30-50% | Many | 20-30% |
| Goods vehicles | 10.1% | 9.1% | 20-40% | Some | 10-20% |

Source: *Energy Efficiency and the Environment,* IEA (1991).
Note: Unit savings shown in the table would result if the best available technology were used to replace the average stock in use today in IEA countries over the next 10 to 20 years. Some of these savings would take place under existing market conditions. For example, for residential lighting, over 50 per cent per unit savings would be possible. But, due to the many market and institutional barriers, there would remain a 30 to 50 per cent economic energy-savings potential that would not be achieved.

### (a) *Industrial Energy End-Use*

Through partnerships with private industry, with utilities and public-sector R&D organisations, significant reductions in energy consumption may be attained through R&D that will improve energy conversion efficiency, recover energy from industrial waste heat, and provide higher-temperature structural materials, also through the related technical information that supports these advances. In all industries opportunities exist to develop technologies that provide industrial processes with energy services offering enhanced energy-efficiency and greater fuel-flexibility than at present. Energy that is currently lost in the manufacturing process can be captured and used, thereby reducing energy requirements to produce goods and services. Savings can thus be achieved from lower energy costs and more efficient plant utilisation.

Technology development programmes should focus on the following: advanced chemical and mechanical heat pumps; process heat exchangers and ceramic recuperators; advanced materials such as continuous fibre-ceramic composites; advanced combustion systems for industry; co-generation technology; sensors and controls; improved membranes for separation systems; and process electrolysis. These technologies address a mix of near- and long-term opportunities to save energy in the industrial sector. Progress in new industrial processes, from raw material to final product, presents a major opportunity for industry to improve its energy efficiency and fuel-flexibility. Potential for saving energy by recreating the production process exists within specific industries, such as steel making, as well as within process steps that cut across industries, such as catalyst or separations technologies.

Reducing the amount of waste generated is an important strategy to control costs, reduce environmental impacts and improve productivity. Potential waste is not produced and therefore does not require treatment and disposal. Waste reduction ensures that more of the raw material becomes the final product, thereby reducing energy requirements, saving natural resources, and lessening environmental impacts. After wastes are reduced to their technical minimum, industry may use or convert unavoidable wastes into feedstocks or fuels. If use or conversion is impossible, it may treat wastes and release them into the environment. More restrictive environmental regulations, rising energy costs, and the requirement for more economical waste control, call for investment and R&D in technologies to reduce industrial wastes.

There are a wide variety of production processes, however, that require individualised waste management strategies. In addition, implementation of new waste-management techniques can require regulatory changes. To overcome the lack of advanced waste reduction and utilisation technology, as well as information barriers and regulatory deficiencies, the range of new actions could include: support for R&D on advanced process technology that reduces wastes, and support for R&D on waste-use and waste-conversion technology. The introduction of regulatory changes, moreover, may help foster improved waste management without compromising environmental quality.

(b) *Residential Energy End-Use*

Many near-term technical options for residential energy conservation exist, namely to improve efficiency of new houses, to "retrofit" existing residences (and heating or cooling systems), and to replace older, inefficient appliances. Over the long term, new technical opportunities should become available. These include: commercial application of new types of building material; factory-based production of structural components or entire homes; advanced equipment and "smart" controls for lighting, space heating and cooling, water heating and household appliances; and more effective use of landscaping and site design to temper the "micro-climates" in residential neighbourhoods. Besides saving money for consumers in the long run, many of these residential energy technologies can make homes more comfortable and improve air quality within them. From a broader perspective, they can contribute to overall efficiency, reliability and environmental acceptability.

Significant advances in energy efficiency depend upon the availability of next-generation technology and technology options for the long term. The following are the specific technical areas for continuing or new R&D effort:

- new building designs and construction methods that make cost-effective use of direct solar gains, that incorporate better insulation, low-heat-loss windows, building thermal mass, and measures to reduce air leakage through the building envelope and heating and cooling ducts;
- energy-efficient appliances and equipment, such as improved refrigerators, furnaces, heat pumps, and air conditioners;
- high-quality fluorescent lights to replace some standard incandescent bulbs in homes;
- high-performance materials for building and equipment applications, including low-emissivity glass, prototypes for evacuated panels and other advanced insulation concepts, and replacements for conventional refrigerants and foam insulation that contain ozone-depleting chlorofluorocarbons compounds;
- industrialised housing techniques, ranging from factory-assembled windows, walls and roof components to complete panels or building modules;
- more effective techniques for retrofitting existing residential buildings, including replacement of inefficient boiler burners and controls, improved techniques for insulating buildings and sealing air leaks, and advanced controls for home appliances to optimise the timing of both thermal and electrical loads;
- landscaping and site design techniques that can reduce cooling and heating loads by tempering the climate around houses.

To ensure that improved energy efficiency enhances rather than harms indoor air quality, support should be directed towards R&D in this area, including investigation of the sources of indoor air pollution, practical methods for evaluating indoor air quality in homes and other locations, and cost-effective means of mitigating air-quality problems in both new and existing housing. Some energy-saving measures, if not properly designed and implemented, may worsen the quality of indoor air. For example, measures that save energy by sealing air leaks can also eliminate too much of the fresh air needed to dilute indoor pollutants. Once problems are properly understood and diagnosed, there are often reliable technical solutions. For example, well-designed mechanical ventilation systems, often with heat recovery to reduce space- or water-heating costs, can actually improve indoor air quality in homes, compared with uncontrolled air infiltration through the building shell or the opening of windows.

(c) *Commercial Energy End-Use*

Through partnerships between private industry, utilities and public-sector R&D organisations, new energy-efficiency and renewable-energy technologies can be developed that are reliable, commercially competitive, and meet energy service needs while maintaining or enhancing indoor environmental quality, occupant comfort and productivity in commercial buildings. For example, natural gas-fired furnaces and boilers with electric ignition and condensing heat exchangers are 10 to 30 per cent more efficient than standard equipment. New designs for commercial-building heat pumps and chillers with variable speed and output require up to 25 per cent less electricity than systems now in place.

R&D programmes can contribute to major efficiency gains in fluorescent lighting ballasts and high-performance window coatings. Also, research should continue to develop more energy-efficient alternatives to the use of chlorofluorocarbons, hydro-fluorocarbons and foam insulation in refrigeration systems. These and many other technologies offer considerable promise for the future. Next-generation development could include: cost-effective passive and active solar technologies for heating and cooling; advanced controls for lighting and heating, ventilation and air-conditioning systems; "smart" windows with optical properties that can adjust to balance heat gains and losses and availability of daylight; building-scale photovoltaics; high-efficiency office equipment; heat pumps; district heating and cooling systems that use thermal storage, and advanced, low-pollution co-generation.

Another important component of the R&D effort could be aimed at maintaining or improving the indoor environmental quality of energy-efficient commercial buildings. Given the potential costs of disruptions in commercial services, or other adverse effects on employee productivity, businesses continue to emphasise that energy-saving measures must not threaten the quality of the environment in offices, stores, or other commercial buildings.

## Technology Prospects and Markets

### *Market Trends*

Energy intensity in the IEA countries is expected to continue to decline at an annual rate of around 1 per cent. This continued decline is based on the assumption of further technological advances, leading to improvements in energy efficiency and to further structural change resulting in lower energy intensity. In addition to direct economic benefits, numerous subsidiary benefits can be expected from energy-efficiency improvements, namely:

- enhanced energy security through extending the lifespan of depletable energy resources and lessening the impact of energy-supply and price disruptions;
- reduced environmental consequences of primary-energy production, conversion and distribution per unit of end-use service without compromising performance characteristics;
- sustainable economic development, especially for newly industrialising nations and countries in transition towards a market economy, since investments in energy efficiency often provide a greater return than investments in energy supply, when evaluated at the margin, while improvements can be achieved incrementally to provide flexibility and match demand.

The future rate of decline in energy intensities in the IEA region, however, is expected to be lower than the average over the previous 20 years, since recent evidence points to many impediments to widescale diffusion and adoption of cost-effective and energy-efficient energy end-use technology, most of them also being barriers to greater economic efficiency. This is of particular relevance to developing countries and Economies in Transition. According to the IEA *World Energy Outlook,* 1996 edition, after the turmoil of initial steps towards a market economy, energy intensity in the countries of the former Soviet Union is projected to improve substantially after peaking in the mid 1990s. From 1996 onwards, energy intensity is projected to fall by 2.3 per cent per annum in the capacity constraints case and 3.2 per cent in the energy savings case. However, at a level of between 1.5 and 1.8 toe per US$1 000 of GDP (at market exchange rates), it remains very high. While there is certainly scope for considerable price-induced conservation, there is considerable uncertainty as to whether such a rapid rate of improvement in energy intensity is sustainable over the next 15 years. The pattern of the industrial growth in countries of the former Soviet Union, other developing countries and Economies in Transition will also play an important role in reducing energy intensity. However, this growth remains very difficult to predict as it depends upon the pace of economic reform. Furthermore, energy-intensive industries might represent one of the few areas where the region has a comparative advantage and these industries could thus be an important engine for growth within the region.

Energy intensity in the developing countries of the rest of the world would appear to have risen by 1.1 per cent per annum from 1981 to 1991. This can be viewed as a result of population pressures and economic growth. Limited financial resources tend to reduce the flexibility developing countries need in order to take advantage of improvements in energy production, distribution and consumption technologies. Furthermore, although evidence is patchy, it can be argued that energy prices in many of these countries are somewhat lower than world prices so there is little incentive to invest scarce capital in newer, more efficient technologies for using energy that is already inexpensive. Finally, the historical increase in energy intensity in the developing countries is probably somewhat overestimated, due to the important, but declining role of non-commercial fuels.

### *Key Players*

Success in energy end-use efficiency and saving depends on bringing together and motivating many individuals, groups and companies which are often not primarily concerned with either energy efficiency or energy-related R&D. The best way of doing so will vary from country to country according to constitutional structures, government organisations and traditional energy-conservation activities.

Governments at all levels are involved in encouraging efficient energy end-use technology and supporting technology deployment into the market. The roles and responsibilities depend, again, on the constitutional framework. Inter-ministerial or inter-departmental co-ordination is not easy. Central government organisation of measures for energy conservation has to strike a balance among conflicting requirements. Strong central organisation can ensure that conservation activities are vigorously pursued and properly co-ordinated across the whole range of government entities, forming a part of not only energy policy but also other policies, such as housing. However, there is a danger that over-centralisation of responsibility may reduce the commitment of those responsible for implementing efficient energy technologies and measures in sectorally-oriented agencies.

Many different individuals, businesses and other organisations are involved in the technology innovation process and application. They are far more numerous and disaggregated than those involved in energy production. The organisations provide equipment, services, advice, motivation or incentives to consumers. Without them, the consumer undoubtedly would not undertake conservation actions as confidently or as carefully. These organisations – whether private or public – must be effectively involved in any government effort to improve energy efficiency. For this reason, this chapter describes some of the characteristics and background of these organisations, and how governments have involved them in ongoing efforts.

Several types of professionals and companies are involved in providing energy conservation services, often as part of wider operations. They include insulation manufacturers and installers, energy auditors, consultants, architects, boiler retrofitters, appliance manufacturers, financing companies and plant constructors. Many existing trade and professional associations in these industries promote efficient energy end-use. A recent innovation in the United States has been the introduction of energy service companies which manage energy use in enterprises by providing, on a contract basis, technical, managerial and financial resources required for a retrofit project. They receive a return on their investment from the savings achieved. There has been less progress in other countries, but similar companies are now beginning to develop in Canada and in Europe, where the European Commission is seeking to encourage their development. Their success, however, will be much influenced by tax practices, which vary between Member countries.

The energy supply industries in some IEA countries play an important role in providing energy efficiency services through their direct dealings with consumers, and their customer service, marketing and technical functions. Energy efficiency and saving are sometimes undertaken by these utilities to improve the commercial outlook, particularly in relation to the need and cost of new capacity. Sometimes conservation activities are the result of government persuasion or legislation. Most of the time, energy supply industries provide conservation services in response to both factors. An increased emphasis is now placed on the integration of efficiency and supply options into the electric and gas utility planning process and demand-side management, as discussed in Chapter 8.

Furthermore, non-governmental groups are trying to encourage technology improvements and adoption of energy-efficient measures with varying degrees of support from government. Special interest organisations concerned with energy efficiency both provide services and act as pressure groups through research, demonstration projects, public education and policy advocacy. There are also groups which have broader interests than energy: consumer groups, service clubs, mortgage lenders, non-profit companies and local initiative groups, as well as the environmental and ecological movements.

### *Market Barriers*

A continuing concern of IEA governments is over the fact that investments in more energy-efficient equipment do not keep pace with the technical and economic availability of new and improved technology. There remains a significant gap between the energy-using characteristics of the present stock of industrial processes, residential and commercial buildings and equipment, and the energy-saving potential of the most efficient systems and equipment available on the market today. A summary of factors that contribute to determining the market potential of energy end-use technology described in this chapter is shown in Table 10.5. It is likely that future improvements in efficiency will continue at a moderate pace, unless there are sudden, significant changes in energy prices, in conjunction with investments in system expansion and restructuring, facility replacement, process improvement, and imposition of stricter energy standards and environmental controls.

Analysts commonly cite a host of barriers or disincentives that have tended to reduce the pace and extent of efficiency savings. These relate to a number of institutional, economic, behavioural and practical issues. Some of the more significant barriers are given below.

- Absence of reliable information on technology advances. For many new energy technologies, and some established ones, industry managers, architects and engineers may be reluctant to invest in energy-saving measures without reliable data on actual performance and costs. The same concerns are shared by many utility programme managers, mortgage lenders and individual energy consumers. The equipment-based information that would allow the cost of realising market or economic potential to be estimated is not generally available in some countries.

- The fragmented nature of the energy end-use market, and the multiplicity of decision-makers. These factors contribute to a reluctance or inability to invest in long-term, generic R&D. In particular, in the residential and commercial sectors, the building industry is split between a large number of small firms, subcontractors and suppliers of equipment and parts. This makes it difficult to generate and sustain support for large-scale industry-sponsored R&D programmes and technology projects.

- Slow turnover. Many of the foregoing problems are exacerbated by the customarily long lifetimes of most industrial processes, of residential and commercial structures and of the heating and cooling systems that serve them. Therefore, an initial decision on design, construction, rehabilitation or appliance purchase that fails to take advantage of cost-effective energy efficiencies will mean a lost opportunity that will be felt for many years to come.

- Regulated energy prices that may not reflect the full cost of energy supply. Utility rates established for electricity and natural gas, for example, do not always incorporate the cost to the economy or society of supplying energy service under various conditions (i.e. non-internalised externalities). Most utilities' pricing includes a fixed component relating to costs and a variable component. A firm's capital expenditure to save energy will normally apply only to the variable component or, in the case of block rates, only to the marginal block, not to the fixed part or higher tariff stocks. Such pricing is unlikely to encourage

*Table 10.5*

**Comparative Market Potential of New and Improved Energy End-Use Technologies: Industrial, Residential and Commercial Sectors**

| Technology | Time-Frame (years) | Nature/Size of Market | Regional Aspects | Potential Marketability |
|---|---|---|---|---|
| **a) Industrial Energy End-Use** | | | | |
| Chemical industry | 0-10 | • Environmental concerns may continue to drive change<br>• Potential for retrofitting and plant upgrading | • Lack of interest by small and medium size industry | H |
| Aluminium production | 0-20 | • Potential for retrofitting and plant upgrading | | M |
| Iron and steel | 0-20 | • Resource-use optimisation may increase economic competitiveness<br>• Potential for retrofitting and plant upgrading | • Steel production in IEA North America shows higher energy intensity | H |
| Pulp and paper processing | 0-20 | • Environmental concerns may continue to drive change | • Larger use of pulp imports in IEA Europe | M |
| Cement production | 0-15 | • Large energy-efficiency gap between best practice and average plant | | M |
| Glass and ceramics | 0-15 | • Environmental concerns may continue to drive change | • Larger market potential for energy intensity reduction in several IEA countries | M |
| Food processing | 0-15 | • Large energy efficiency gap between best practice and average plant | • Notable variations in energy intensity between industries and products | M |
| Cross-cutting technologies | 0-10 | • Energy auditing may help to identify cost-effective opportunities | • Potential for energy intensity reduction depends on industry and process | H |

Note: L, M, H represent low, medium, high.

*Table 10.5 (continued)*

**Comparative Market Potential of New and Improved Energy End-Use Technologies: Industrial, Residential and Commercial Sectors**

| Technology | Time-Frame (years) | Nature/Size of Market | Regional Aspects | Potential Marketability |
|---|---|---|---|---|
| **b) Residential Energy End-Use** | | | | |
| Space heating and cooling | 0-10 | • Large market potential in the refurbishment of existing buildings | • Notable differences in the energy requirements for space heating and cooling between IEA countries | H |
| Water heating | 0-10 | • Large market potential through replacement of existing units | • Energy tariff structures reduce market potential in some IEA countries | L |
| Lighting | 0-10 | • Large market potential in the refurbishment of existing buildings | • Electricity tariff structures reduce market potential in some IEA countries | H |
| Refrigeration | 0-10 | • Energy labelling and information campaigns may influence consumer behaviour | • Average energy efficiency of refrigerators and freezers shows notable differences between IEA countries | H |
| Cooking | 0-10 | • Energy labelling and information campaigns may influence consumer behaviour | • Average energy efficiency of electric cookers shows notable differences between IEA countries | M |
| Washing machines | 0-10 | • Energy labelling and information campaigns may influence consumer behaviour | | M |
| **c) Commercial Energy End-Use** | | | | |
| Space heating and cooling | 0-10 | • Large market potential in the refurbishment of existing buildings | • Notable differences in energy intensity of commercial premises between IEA countries | H |
| Lighting | 0-10 | • Large market potential for improvements and savings | | M |
| Office equipment | 0-10 | • Improved service requirements may encourage change | | M |

Note: L, M, H represent low, medium, high.

capital outlay on energy savings. Also, the regulatory framework of utilities may limit opportunities for demand-side management initiatives if the result is a loss of revenue, for instance. However, the effects of rapid restructuring and deregulation may also be harmful because of the instability created and sharpened price competitiveness, which may discourage capital investments.

- Lack of customer incentives. Market mechanisms often fail to encourage the adoption of an economical energy-efficient technology or measure in situations where those who must pay for it cannot count on receiving the resulting economic, environmental and other benefits. For instance, builders and home buyers both have a strong tendency to favour the lower "up-front" cost of a new residential property not incorporating energy-efficiency features, even at the expense of attractive potential energy savings in the future.

- Limited capital and means. Industries that are highly energy-intensive have a stronger incentive to invest in efficient energy end-use technology, while others do not even think there may exist substantial and cost-effective opportunities in better technology. Most firms regard energy-efficient technology in the larger context of strategic planning. Investments are evaluated and ranked according to a variety of elements, namely product demand, competition, cost of capital labour and energy. Rapid payback of investment would be expected in a regime of high capital costs. Energy efficiency is only one consideration, moreover, in decisions regarding investments affecting energy use in the industrial, residential and commercial sectors. Building owners and tenants tend to attach greater importance to occupant comfort and overall productivity and may be reluctant to make any changes that might affect building operations.

## Technology Policy Issues

### *Role of Governments*

Achieving reductions in energy consumption through energy efficiency is both a short-term and long-term undertaking. Because of the many barriers, government policies should be consistent and coherent and they should aim at removing or reducing obstacles to increased deployment of more efficient energy end-use technologies, while at the same time fostering continuing progress in new and improved technologies for the long term. In many cases, energy-efficiency policy and environmental protection policy use the same basic instruments. Of particular interest is the effect of such instruments on decisions to carry out new technology development programmes. Energy-efficiency policies and programmes should also improve the general public's awareness of the benefits of rational energy use and savings. Multi-level education and training for personnel involved in design, installation and maintenance of energy end-use equipment should be encouraged. While the preceding analysis has focused on energy efficiency in parallel with improved economics and environmental enhancement, it is equally important for alternative end-use devices to be developed to allow the shift of existing consumption to more diverse fuel sources. Here, the objective of sustainable energy enters at the system level. For example, the selection between a natural gas or an electric-powered heat pump transcends a simple focus on efficiency and addresses other energy system factors including energy diversification.

An end-use service can potentially exploit a different fuel source that, from a longer-term perspective, may be less expensive, more secure, more readily available, more environmentally benign, or allow use of an indigenous resource. In achieving system integration, there is likely to be an overall benefit stemming from one or more attributes, such as efficiency, cost, environmental impact, security or performance. Because numerous trade-offs are possible among such diverse objectives, a clear articulation of national energy policy and environmental priorities is essential before extensive efforts are channelled towards new and improved technology development and deployment.

The energy efficiency of current and future technology is largely determined by equipment vendors and based on their customers' most pressing requirement in terms of product or service. R&D organisations can identify pathways to increased efficiency and develop end-use systems to incorporate such advances. In the industrial sector, while the industrialist both pays for the energy efficiency improvement and reaps its benefits, efficiency research and development remain underfunded. It is hazardous for any single firm to finance and conduct the efficiency R&D necessary when the benefits of that R&D may soon be reaped by other firms. Government and institutional decision-makers, in partnership with manufacturers, can inform potential users of the value of new end-use products to facilitate successful commercialisation. It is also possible to integrate R&D into this chain, where governments recognise that new end-use products are desirable even if not yet available for commercialisation. Technology deployment thus extends to technology procurement. It can be seen from Table 10.6 which areas need government support and which possible technology deployment measures are applicable.

Life-cycle and fuel-cycle assessment can provide decision-makers with powerful means to evaluate the energy, environmental and economic impacts associated with an end-use technology product, process or activity. This can be done by identifying and quantifying the impact on human beings or on the environment of use of a form of energy or a material, as well as any associated releases into the environment, and by evaluating opportunities for new energy technologies and environmental improvements. The assessment includes the entire life cycle of the product, process or activity and encompasses the following: exploration, extracting and processing of raw material; technology development, manufacturing, transportation and distribution; use/re-use/maintenance; and safe final disposal. But the methodological problems associated with life-cycle and fuel-cycle assessment are significant and there is no way to include all social, environmental and macro-economic elements in a closed form. Nevertheless, the process itself can be heuristic, since the impact of attempting to perform life-cycle analyses regularly as part of the decision-making process may help to raise the quality of decisions by creating an awareness of issues and connections between them that might otherwise have been overlooked.

R&D budgets in IEA countries can support energy efficiency through basic scientific and applied R&D in end-use technologies, and by contributing to the demonstration of technology feasibility. R&D can be carried out on a risk-sharing basis in co-operation with the more fragmented industries such as the building industry and appliance manufacturers. Most

*Table 10.6*
**Industrial, Residential and Commercial Energy Use: Government Role in Technology Deployment**

| Technology | Level of Market Activity | Need for Government Support | Possible Government Measures |
|---|---|---|---|
| Industrial Energy End-Use | • Low to moderate in most IEA countries<br>• New environmental concerns drive technological progress in many cases<br>• Focus on cross-cutting technologies<br>• Process restructuring to increase competitiveness in the global market | • Sharing of technology information<br>• Removal of subsidies and trade barriers<br>• Streamlining of regulatory practices and standards<br>• Promoting fuel- and life-cycle analysis | • R&D funding of new technologies and production-process upgrading<br>• Technology partnership with industry and use of voluntary targets<br>• Energy auditing and monitoring<br>• Supporting demand-side management programmes |
| Residential Energy End-Use | • Moderate in most IEA countries<br>• Integration of energy-efficient and environmentally sound technology<br>• Rehabilitation of existing buildings<br>• Recycling of appliances and other components | • Establishment of minimum efficiency standards<br>• Assistance to local housing authorities and administrations<br>• Demonstration of new technology applications and intelligent housing<br>• Demonstration of retrofitting approaches | • R&D partnership with professional associations and industry<br>• Funding R&D on advanced components<br>• Energy labelling<br>• Information exchange and benchmarking<br>• Support for new financing schemes |
| Commercial Energy End-Use | • Possible leading role of public and commercial sector<br>• Cost-sharing technology arrangements<br>• Integration of energy-efficient and renewable energy technologies into new architecture | • Sharing of technology information<br>• Promoting demonstration of new and improved technology and systems<br>• Support for retrofitting experience | • Technology data collection, and information exchange on best-case practice<br>• Long-term building operation and maintenance programmes<br>• Third-party financing |

energy-efficiency research initiatives undertaken by IEA Member countries consists of applied research in order to improve the efficiency of existing equipment, materials or process design. And the most important goal of such activities is to facilitate market entrance for new products, through co-operation in the demonstration of a new technology. Examples include co-operation with the building industy and the architectural profession to design and demonstrate much more efficient buildings, as well as funding for organisations to demonstrate new ways to use energy more efficiently. The goal here is to reduce barriers to improvements in more conventional end-use products tending to require a higher initial investment today, and to obtain a future (but perhaps not guaranteed) benefit in terms of cost.

Therefore, to achieve progress, it may be appropriate for industry to explore – and for governments to support – more extensive evaluations of innovation in end-use services and the resulting changes in the fundamental nature of energy consuming end-use products.

It is an historical fact that IEA governments' R&D expenditure on energy efficiency decline at precisely those times when market mechanisms that would support the development of the technology needed for the future no longer find this research an attractive investment. When energy is relatively inexpensive, as it has been since the mid-1980s, the development of new, more energy-efficient technology appears less attractive than hitherto.

From 1981 to 1993 IEA countries' R&D budgets for energy conservation in all the energy end-use sectors (transportation included) fluctuated considerably. They peaked in 1980/81 at about US$ 775 million (adjusted to 1993 prices) and fell in 1993 to US$ 650 million.

Reductions in spending on energy conservation have been particularly pronounced, because of two major factors, namely: the fall in energy prices in the early 1980s; and a greater reliance on market forces to stimulate R&D activities. Although coherent and comparable figures for R&D expenditures in the private sector are not available, it would appear that industry has also substantially reduced energy-related research activities since the mid-1980s. Nevertheless, recent government energy R&D budget figures show that appropriations for energy efficiency have increased in several countries as a result of environmental concerns. The most immediate and direct benefit of these new R&D programmes is a reduction in the use of resources and in the emissions of pollutants that occur upstream in the fuel cycles.

Governments have a clear responsibility for ensuring that energy is used efficiently in their own buildings and sites. This is often difficult because government accounting systems rarely allow a government department to retain any savings arising from efficiency investments. But some have made efforts in this area, and are continuing to do so. A number of government-wide programmes have been launched as a means of reducing overall government expenditures (notably in Canada, the Netherlands and the United States). Government efforts to stimulate energy efficiency in areas for which they are responsible, such as public buildings, can in principle be grouped in all the categories of endeavour previously described. They can range from information campaigns to increasing civil servants' energy awareness, or to controlling temperatures in public buildings, or direct financial support. Several IEA countries have highlighted the sorts of initiative that government can develop in the demonstration of new technologies in their areas of immediate interest. Such initiatives can generate success stories, show leadership and provide the basis for industry growth and spin-offs to other areas of the economy. And, if the investments required are made prudently with low payback times, this demonstrated success can be emulated in the private sector.

### *Role of International Co-operation*

Energy efficiency can contribute simultaneously to the goals of economic growth, protection of the environment and energy security. While IEA countries have increased their energy efficiency remarkably in the past, there still exists a very large technical potential for further improvements, the full realisation of which is hampered by market and institutional barriers.

The IEA's work to further enhance energy efficiency includes monitoring energy efficiency and demand development, conducting studies on energy efficiency, exchange of experience among Member countries and evaluation of national conservation programmes.

International technology collaboration promises to be most fruitful in the following five areas: fundamental R&D; exploratory development of longer-term high-impact concepts; joint demonstration of the benefits of market-ready systems; development of international standards, preparation of public-information and educational material and action to reduce institutional and attitudinal barriers to deployment; and technology transfer to newly industrialising countries and countries in transition towards a market economy.

International co-operation is an important part of R&D efforts. Participation in international fora or data networks helps circulate technical know-how, programme information and evaluation; it also prevents unnecessary duplication of work and wasting of funds. IEA Member countries have often avoided repeating each other's mistakes by co-operating in the exchange of information on efficient technologies and practices, and particularly on the effectiveness of various government and co-operative government/industry programmes (such as joint procurement of more efficient technologies). Fundamental cross-cutting R&D has the best possibility for technology collaboration. At the other end of the technology innovation cycle, collaborative projects may be important in the dissemination of quality technical data and analysis of new technological possibilities. Technology collaboration may be at its most relevant with projects receiving insufficient industrial support, due to limited short-term economic possibilities, but offering significant potential in the longer term for energy-efficiency along with associated advantages in cost, security and environmental quality. Co-operation may also encourage industry participation in order to encourage more rapid technology deployment. Table 10.7 presents prospects and means for international co-operation focusing on the principal technologies discussed in this chapter.

IEA collaboration in energy end-use technology has traditionally been comprehensive and has promoted strong interest. More recently, activities are revealing an even greater potential for expansion through recognition that cost-effective energy efficiency and conservation technology can be an excellent means for increasing competitiveness, reducing pollution, enhancing energy security and promoting sustainable growth.

The Implementing Agreement on Energy Technology Data Exchange (ETDE) is providing participants with a common database and distribution system for bibliographic energy information. The IEA Information Centre for the Analysis and Dissemination of Demonstrated Energy Technologies (CADDET) publishes brochures and reports on demonstration projects spanning the entire energy and electricity end-use area, including buildings, industrial processes, small-scale co-generation of heat and electricity and electrical appliances. Other Implementing Agreements on technology information exchange and diffusion deal with heat pumps, heat transfer and heat exchangers.

In the residential, commercial and building sectors, international collaboration is very active through the multi-task Implementing Agreement on Energy Conservation in Buildings and Community Systems, the IEA Air Infiltration and Ventilation Centre, as well as co-operative activity in district

*Table 10.7*
**Industrial, Residential and Commercial Energy Use: Role of International Co-operation in Technology Progress**

| Technology | Prospects for International Co-operation | Modes of Co-operation | Technology Transfer Issues |
|---|---|---|---|
| Industrial Energy End-Use | • Industrial process integration<br>• Small-scale co-generation<br>• Waste and emissions reduction<br>• Advanced heat exchangers and ceramic recuperators<br>• Advanced chemical and mechanical heat pumps | • Collaborative R&D in new components and advanced processes<br>• Information exchange on new technology<br>• Fuel- and life-cycle analysis and energy indicators | • Partnership with industrial associations<br>• Promotion of voluntary agreements<br>• Co-operation on international standards<br>• Collaboration with developing countries and countries in transition towards a market economy |
| Residential Energy End-Use | • Integration of efficient energy end-use and renewable-energy technology<br>• Energy-efficient appliances and equipment<br>• New building designs and construction methods; industrialised housing techniques<br>• High-performance materials for building and equipment applications<br>• Indoor air quality<br>• Advanced heat pumps and heat storage | • Collaborative R&D in new components and systems<br>• Demonstration of new and improved systems<br>• Information exchange on new technology and best-case practice<br>• Fuel- and life-cycle analysis and energy efficiency indicators | • Partnership with professional associations<br>• Harmonisation of national technical standards<br>• Collaboration with developing countries and countries in transition towards a market economy |
| Commercial Energy End-Use | • Cost-effective new energy end-use and renewable energy technology integration<br>• High-efficiency office equipment<br>• Intelligent buildings and advanced architecture<br>• Indoor air quality<br>• Advanced heat pumps and storage | • Collaborative R&D in new components and systems<br>• Demonstration of advanced technology integration<br>• Information exchange on best-case practice in public buildings | • Partnership with local communities and utilities<br>• Harmonisation of national technical standards |

heating, energy storage and advanced fuel cells. A total of 14 Agreements maintain a strong pace of activity in energy end-use technologies, including the recently signed Agreements on co-operative activity in industrial process integration and demand-side management.

## Approach

Analysis shows impressive technical opportunities for using energy more efficiently and effectively in the industrial, residential and commercial sectors. It should be ensured that reliable information is available on energy end-use, on the cost of new technologies and the actual energy efficiency savings they offer. Such market information is an essential prerequisite for evaluating the effectiveness of efficiency programmes and for developing policies that accelerate the deployment of more efficient technologies and lead to the resulting improvement in the economy. Energy markets work best when they are competitive and when trade and investment distortions are limited. But the many technical and institutional barriers may discourage efforts and limit technological progress. To meet the technology priorities identified in this chapter, IEA Member countries may therefore wish to work towards a technology strategy and collaborative R&D programme that includes the measures listed below.

- Conducting aggressive cost-shared government-industry projects focusing on the demonstration of innovative energy-efficient processes in energy-intensive industries, particularly in the aluminum, cement, chemical, food processing, glass and ceramics, iron and steel, and pulp and paper industries.
- Accelerating progress on next-generation and cross-cutting technologies and techniques to promote optimisation of energy and resource use in industrial production cycles, taking into account use of materials, curbing of emissions and opportunities for fuel switching.
- Promoting energy efficiency of new residential and commercial buildings by providing technical information to energy users, engineers and equipment suppliers, and by facilitating the creation and enforcement of energy-efficiency standards through building codes.
- Improving the energy efficiency of new appliances for the residential and commercial sector by reducing their cost and improving their performance (particularly in space heating and cooling, water heating, lighting, refrigeration, cooking, and washing machines), also by developing methods for monitoring and enhancing indoor comfort and air quality.
- Contributing to retrofit energy technology in existing residential and commercial buildings while supporting efficient technology demonstration and practice in publicly owned housing.
- Conducting energy audits in manufacturing plants, in residential and in commercial facilities to accelerate adoption of cost-effective energy end-use technology and measures, with a view to establishing component life, fuel-cycle flexibility and total-cycle analysis.
- Assisting non-Member countries through the dissemination of information on available energy end-use technologies, on opportunities for efficiency improvements, on success stories, and on practical experiences and potential gains.

# ANNEX I

## MEMBERSHIP OF EXPERTS' GROUP AND PANELS

### EXPERTS' GROUP

**Australia**
Mr. Barry Jones
Minister, Energy and Agriculture
Delegation of Australia to the OECD
Paris

**Canada**
Mr. Peter Reilly-Roe
Director, Technology and Programmes Division
Transport and Energy Branch
Energy, Mines and Resources Canada
Ottawa

**Denmark**
Mr. Steen Rolf Jacobsen
Director for Energy R&D
Ministry of Energy
Copenhagen

**Germany**
Prof. Dr. W. Koese
Member of the Board of Directors
Kernforschungszentrum
Karlsruhe

Dr. Hanns -J. Neef
Deputy Director, PBE
Kernforschungsanage
Jülich

Dr. Hermann-Friedrich Wagner
Director, Energy R&D Poicy Division
Bundesministerium für Forschung und Technologie
Bonn

**Japan**
Mr. Michio Kobayashi
Director
Engineering Research & Development Administration
Tokyo Electric Power Company, Tokyo

Mr. Seiji Oshima
First Secretary, Scientific Affairs
Delegation of Japan to the OECD
Paris

**The Netherlands**
Mr. Alfred R. Braun
Braun Consutants
Hengelo

Mr. T.M.P. Schoustra
Directorate for Energy Conservation
Ministry of Economic Affairs
The Hague

**Norway**
Mr. Kjell Oppegaard
SPUNG Programme Manager
Royal Norwegian Council for Scientific and Industrial Research (NTNF)
Oslo

**Sweden**
Dr. Leif Brandels
Head of Department National Energy Administration
Ministry of Environment and Energy
Stockholm

Dr. Lars A. Kristoferson
Stockholm Environment Institute
Stockholm

**Switzerland**
Dr. Alec Jean Baer
Deputy Director
Federal Energy Office
Bern

**United Kingdom**
Dr. Barrie W. Dale
Chief, Scientists Group
Energy Technology Support Unit
UK Department of Energy
Harwell

Mr. B. Darbyshire
Offshore Supplies Office
UK Department of Energy
Glasgow

**United States of America**
Dr. Roger Le Gassie
Senior Vice-President
Technology and Management Services Inc.
Germantown, Maryland

Mr. Charles R. Mandelbaum
Office of Planning and Analysis
US Department of Energy
Washington DC

Dr. Robert L. San Martin
Deputy Assistant Secretary for Renewable Energy
US Department of Energy
Washington DC

**European Commission**
Dr. Pierre Bourdeau
Director, Energy R&D
Directorate General for Science, R&D
Brussels

**Nuclear Energy Agency**
Mr. Geoffrey Stevens
Head, Nuclear Development Division
Nuclear Energy Agency, OECD
Paris

**IEA Secretariat**
Mr. John Brady
Head, Division of Energy Technology Collaboration

Dr. Kenneth Friedman
Head, Division of Energy Technology Policy

Dr. Sergio F. Garribba
Director, Energy Technology and R&D Office

Dr. Samuel Schweitzer
Assistant Director, Energy Technology and R&D Office

Dr. Roger Stuart
Principal Administrator, Division of Energy Technology Studies

**PANEL ON CLEAN USE OF COAL**

Dr. Hanns-J. Neef (Co-ordinator)
Kernforschungsanage
Jülich
Germany

Mr. Tsuyoshi Hanada
Electricity Power Development Company
Japan

Prof. Dr. Ulf Hansen
University of Essen
Germany

Dr. Heinz Hiller
Lurgi GmbH
Germany

**PANEL ON OIL AND NATURAL GAS PRODUCTION**

Mr. B. Darbyshire (Co-ordinator)
Offshore Supplies Office
UK Department of Energy
United Kingdom

Mr. R. Baiey
Alberta Oil Sands Technology and Research Authority
Canada

Mr. J. Conway
Offshore Supplies Office
United Kingdom

Dr. C. Cotterell
Winfrith Atomic Energy Establishment
United Kingdom

Dr. B.W. Dale
Energy Technology Support Unit
United Kingdom

Mr. J. Field
Arco Oil
United Kingdom

Dr. W. Fox
Winfrith Atomic Energy Establishment
United Kingdom

Dr. J. Gilbert
British Petroleum
United Kingdom

Mr. J. Henley
Mobil
United Kingdom

Prof. A.G. Kemp
University of Aberdeen
United Kingdom

Mr. J. Mackley
British Petroleum
United Kingdom

Dr. Langley Muir
Energy, Mines and Resources Canada
Canada

Mr. W. Olsen
Statoil
Norway

Mr. C. Ryan
Statoil
Norway

Mr. W. Scheidecker
Arco Oil
United Kingdom

Mr. J. Silcock
Offshore Supplies Office
United Kingdom

Mr. Nobuo Tezuka
Japan National Oil Corporation
Japan

Mr. R. Utseth
Statoil
Norway

Mr. C. Wakefied
Shell
United Kingdom

Mr. D. Wilson
Robertson ERC
United Kingdom

**PANEL ON NATURAL GAS AND ITS TRANSPORTABILITY**

Mr. Kje Oppegaard (Co-ordinator)
SPUNG Programme Manager
Royal Norwegian Council for Scientific and Industrial Research (NTNF)
Norway

Mr. Lars Bugge
Royal Ministry of Petroleum and Energy
Norway

Mr. Kjell Hagenmark
Statoil
Norway

Mr. Kaus-J. Jens
Centre for Industrial Research
Norway

Mr. Olav Kaarstad
Statoil
Norway

Mr. Øystein Lind
Norsk Hydro AS
Norway

**PANEL ON NUCLEAR FISSION TECHNOLOGIES**

Mr. Geoffrey Stevens (Co-ordinator)
Nuclear Energy Agency
OECD
Paris

Prof. P.M.S. Jones
UK Atomic Energy Authority
United Kingdom

Dr. Luigi Noviello
ENEL
Italy

Mr. J. Taylor
Electric Power Research Institute
United States

Mr. G. Vendryes
Nuclear Energy Agency
OECD
Paris

Dr. W. von Lensa
Kernforschungsanage Jülich
Germany

Dr. A. Watanabe
Power Reactor and Nuclear Fuel
Development Corp.
Japan

**PANEL ON NUCLEAR FUSION**

Dr. Günter Grieger (Co-ordinator)
Member of the Board
Max-Planck-Institut für Plasmaphysik
Germany

Dr. D. P. Jackson
Atomic Energy of Canada Ltd
Canada

Mr. H. Kishimoto
Japan Atomic Energy Research Institute
Japan

Mr. G. Leman
Nuclear Fusion Research
Sweden

Mr. H. Obayashi
NIFS
Japan

Dr. Michael Roberts
US Department of Energy
United States

Mr. R. Verbeek
EURATOM
European Commission

**PANEL ON RENEWABLE ENERGY**

Dr. Robert L. San Martin (Co-ordinator)
US Department of Energy
United States

Mr Stephen Bolcso
Energy, Mines and Resources Canada
Canada

Dr. Steffan Engstroem
National Energy Administration
Sweden

Dr. Pau Kesserling
Paul Scherrer Institute
Switzerand

Dr. Geoffrey Long
Aeoilan House
United Kingdom

Dr. Frederick H. Morse
US Department of Energy
United States

Dr. Hans-Joachim Siesing
Deutsche Institut für Wirtschfatsforschung
Germany

Dr. Achille Taschini
ENEL
Italy

Mr. Katsuyuki Uesugi
New Energy Development Organisation
Japan

**PANEL ON ELECTRICITY PRODUCTION AND DISTRIBUTION**

Mr. Michio Kobayashi (Co-ordinator)
Tokyo Electric Power Company
Japan

Mr. J.M. Bell
Ontario Hydro
Canada

Dr. Ing. Wilfried Dicke
Fraenkisches Ueberandwerk AG
Germany

Dr. Milton Klein
Electric Power Research Institute
United States

Dr. E. Metcalfe
Central Electricity Research Laboratories
United Kingdom

Mr. Lars Sjunnesson
SYDCRAFT
Sweden

**PANEL ON TRANSPORT TECHNOLOGY AND FUELS**

Mr. Peter Reilly-Roe (Co-ordinator)
Energy, Mines and Resources Canada
Canada

Dr. Pierpaolo Garibaldi
Ecofuel SpA
Italy

Dr. David Greene
Oak Ridge National Laboratory
United States

Mr. Gunnar Kinbom
Swedish National Board for Technical Development
Sweden

Dr. John Marrow
Energy Technology Support Unit
United Kingdom

Dr. David Martin
Energy Technology Support Unit
United Kingdom

Dr. -Ing. H. Quadflieg
Technischer Ueberwachungs-Verein
Rheinland eV
Germany

**PANEL ON ENERGY END USES**

Mr. Afred R. Braun (Co-ordinator)
Braun Consultants
The Netherlands

Mr. John J. Brogan
US Department of Energy
United States

Dr. D. Cioccio
Energy, Mines and Resources Canada
Canada

Prof. Noboru Itoh
Chuo University
Japan

Dr. - Ing. M. Rudolph
Technische Universität München
Germany

Prof. Ugo Farinelli
ENEA
Italy

Dr. Paul Hofseth
Ministry of Environment
Norway

Prof. John Holdren
University of California
United States

Prof. Cas Otto Wene
Chalmers Institute for Technology
Sweden

Dr. Osayuki Yokoyama
Agency of Industrial Science and Technology
MITI
Japan

**PANEL ON GREENHOUSE GAS TECHNOLOGIES**

Dr. Lars Kristoferson (Co-ordinator)
Stockholm Environment Institute
Sweden

# ANNEX II

# INTERNATIONAL ENERGY AGENCY

## "SHARED GOALS"

The 23 Member countries* of the International Energy Agency (IEA) seek to create the conditions in which the energy sectors of their economies can make the fullest possible contribution to sustainable economic development and the well-being of their people and of the environment. In formulating energy policies, the establishment of free and open markets is a fundamental point of departure, though energy security and environmental protection need to be given particular emphasis by governments. IEA countries recognise the significance of increasing global interdependence in energy. They therefore seek to promote the effective operation of international energy markets and encourage dialogue with all participants.

In order to secure their objectives they therefore aim to create a policy framework consistent with the following goals:

1 **Diversity, efficiency and flexibility within the energy sector** are basic conditions for longer-term energy security: the fuels used within and across sectors and the sources of those fuels should be as diverse as practicable. Non-fossil fuels, particularly nuclear and hydro power, make a sub-stantial contribution to the energy supply diversity of IEA countries as a group.

2 **Energy systems should have the ability to respond promptly and flexibly to energy emergencies.** In some cases this requires collective mechanisms and action: IEA countries co-operate through the Agency in responding jointly to oil supply emergencies.

3 **The environmentally sustainable provision and use of energy** is central to the achievement of these shared goals. Decision-makers should seek to minimise the adverse environmental impacts of energy activities, just as environmental decisions should take account of the energy consequences. Government interventions should where practicable have regard to the Polluter Pays Principle.

4 **More environmentally acceptable energy sources** need to be encouraged and developed. Clean and efficient use of fossil fuels is essential. The development of economic non-fossil sources is also a priority.

* Australia, Austria, Belgium, Canada, Denmark, Finland, France, Germany, Greece, Ireland, Italy, Japan, Luxembourg, Netherlands, New Zealand, Norway, Portugal, Spain, Sweden, Switzerland, Turkey, United Kingdom, United States.

A number of IEA members wish to retain and improve the nuclear option for the future, at the highest available safety standards, because nuclear energy does not emit carbon dioxide. Renewable sources will also have an increasingly important contribution to make.

5 **Improved energy efficiency** can promote both environmental protection and energy security in a cost-effective manner. There are significant opportunities for greater energy efficiency at all stages of the energy cycle from production to consumption. Strong efforts by Governments and all energy users are needed to realise these opportunities.

6 Continued **research, development and market deployment of new and improved energy technologies** make a critical contribution to achieving the objectives outlined above. Energy technology policies should complement broader energy policies. International co-operation in the development and dissemination of energy technologies, including industry participation and co-operation with non-Member countries, should be encouraged.

7 **Undistorted energy prices enable markets** to work efficiently. Energy prices should not be held artificially below the costs of supply to promote social or industrial goals. To the extent necessary and practicable, the environmental costs of energy production and use should be reflected in prices.

8 **Free and open trade** and a secure framework for investment contribute to efficient energy markets and energy security. Distortions to energy trade and investment should be avoided.

9 **Co-operation among all energy market participants** helps to improve information and understanding, and encourage the development of efficient, environmentally acceptable and flexible energy systems and markets worldwide. These are needed to help promote the investment, trade and confidence necessary to achieve global energy security and environmental objectives.

(The “Shared Goals” were adopted by IEA Ministers at their 4 June 1993 meeting in Paris.)

# ANNEX III

## GLOSSARY OF TERMS AND ABBREVIATIONS

In this study, abbreviations are frequently substituted for a number of terms. While these terms are often written in full on first mention and subsequently abbreviated, this glossary provides a quick central reference for many of the abbreviations used, as well as conversion factors for the principal measurement units.

| | |
|---|---|
| ABWR | advanced boiling light water-cooled (nuclear) reactor |
| AC | alternating current |
| AFBC | atmospheric fluidised-bed combustion |
| AGR | Advanced Gas (nuclear) Reactor |
| bar | measure of pressure (1 bar = 750 mmHg = 1.0197 kg of force per square centimetre) |
| bcm | billion cubic metres (at standard temperature and pressure of 15°C and 760 mmHg; 1 bcm = 36.602 billion cubic feet) |
| BOT | build-operate-and-transfer |
| BTU | British Thermal Unit (1 BTU = 1,054 Joules = 0.252 kcalories) |
| BWR | boiling light water-cooled (nuclear) reactor |
| °C | degree Celsius |
| $C_1$ chemistry | chemical reactions and processes for the conversion of the carbon-hydrogen molecule |
| CAD | computer-aided design |
| CANDU | Canadian Deuterium Uranium (nuclear) reactor |
| CFBC | circulating fluidised-bed combustion |
| CFCs | chlorofluorocarbons |
| $CH_4$ | methane |
| CHP | combined heat and power (co-generation) |
| CNG | compressed natural gas |
| CO | carbon monoxide |
| $CO_2$ | carbon dioxide |
| CRGT | chemically-recuperated gas turbine |
| CVT | continuously variable transmission |
| DC | direct current |
| DCCD | direct coal-fired combustion devices (diesel engine and gas turbine) |
| DSM | demand-side management |
| 3D | three-dimensional |

| | |
|---|---|
| EC | European Commission |
| EGR | exhaust gas recirculation |
| EOR | enhanced oil recovery |
| EU | European Union |
| EV | electric vehicle |
| FBC | fluidised bed combustion |
| FBR | fast breeder (nuclear) reactor |
| FGD | flue gas desulphurisation |
| FT synthesis | Fischer-Tropsch synthesis |
| GCR | gas-cooled graphite-moderated (nuclear) reactor |
| GJ | gigaJoule (1 billion Joules) |
| GJ/kg | gigaJoule per kilogramme |
| GJ/tonne | gigaJoule per tonne |
| GTID | geologically targeted infill drilling |
| GW | gigaWatt (1 billion Watts; GWe denotes gigaWatts of electric power) |
| GWe | gigaWatt of electricity |
| HWR | heavy water-cooled and -moderated (nuclear) reactor |
| IAEA | International Atomic Energy Agency |
| IAQ | indoor air quality |
| ICEV | internal combustion engine vehicle |
| IEA | International Energy Agency |
| IGCC | integrated coal-gasification combined cycle |
| IGFC | integrated coal-gasification fuel cell |
| ISTIG | intercooled steam-injected gas turbine |
| ITER | International Thermonuclear Experimental Reactor |
| IVT | intermittently variable transmission |
| J | Joule |
| HAT | humid air turbine |
| HC | unburnt hydrocarbons |
| He3 | isotope 3 of helium (or helium 3) |
| hhv | higher heating value (of fuels) |
| HLW | high-level nuclear waste |
| HT | high temperature |
| HTR, HTGR | high-temperature gas-cooled (nuclear) reactor |
| kcal | kilocalorie (1 kcal = 4,187 Joules = 3.968 BTUs) |
| kg | kilogram (1 kilogram = 2.205 pounds) |
| km | kilometre (1 kilometre = 1,000 metres = 0.621 miles) |
| kW | kiloWatt (1 thousand Watts; kWe denotes kiloWatts of electric power) |
| kWe | kiloWatt of electricity |
| kWh | kiloWatt-hour (1,000 Watts during one hour) |
| LHR | low heat rejection (engine) |
| lhv | lower heating value (of fuels) |
| LMR | liquid metal-cooled (nuclear) reactor |
| LNG | liquefied natural gas (methane) |
| LPG | liquefied petroleum gas (propane and butane) |

| | |
|---|---|
| LWR | light water-cooled (nuclear) reactor |
| m | metre (1 metre = 100 centimetres = 1,000 millimetres = 39.37 inches = 3.28 feet) |
| mbd | million barrels per day (1 barrel = 158.98 litres; 1 mbd = 49.5 million metric tons of oil per year for 34° API crude) |
| MCFC | molten carbonate fuel cell |
| MHD | magnetohydrodynamics |
| mill | one-tenth of one US cent (.001 US $ at 1993 value, unless stated otherwise) |
| mm | millimetre (one-tenth of one centimetre; 1 mm = 0.001 metres) |
| MOX | mixed uranium and plutonium oxide (nuclear fuel) |
| MTG | methanol to gasoline conversion |
| Mtoe | million metric tonnes of oil equivalent |
| MW | megaWatt (1 million Watts; MWe denotes megaWatts of electric power) |
| MWd | megaWatt days |
| MWe | megaWatt of electricity |
| MWD | measurement while drilling |
| MWd/kg | megaWatt-day per kilogram (thermal energy of one million Watts during one day per kilogram of material) |
| M85 | fuel blend of 85 per cent methanol and 15 per cent gasoline |
| NA | not applicable or not available |
| NEA | Nuclear Energy Agency |
| NGV | natural gas vehicle |
| $NO_x$ | oxides of nitrogen |
| NSSS | nuclear steam supply system |
| $O_3$ | ozone |
| OECD | Organisation for Economic Co-operation and Development |
| OEM | original equipment manufacturer |
| ORC | organic Rankine cycle |
| OTEC | ocean thermal energy conversion |
| PAFC | phosphoric acid fuel cell |
| PCFC | pulverised coal-fired combustion |
| PFBC | pressurised fluidised-bed combustion |
| PHWR | pressurised heavy water-cooled and -moderated (nuclear) reactor |
| PWR | pressurised light water-cooled (nuclear) reactor |
| Quad | 1 Quad = 1x1015 BTUs = 1.05x1018 Joules = 1.05 exaJoules) |
| R&D | research and development |
| ROV | remotely operated vehicle |
| RVP | Reid vapor pressure (measure of volatility of gasoline) |
| SCR | selective catalytic reduction |
| SNG | synthetic natural gas, synthesis gas (or syngas) |
| $SO_2$ | sulphur dioxide |
| $SO_x$ | oxides of sulphur |
| SOFC | solid oxide fuel cell |
| STIG | steam-injected gas turbine |
| SWU | separative work unit |
| tC | tonne of carbon |

| | |
|---|---|
| ton | short ton (1 ton = 2,000 pounds) |
| tonne | metric ton (1 tonne = 1,000 kilograms) |
| toe | metric ton of oil equivalent (1 toe = 10 million kcal) |
| TW | teraWatt (1012 Watts; TWe denotes teraWatts of eletric power) |
| TWh | teraWatt-hour (1012 Watts during one hour) |
| $u^{235}$ | isotope 235 of uranium (or uranium 235) |
| VOC | volatile organic compounds, including hydrocarbon vapor emissions |
| W | Watt (1 Watt = 1 Joule per second) |
| WEC | World Energy Council |

# ANNEX IV

# BIBLIOGRAPHY

## General References and Sources

Clinton, President William J. and Vice-President Albert Gore, Jr. (1993) *The Climate Change Action Plan,* Executive Office of the President, Washington DC.

Danish Energy Agency (1993), *Evaluation of the Ministry of Energy's Energy Research Programmes 1986-91,* Ministry of Energy, Copenhagen.

Doyle, J. (1992), *Building a Stronger Environmental Technology Exploitation Capability in Canada,* Environment Canada, and Industry, Science and Technology Canada, Ottawa.

*Energy Use in Industry and Buildings* (London, UK, 1995).

European Commission (1996), *European Energy to 2020: A Scenario Approach,* Luxembourg.

European Commission (1996), *Overview of Energy RD&D Options for a Sustainable Future,* Luxembourg.

Federal Environment Ministry (1993), *Environment Policy. Climate Protection in Germany,* National Report of the Federal Government of the Federal Republic of Germany, Bonn.

Gray, J.E., H.-C. Bailly and D.L. Guertin (1992), *Energy Technology Co-operation for Sustainable Economic Development,* The Atlantic Council of the United States, Washington DC.

Grubb, Michael, et al. (1991), *Energy Policies and the Greenhouse Effect,* Vols. 1 and 2, The Royal Institute of International Affairs, Dartmouth.

Guertin, Donald L., W.K. Davis and J.E. Gray (1992), *US Energy Imperatives for the 1990s: Leadership, Efficiency, Environmental Responsibility and Sustained Growth,* University Press of America, New York.

Haefele, Wolf, ed. (1981), *Energy in a Finite World: A Global Systems Analysis,* Report by the Energy Systems Program Group of the International Institute for Applied Systems Analysis, Ballinger, Cambridge.

Intergovernmental Panel on Climate Change (1990), *Climate Change - The IPCC Response Strategies,* IPCC-World Meteorological Organisation, Geneva.

International Energy Agency (1980), *A Group Strategy for Energy Research, Development and Demonstration,* OECD, Paris.

International Energy Agency (1985), *Energy Technology Policy,* OECD, Paris.

International Energy Agency (1989), *Energy and the Environment: Policy Overview,* OECD, Paris

International Energy Agency (1992), *Collaboration in Energy Technology 1987-1990,* OECD, Paris

International Energy Agency (1992), *The Role of IEA Governments in Energy,* OECD, Paris.

International Energy Agency (1993), *Energy Policies of IEA Countries: 1992 Review,* OECD, Paris.

International Energy Agency (1993), *World Energy Outlook to the Year 2010,* OECD, Paris.

International Energy Agency/OECD (1989), *Energy Technologies for Reducing Emissions of Greenhouse Gases,* Proceedings, OECD, Paris.

International Energy Agency/OECD (1991), *Greenhouse Gas Emissions. The Energy Dimension,* OECD, Paris.

International Energy Agency/OECD (1991), *Technology Responses to Global Environmental Challenges: Energy Collaboration for the 21st Century*, Proceedings, OECD, Paris.

International Energy Agency/OECD (1992), *Energy Technology Policy for Sustainable Development: Comparing Long-term Approaches,* Proceedings, OECD, Paris.

Ministry of International Trade and Industry (1987), *The Twenty-first Century Energy Vision. Entering the Multiple Energy Era,* MITI, Tokyo.

Mintzer, Irving M., ed. (1992), *Confronting Climate Change: Risks, Implications and Responses,* Cambridge University Press, Cambridge, UK.

Nelson, Richard R., ed. (1993), *National Innovation Systems. A Comparative Analysis,* Oxford University Press, New York.

Ohta, Tokio (1993), *Energy Technology. Sources, Systems and Frontier Conversion,* Yokohama National University, Yokohama.

Organisation for Economic Co-operation and Development (1992), *Technology and Economy: The Key Relationships,* OECD, Paris.

Royal Swedish Academy of Engineering Sciences (1993), *Energy for Coming Generations. Conclusions and Recommendations,* IVA, Stockholm.

Science and Technology Agency (1988), *Future Technology in Japan: Forecast to the Year 2015,* Institute for Future Technology, Tokyo.

UK Department of Energy (1987), *Background Papers Relevant to the 1986 Appraisal of UK Energy Research Development and Demonstration,* Department of Energy, London.

United Nations, Advanced Technology Assessment System (1992), *Environmentally Sound Technology for Sustainable Development,* United Nations, New York.

US Congress, Office of Technology Assessment (1991), *Energy Technology Choices: Shaping Our Future,* OTA-E-493, US Government Printing Office, Washington DC.

US Department of State, Office of Global Change (1992), *National Action Plan for Global Climate Change,* Washington DC.

World Commission on Environment and Development (1987), *Our Common Future,* Oxford University Press, Oxford.

World Energy Council Commission (1993), *Energy for Tomorrow's World . The Realities, the Real Options and the Agenda for Achievement,* St. Martin's Press, London.

World Energy Council (1995), *Global Transport Sector Energy Demand Towards 2020,* London.

World Energy Council (1995), *Energy Efficiency Improvement Utilising High Technology: An Assessment of Energy Use in Industry and Buildings,* London.

**References by Technology Area**

***Clean Use of Coal***

Couch, G.R. (1993), *Coal Specifications - Impact on Power Station Performance,* IEA Coal Research, London.

Electric Power Research Institute (1990), *Coal Water and Gasification Program,* EPRI, Palo Alto, California.

International Energy Agency (1992), *Coal, The Environment and Development: Technologies to Reduce Greenhouse Gas Emissions,* Proceedings, OECD, Paris.

Jones, T. (1991), *Environmental Impact Assessment for Coal,* IEA Coal Research, London.

Maude, Chris (1993), *Advanced Power Generation: A Comparative Study of Design Options for Coal,* IEA Coal Research, London.

Singer, J.G. (1991), *Combustion: Fossil Power. A Reference Book on Fuel Burning and Steam Generation,* Combustion Engineering, Windsor, Connecticut.

Smith, Irene and K. Thambimuthu (1991), *Greenhouse Gases Abatement and Control: The Role of Coal,* IEA Coal Research, London.

Soud, H.N. (1991), *Emission Standards Handbook: Air Pollutant Standards for Coal-fired Plants,* IEA Coal Research, London.

Takematsu, Toshi'ichi and C. Maude (1991) *Coal Gasification for IGCC Power Generation,* IEA Coal Research, London.

United Nations, Economic Commission for Europe (1990), *Clean Combustion of Brown Coal and Lignite,* New York.

US Department of Energy, Assistant Secretary for Fossil Energy, (1990), *Clean Coal Technology. The New Coal Era,* US Department of Energy, Washington DC.

***Oil and Natural Gas Production***

American Association of Petroleum Geologists (1993), *New Views on Old World Oil - Technology Leads the Way,* Proceedings, AAPG, Tulsa, Oklahoma.

Energy and Environmental Analysis, Inc. (1993), *Chemical Composition of Discovered and Undiscovered Natural Gas in the United States,* Report No. 93/0456.1, Gas Research Institute, Chicago, Illinois.

Flannery, B.P. and R. Clarke, eds. (1991), *Global Climate Change. A Petroleum Industry Perspective,* International Petroleum Industry Environmental Conservation Association, London.

Groth, Peter K. and L.W. Groth (1993), *Bibliography for Surface and Non-Surface Hydrocarbon Prospecting Methods,* Association of Petroleum Geochemical Explorationists, Denver, Colorado.

International Energy Agency (1991), *Natural Gas Prospects and Policies,* OECD, Paris.

International Energy Agency (1992), *Natural Resource Management: Crude Oil Sector,* Proceedings, OECD, Paris.

Ivanhoe, L.F. and G.G. Leckie (1993), "Global Oil Gas Fields, Sizes Tallied, Analyzed", *Oil & Gas Journal,* Vol. 91, No. 7, p. 87-91.

Leckie, George G. (1993), "Hydrocarbon Reserves and Discoveries", *Energy Exploration & Exploitation,* Vol. 11, No. 1, p. 3-22.

National Petroleum Council (1995), *Research Development and Demonstration Needs of the Oil and Gas Industry,* United States.

Oil and Gas Journal Special (1993), "Drilling Technology Report", *Oil & Gas Journal,* Vol. 91, No. 7, p. 49-66.

Parums, A.M. (1993), "Environmental Impact of Oil and Gas Production: A Review of the Impacts of Current Systems and Some Trends for the Future", *Energy & Environment,* Vol. 4, No. 3, p. 253-267.

Society of Petroleum Engineers (1993), *International Symposium on Oilfield Chemistry,* Proceedings, SPE, Richardson, Texas.

US Department of Energy, The Yergin Committee Report to the US Secretary of Energy (1995), *Energy R&D: Shaping our Nation's Future in a Competitive World.*

***Natural Gas and Its Transportability***

G. Cacciola, V. Recupero and N. Giordano, "Economic Evaluation of Long Distance Hydrogen Transmission by Chemical Closed-loop Cycle", *International Journal of Hydrogen Energy,* Vol. 10.

Commission of the European Communities (1992), *European Conference on Natural Gas Policies and Technologies,* Proceedings, European Commission, Brussels.

Davis, R.N. and R.J. Kirkland (1989), *Liquid Methane as a Transportation Fuel,* LNG-9 Conference.

Fischer, F.L. (1983), *Introduction of a Commercial System for Liquid Methane Vehicles,* Non-Petroleum Vehicular Fuels III, Institute of Gas Technology, United States.

International Energy Agency (1993), N*atural Gas Technologies: Energy Security, Environment and Economic Development,* Proceedings, OECD, Paris.

Lee, J.S. and S.T. Oyama (1988), "Oxidative Coupling of Methane to Higher Hydrocarbons", *Catal. Review Science Energy,* Vol. 30, p. 249.

Minet R.G. and J. Kim (1983), "Development of the Benson Process for Ethylene and Acetylene from Methane", *Chemical Economy & Engineering Review,* Vol. 15, p. 35.

Noceti, R.P. and C.E. Taylor (1988), *Process for Converting Light Alkanes into Higher Hydrocarbons,* US Patent 4, 769, 504.

OGJ Special (1993), "Annual Pipeline Report", *Oil & Gas Journal,* Vol. 91, No. 36, p. 34-74.

Olifirov, F. N.,V.M. Kalmin, and A.I.Gulienko (1989), *Fuel Supply and Control Systems for Commercial Aircraft Engines using Liquified Natural Gas,* LNG-9 Conference.

US Department of Energy (1992), *International Gas Research Conference,* Proceedings, Gas Research Institute, Chicago.

US Department of Energy, Energy Information Administration (1992), *Natural Gas 1992 - Issues and Trends,* US Department of Energy, Washington DC.

US Environmental Protection Agency, US Agency for International Development, and Environment Agency of Japan (1990), *International Workshop on Methane Emissions from Natural Gas Systems, Coal Mining and Waste Management Systems,* Proceedings, Washington DC, April.

***Nuclear Fission Technologies***

Adamantiades, A.G. (1991), *Radioactive Waste Management. A Background Study,* World Bank, Washington DC.

American Nuclear Society (1993), *Global '93: Future Nuclear Systems - Emerging Fuel Cycles and Waste Disposal Options,* Proceedings, ANS, La Grange Park, Illinois.

International Atomic Energy Agency (1990), "Decommissioning Nuclear Facilities: International Overview", *IAEA News Features,* No. 6, Vienna.

International Atomic Energy Agency (1993), *Operating Experience with Nuclear Power Stations in Member States in 1992,* IAEA, Vienna.

Kuczera, B. (1993), "R&D Activities on Safety Aspects of Future PWR Plants Performed at KfK", *Nuclear Safety,* Vol. 34, No. 3, p. 213-229.

Larsson, A. (1989), "State-of-the-Art Report on Radioactive Waste Disposal", *IAEA Bulletin,* Vol. 31, No. 4.

Marth, W. (1993), *The Story of the European Fast Reactor Co-operation,* Report KfK 5255, Kernforschungszentrum, Karlsruhe.

Nuclear Energy Agency (1989), *Advanced Water-Cooled Reactors Technologies: Rationale, State of Progress and Outlook,* OECD, Paris.

Nuclear Energy Agency (1991), *Small and Medium Reactors,* Report by an Expert Group, OECD, Paris.

Nuclear Energy Agency (1992), *Broad Economic Impact of Nuclear Power,* OECD, Paris.

Nuclear Energy Agency (1993), *Power Generation Choices: Costs, Risks and Externalities,* Proceedings, OECD, Paris.

Nuclear Energy Agency/International Energy Agency (1991), P*rojected Costs of Generating Electricity from Power Stations for Commissioning in the Period 1995-2000,* OECD, Paris.

Nuclear Energy Agency/International Energy Agency (1992), *Uranium. Resources, Production and Demand,* OECD, Paris.

Tsyplenkov, V. (1993), "Electricity Production and Waste Management: Comparing the Options", *IAEA Bulletin,* Vol. 35, No. 4, p. 27-33.

UK House of Commons Energy Committee (1990), *The Fast Breeder Reactor,* HMSO, London.

US Department of Energy, Energy Information Administration (1993), *World Nuclear Capacity and Fuel Cycle Requirements 1993,* DOE/EIA - 0436(93), US Department of Energy, Washington DC.

***Nuclear Fusion***

Colombo, Umberto, et al. (1990), *Report of the Fusion Evaluation Board,* Commission of the European Communities, Brussels.

Deutsche Physikalische Gesellschfat (1992), *Wall Component Materials for Fusion Reactors of the Future,* Proceedings, Forschungszentrum Jülich, Germany.

Fusion Council of Japan (1990), *Interim Report of the Subcommittee on Technical Evaluation of Research and Development in Nuclear Fusion,* Fusion Council of Japan, Tokyo.

International Atomic Energy Agency (1993), *ITER Conceptual Design Activities: Final Report,* ITER Documentation Series No. 16, IAEA, Vienna.

International Atomic Energy Agency, International Fusion Research Council (1990), *Status Report on Controlled Thermonuclear Fusion.* Executive Summary and General Overview, IAEA, Vienna.

Japan Atomic Energy Research Institute (1993), *ICENES '93 - Seventh International Conference on Emerging Nuclear Energy Systems,* Proceedings, JAERI, Tokyo.

Please, R.S. et al. (1989), *Environmental Safety-Related and Economic Potential of Fusion Power,* EEF Study Group, Brussels.

Science Council of Monbusho (1986), *On Fusion Research Planning in Japanese Universities,* Report of the Fusion Division of the Science Council, Tokyo.

Sever, H.G. et al. (1990), *Final Report of the Fusion Policy Advisory Committee,* US Department of Energy, Washington DC.

US Congress, Office of Technology Assessment (1987), *Starpower: The US and the International Quest for Fusion Energy,* US Congress, US Government Printing Office, Washington DC.

US Department of Energy, Fusion Energy Advisory Committee (1993), *Advice and Recommendations to the US Department of Energy in Response to the Charge Letter of September 18, 1992,* DOE/ER-0594T, US Department of Energy, Washington DC.

***Renewable Energy***

Bolcso, S., *Input Materials,* Canada, 1989.

Clayton, B.R., ed. (1992), *Wind Energy Conversion 1992,* Proceedings, Mechanical Engineering Publications Ltd., London.

Energy Technology Support Unit (1989) *Prospects for Renewable Energy in the Norweb Area,* Overview and Main Report, ETSU, Harwell and Norweb, Manchester.

Forum für Zukunftsenergien (1992), *Geothermal Energy: Technology, Ecology, Economy,* Proceedings, FZE, Bonn.

International Atomic Energy Agency, *Electricity and the Environment,* Background papers for a Senior Expert Symposium held in Helsinki, Finland, 13-17 May 1991.

International Energy Agency (1990), *Photovoltaic Systems for Electric Utility Applications,* Proceedings, OECD, Paris.

International Energy Agency (1991), *Guidelines for the Economic Analysis of Renewable Energy Technology Applications,* OECD, Paris.

International Energy Agency (1987), *Renewable Sources of Energy,* OECD, Paris.

International Energy Agency/Organisation for Economic Co-operation and Development (1993), *Hydropower, Energy and the Environment,* Proceedings, OECD, Paris.

International Energy Agency/International Union of Producers and Distributors of Electric Energy, *New Electricity 21, Designing a Sustainable Electric System for the Twenty-first Century* (1996), Proceedings, OECD, Paris.

Johansson, Thomas B., H. Kelly, A.K.N. Reddy and R.H. Williams, eds. (1993), *Renewable Energy: Sources for Fuels and Electricity,* report commissioned by the United Nations Solar Energy Group for Environment and Development as input to the 1992 United Nations Conference on Environment and Development in Rio de Janeiro, Island Press, Washington.

Knox, Richard, (1993), *New Renewable Energy Sources: Technical Realities and Commercial Opportunities,* MDIS Publications Ltd, Chichester, UK.

Kesselring, P., *Input Materials,* Switzerland, 1989.

Long, G., *Input Materials,* United Kingdom, 1989.

Meridian Corporation (1989), *Characterization of US Energy Resources and Reserves,* Washington DC.

O'Dwyer, et. al., *The Case for Wind Energy,* Report No. 37-102. Presented at the CIGRE Meeting, Paris, 1990.

Solar Energy Research Institute (1990), *The Potential of Renewable Energy,* US Department of Energy, Washington DC.

Swiss Federal Committee on Energy R&D (1987), *Federal Energy R&D Concept.*

Swiss Federal Institute for Reactor Research (1988), *New Renewable Energy Sources,* Bern.

United Nations Economic Commission for Europe (1993), *Solar Power Systems,* United Nations, New York.

UN Solar Energy Group on Environment and Development (1991), *Solar Energy. A Strategy in Support of Environment and Development,* UNSEGED, United Nations, New York.

US Agency for International Development (1989), *Biomass Energy Systems and Technology Report,* AID, Washington DC.

US Department of Energy, Energy Information Administration (1993), *Renewable Resources in the US Electricity Supply,* DOE/EIA-0561 (93), US Department of Energy, Washington DC.

US Department of Interior, Bureau of Reclamation (1991), *Hydropower: Reclamation's Energy Initiative,* US Department of Interior, Washington DC.

World Energy Conference 14th Conference, Session 1.1, *Progress and Prospects for Renewable Energy Sources: A European Community View.*

World Energy Council (1993), *Renewable Energy Resources: Opportunities and Constraints 1990-2020,* London.

***Electricity Production and Distribution***

Cambridge Energy Research Associates (1990), *Lightening the Load: Electric Utilities and Demand-Side Management,* CERA, Cambridge, Massachusetts.

Grubb, Michael (1991), "The Integration of Renewable Electricity Sources", *Energy Policy,* Vol. 19, p. 670-686.

International Atomic Energy Agency (1991), *Electricity and the Environment,* Proceedings of Senior Expert Symposium, IAEA, Vienna.

International Energy Agency (1991), *Advanced Technologies for Electric Demand-Side Management,* Proceedings, OECD, Paris.

International Energy Agency (1992), *Electricity Supply in the OECD,* OECD, Paris.

International Energy Agency (1993), *New Electricity 21: Power Industry Technology and Management Strategies for the Twenty-first Century,* Proceedings, OECD, Paris.

International Energy Agency (1993), *Electric Power Technologies: Environmental Challenges and Opportunities,* OECD, Paris.

International Energy Agency (1993), *Electricity Information,* OECD, Paris.

Johansson, T. B., B. Bodlund and R.H. Williams, eds. (1989), *Electricity: Efficient End-Use and New Generation Technologies, and Their Planning Implications,* Lund University Press, Lund, Sweden.

Jones, David A., ed. (1993), "Power Generation Technology", *The International Review of Primary Power Production,* Sterling Publications Ltd., London.

Scott, David H. (1991), *Advanced Power Generation from Fuel Cells - Implications for Coal,* IEA Coal Research, London.

***Transport Technology and Fuels***

Bernard, M.J., and D.J.Santini (1989), "Enhancing Energy Price Stability Through Consistent And Balanced Energy Technology R&D," *Energy Policy,* pp. 554-566, December.

Bleviss, D.L (1988), *The New Oil Crisis And Fuel Economy Technologies,* Quorum Books, Westport, Connecticut.

Cerero, R., *America's Suburban Centers: A Study of the Land Use-Transportation Link* (1988), U.S. Department Of Transportation, Urban Mass Transit Administration, DOT-T-88-14, Washington, DC.

Davis, S.C., et al. (1995), *Transportation Energy Data Book: Edition 15,* Oak Ridge National Laboratory, Oak Ridge, Tennessee.

Deluchi, M.A. (1989), *Greenhouse Gases From Alternative-Fuel Vehicles,* Argonne National Laboratory, Argonne, Illinois.

Deluchi, M.A. (1989), "Hydrogen Vehicles: An Evaluation of Fuel Storage, Performance, Safety, Environmental Impacts and Cost", *International Journal of Hydrogen Energy,* Vol. 14, No. 2, p. 81-130.

Deluchi, M.A., Q. Wang and D. Sperling (1989), "Electric Vehicles: Performance, Life-Cycle Costs, Emissions and Recharging Requirements", *Transportation Research,* No. 5, Vol. 22A.

Energy And Environmental Analysis Inc. (1989), *Domestic Manufacturers' Fuel Economy Capability to 2001, An Update,* Oak Ridge National Laboratory, Oak Ridge, Tennessee.

European Conference of Ministers of Transport (1993), *Transport Growth in Question,* 12th Int. Symposium on Theory and Practice in Transport Economics, Proceedings, OECD, Paris.

European Conference of Ministers of Transport (1993), *Transport Policy and Global Warming,* Proceedings, OECD, Paris.

Fédération Internationale de l'Automobile (FIA) (1989), "Stakes and Strategies: Orientation Report," *International Journal Of Vehicle Design,* Vol. 10, No. 4, pp. 387-431, Geneva, Switzerland.

French, T. ( 1989), "Airlines On Track?," *Airline Business,* August.

Gilmore, D.B. (1988), "Fuel Economy Goals For Future Powertrain And Engine Components", *International Journal of Vehicle Design,* Vol. 9, No. 6, pp. 616-63.

Greene, D.L. (1989), *Energy Efficiency Improvement Potential of Commercial Aircraft to 2010,* Oak Ridge National Laboratory, Oak Ridge, Tennessee.

Greene D.L. (1994), *Transportation Energy Efficiency Trends, 1972-1992,* Oak Ridge National Laboratory. Oak Ridge, Tennessee.

Grey, C.L., and J.A. Alson (1989), "The Case for Methanol," *Scientific American,* pp. 108-114, November.

Heavenrich, Robert H.M., J.D. Murrell, and K.H. Hellman (1989), *Options for Controlling the Global Warming Impact From Motor Vehicles,* EPA/AA/CTAB/89-08, Environmental Protection Agency, Ann Arbour, Michigan.

Hillsman, E.L., and F. Southworth (1989), *Factors That May Influence Responses Of The US Transportation Sector To Policies For Reducing Greenhouse Gas Emissions,* Oak Ridge National Laboratory, Oak Ridge, Tennessee.

Hu, P.S., L.S.Williams, and D.J. Beal (1989), *Light-Duty Vehicle MPG and Market Shares Report: Model Year 1988,* Oak Ridge National Laboratory, ORNL-6549, Oak Ridge, Tennessee.

International Energy Agency (1990), *Substitute Fuels for Road Transport. A Technology Assessment,* OECD, Paris.

International Energy Agency (1993), *Cars and Climate Change,* OECD, Paris.

International Energy Agency (1993), *Electric Vehicles: Technology, Performance and Potential,* OECD, Paris.

International Energy Agency/Organisation for Economic Co-operation and Development (1991), *Low Consumption/Low Emission Automobile,* Proceedings of an Expert Panel, OECD, Paris.

International Energy Agency/Organisation for Economic Co-operation and Development (1992), *The Urban Electric Vehicle: Policy Options, Technology Trends and Market Prospects,* Proceedings, OECD, Paris.

Johnson, L.R., D.M. Rote, et al. (1989), *Maglev Vehicles And Superconductor Technology: Integration Of High-speed Ground Transportation Into The Air System,* Argonne National Laboratory Report ANL/CNSV-67, Argonne National Laboratory, Argonne, Illinois.

Kitamura, R., J.M. Nilles, et al. (1989), *Telecommuting as a Transportation Planning Measure: Initial Results of State of California Pilot Project,* paper #890753, Transportation Research Board, Washington, DC.

Kunert, U. (1988), "National Policy Towards Cars: The Federal Republic Of Germany," *Transport Reviews,* No. 1, pp. 59-74.

Lawrence, E., *Fuel Consumption Data Book* (1989), Transport Canada, Road Safety, Ottawa, Ontario, TMSE#8902.

Lesley, L. (1988), "Cities - Will Buses Cope Economically With Traffic?" *International Journal of Vehicle Design,* No. 1, pp. 122-130.

Mage, David, and O. Zali, eds. (1992), *Motor Vehicle Air Pollution. Public Health Impact and Control Measures,* World Health Organisation, Geneva.

Mitchell, B.R. (1976), *European Historical Statistics 1750-1970,* Columbia Press, New York, NY.

Organisation for Economic Co-operation and Development (1993), *Choosing an Alternative Transportation Fuel. Air Pollution and Greenhouse Gas Impacts,* OECD, Paris.

Organisation for Economic Co-operation and Development/European Conference of Ministers of Transport/International Energy Agency (1992), *Toward Clean and Fuel Efficient Automobiles,* Proceedings, OECD, Paris.

Ogden, J.M. and R.H.Williams, *New Prospects For Solar Hydrogen Energy: Implications Of Advances In Thin-Film Solar Cell Technology,* Centre for Energy and Environmental Studies, Princeton University, Princeton, NJ, presented at IEA/OECD Expert Seminar, April, 1989.

Parson, E.A. (1989), *The Transport Sector And Global Warming,* Kennedy School Of Government, Cambridge, Massachusetts.

Premo, D.J. (1989), "Surpassing Capacity," *Air Cargo World,* October.

Santini, D.J., A.V. Deluchi, and M. Walsh, *Greenhouse Gas Emissions From Selected Alternative Transportation Fuels Market Niches,* American Institute Of Chemical Engineers Summer meeting, Argonne National Laboratory, Argonne, Illinois, 1989.

Saricks, C.L. (1990), *Technology And Policy Options For Mitigating Greenhouse Gas Emissions From Mobile Sources,* Transportation Research Board, Washington, DC.

Schipper, L. (1989), *Lifestyles, Transportation and Energy Demand: The Energy/Climate Link,* International Energy Studies, Lawrence Berkeley Laboratory, Berkeley, California.

Showers, V. (1989), *World Facts and Figures,* 3rd Edition, John Wiley and Sons Ltd., New York, NY.

Sperling, D. (1989), *Alternative Transportation Fuels,* Quorum Books, Westport, Connecticut.

Sperling, D. (1988), *New Transport Fuels: A Strategic Approach to Technological Change,* University of California Press, Berkeley.

Sperling, D. and M.A. Deluchi, *Transportation Energy Strategies and the Greenhouse Effect,* University of Davis, Davis, CA, presented at IEA/OECD Expert Seminar, April 1989.

Taylor, G.W.R., R.A. Tarkir and J. Gunsing (1989), *Development of a Speed Modulated Accessory Drive System for Transit Buses,* paper #892531, Society of Automotive Engineers, Warrendale, Pennsylvania.

Underwood, S.E., K. Chen and R.D. Ervin (1990), *The Future Of Intelligent Vehicle-Highway Systems: A Delphi Forecast Of Markets And Sociotechnological Determinants,* paper #890804, Transportation Research Board, Washington, DC.

US Congress, Office of Technology Assessment (1993), *Energy Efficiency: Challenges and Opportunities for Electric Utilities,* US Government Printing Office, Washington DC.

US Department of Energy, Energy Information Administration (1993), *Alternatives to Traditional Transportation Fuels. An Overview,* DOE/EIA-0585/0, Department of Energy, Washington DC.

Wang, Q., M.A. Deluchi and D. Sperling (1989), *Emission Impacts Of Electric Vehicles,* paper #890682, Transportation Research Board, Washington, DC.

Whitaker, R. (1989), "The Quest For Speed," *Airline Business,* April.

***Industrial, Residential and Commercial Energy Use***

Birtles, A.B. (1993), "Getting Energy Efficiency Applied in Buildings", *Energy & Environment,* Vol. 4, No. 3, p. 221-252.

Electric Power Research Institute (1990), *Efficient Electricity Use: Estimates of Maximum Energy Savings,* Report CU-6746, EPRI, Palo Alto, California.

Fitzgerald, K.B., D. Barnes and G. Mc Granahan (1990), *Interfuel Substitution and Changes in the Way Households Use Energy,* World Bank, Washington DC.

International Energy Agency (1987), *Energy Conservation in IEA Countries,* OECD, Paris.

International Energy Agency (1991), *Energy Efficiency and the Environment,* OECD, Paris.

International Energy Agency (1992), *Use of Efficiency Standards in Energy Policy,* Proceedings, OECD, Paris.

International Energy Agency/OECD (1993), *Expert Workshop on Life-Cycle Analysis of Energy Systems,* Proceedings, OECD, Paris.

Morovic, Tihomir, et al. (1987), *Energy Conservation Indicators,* Springer-Verlag, Berlin.

Netherlands Ministry of Economic Affairs (1990), *Memorandum on Energy Conservation: Strategy for Energy Conservation and Renewable Energy Resources,* SDU, The Hague.

Organisation for Economic Co-operation and Development (1992), *Cities and New Technologies,* Proceedings, OECD, Paris.

Schipper, Lee, et al. (1992), *Energy Efficiency and Human Activity: Past Trends, Future Prospects,* Cambridge University Press, Cambridge, UK.

Springmann, Frank (1991), *Analysis of the Ecological Impact of Demonstration Projects in the Field of Rational Use of Energy,* Study on Behalf of the European Communities, Regio-Tec GmbH, Starnberg.

UK Department of Environment (1992), *Climate Change: Our National Programme for* $CO_2$ *Emissions,* Department of Energy, London.

# MAIN SALES OUTLETS OF OECD PUBLICATIONS
# PRINCIPAUX POINTS DE VENTE DES PUBLICATIONS DE L'OCDE

**AUSTRALIA – AUSTRALIE**
D.A. Information Services
648 Whitehorse Road, P.O.B 163
Mitcham, Victoria 3132 Tel. (03) 9210.7777
Fax: (03) 9210.7788

**AUSTRIA – AUTRICHE**
Gerold & Co.
Graben 31
Wien I Tel. (0222) 533.50.14
Fax: (0222) 512.47.31.29

**BELGIUM – BELGIQUE**
Jean De Lannoy
Avenue du Roi, Koningslaan 202
B-1060 Bruxelles Tel. (02) 538.51.69/538.08.41
Fax: (02) 538.08.41

**CANADA**
Renouf Publishing Company Ltd.
5369 Canotek Road
Unit 1
Ottawa, Ont. K1J 9J3 Tel. (613) 745.2665
Fax: (613) 745.7660

Stores:
71 1/2 Sparks Street
Ottawa, Ont. K1P 5R1 Tel. (613) 238.8985
Fax: (613) 238.6041

12 Adelaide Street West
Toronto, QN M5H 1L6 Tel. (416) 363.3171
Fax: (416) 363.5963

Les Éditions La Liberté Inc.
3020 Chemin Sainte-Foy
Sainte-Foy, PQ G1X 3V6 Tel. (418) 658.3763
Fax: (418) 658.3763

Federal Publications Inc.
165 University Avenue, Suite 701
Toronto, ON M5H 3B8 Tel. (416) 860.1611
Fax: (416) 860.1608

Les Publications Fédérales
1185 Université
Montréal, QC H3B 3A7 Tel. (514) 954.1633
Fax: (514) 954.1635

**CHINA – CHINE**
Book Dept., China Natinal Publiations
Import and Export Corporation (CNPIEC)
16 Gongti E. Road, Chaoyang District
Beijing 100020 Tel. (10) 6506-6688 Ext. 8402
(10) 6506-3101

**CHINESE TAIPEI – TAIPEI CHINOIS**
Good Faith Worldwide Int'l. Co. Ltd.
9th Floor, No. 118, Sec. 2
Chung Hsiao E. Road
Taipei Tel. (02) 391.7396/391.7397
Fax: (02) 394.9176

**CZECH REPUBLIC – RÉPUBLIQUE TCHÈQUE**
National Information Centre
NIS – prodejna
Konviktská 5
Praha 1 – 113 57 Tel. (02) 24.23.09.07
Fax: (02) 24.22.94.33
E-mail: nkposp@dec.niz.cz
Internet: http://www.nis.cz

**DENMARK – DANEMARK**
Munksgaard Book and Subscription Service
35, Nørre Søgade, P.O. Box 2148
DK-1016 København K Tel. (33) 12.85.70
Fax: (33) 12.93.87

J. H. Schultz Information A/S,
Herstedvang 12,
DK – 2620 Albertslung Tel. 43 63 23 00
Fax: 43 63 19 69
Internet: s-info@inet.uni-c.dk

**EGYPT – ÉGYPTE**
The Middle East Observer
41 Sherif Street
Cairo Tel. (2) 392.6919
Fax: (2) 360.6804

**FINLAND – FINLANDE**
Akateeminen Kirjakauppa
Keskuskatu 1, P.O. Box 128
00100 Helsinki

Subscription Services/Agence d'abonnements :
P.O. Box 23
00100 Helsinki Tel. (358) 9.121.4403
Fax: (358) 9.121.4450

***FRANCE**
OECD/OCDE
Mail Orders/Commandes par correspondance :
2, rue André-Pascal
75775 Paris Cedex 16 Tel. 33 (0)1.45.24.82.00
Fax: 33 (0)1.49.10.42.76
Telex: 640048 OCDE
Internet: Compte.PUBSINQ@oecd.org

Orders via Minitel, France only/
Commandes par Minitel, France exclusivement :
36 15 OCDE

OECD Bookshop/Librairie de l'OCDE :
33, rue Octave-Feuillet
75016 Paris Tel. 33 (0)1.45.24.81.81
33 (0)1.45.24.81.67

Dawson
B.P. 40
91121 Palaiseau Cedex Tel. 01.89.10.47.00
Fax: 01.64.54.83.26

Documentation Française
29, quai Voltaire
75007 Paris Tel. 01.40.15.70.00

Economica
49, rue Héricart
75015 Paris Tel. 01.45.78.12.92
Fax: 01.45.75.05.67

Gibert Jeune (Droit-Économie)
6, place Saint-Michel
75006 Paris Tel. 01.43.25.91.19

Librairie du Commerce International
10, avenue d'Iéna
75016 Paris Tel. 01.40.73.34.60

Librairie Dunod
Université Paris-Dauphine
Place du Maréchal-de-Lattre-de-Tassigny
75016 Paris Tel. 01.44.05.40.13

Librairie Lavoisier
11, rue Lavoisier
75008 Paris Tel. 01.42.65.39.95

Librairie des Sciences Politiques
30, rue Saint-Guillaume
75007 Paris Tel. 01.45.48.36.02

P.U.F.
49, boulevard Saint-Michel
75005 Paris Tel. 01.43.25.83.40

Librairie de l'Université
12*a*, rue Nazareth
13100 Aix-en-Provence Tel. 04.42.26.18.08

Documentation Française
165, rue Garibaldi
69003 Lyon Tel. 04.78.63.32.23

Librairie Decitre
29, place Bellecour
69002 Lyon Tel. 04.72.40.54.54

Librairie Sauramps
Le Triangle
34967 Montpellier Cedex 2 Tel. 04.67.58.85.15
Fax: 04.67.58.27.36

A la Sorbonne Actual
23, rue de l'Hôtel-des-Postes
06000 Nice Tel. 04.93.13.77.75
Fax: 04.93.80.75.69

**GERMANY – ALLEMAGNE**
OECD Bonn Centre
August-Bebel-Allee 6
D-53175 Bonn Tel. (0228) 959.120
Fax: (0228) 959.12.17

**GREECE – GRÈCE**
Librairie Kauffmann
Stadiou 28
10564 Athens Tel. (01) 32.55.321
Fax: (01) 32.30.320

**HONG-KONG**
Swindon Book Co. Ltd.
Astoria Bldg. 3F
34 Ashley Road, Tsimshatsui
Kowloon, Hong Kong Tel. 2376.2062
Fax: 2376.0685

**HUNGARY – HONGRIE**
Euro Info Service
Margitsziget, Európa Ház
1138 Budapest Tel. (1) 111.60.61
Fax: (1) 302.50.35
E-mail: euroinfo@mail.matav.hu
Internet: http://www.euroinfo.hu//index.html

**ICELAND – ISLANDE**
Mál og Menning
Laugavegi 18, Pósthólf 392
121 Reykjavik Tel. (1) 552.4240
Fax: (1) 562.3523

**INDIA – INDE**
Oxford Book and Stationery Co.
Scindia House
New Delhi 110001 Tel. (11) 331.5896/5308
Fax: (11) 332.2639
E-mail: oxford.publ@axcess.net.in

17 Park Street
Calcutta 700016 Tel. 240832

**INDONESIA – INDONÉSIE**
Pdii-Lipi
P.O. Box 4298
Jakarta 12042 Tel. (21) 573.34.67
Fax: (21) 573.34.67

**IRELAND – IRLANDE**
Government Supplies Agency
Publications Section
4/5 Harcourt Road
Dublin 2 Tel. 661.31.11
Fax: 475.27.60

**ISRAEL – ISRAËL**
Praedicta
5 Shatner Street
P.O. Box 34030
Jerusalem 91430 Tel. (2) 652.84.90/1/2
Fax: (2) 652.84.93

R.O.Y. International
P.O. Box 13056
Tel Aviv 61130 Tel. (3) 546 1423
Fax: (3) 546 1442
E-mail: royil@netvision.net.il

Palestinian Authority/Middle East:
INDEX Information Services
P.O.B. 19502
Jerusalem Tel. (2) 627.16.34
Fax: (2) 627.12.19

**ITALY – ITALIE**
Libreria Commissionaria Sansoni
Via Duca di Calabria, 1/1
50125 Firenze Tel. (055) 64.54.15
Fax: (055) 64.12.57
E-mail: licosa@ftbcc.it

Via Bartolini 29
20155 Milano Tel. (02) 36.50.83

Editrice e Libreria Herder
Piazza Montecitorio 120
00186 Roma Tel. 679.46.28
Fax: 678.47.51

Libreria Hoepli
Via Hoepli 5
20121 Milano Tel. (02) 86.54.46
Fax: (02) 805.28.86

Libreria Scientifica
Dott. Lucio de Biasio 'Aeiou'
Via Coronelli, 6
20146 Milano Tel. (02) 48.95.45.52
Fax: (02) 48.95.45.48

**JAPAN – JAPON**
OECD Tokyo Centre
Landic Akasaka Building
2-3-4 Akasaka, Minato-ku
Tokyo 107 Tel. (81.3) 3586.2016
Fax: (81.3) 3584.7929

**KOREA – CORÉE**
Kyobo Book Centre Co. Ltd.
P.O. Box 1658, Kwang Hwa Moon
Seoul Tel. 730.78.91
Fax: 735.00.30

**MALAYSIA – MALAISIE**
University of Malaya Bookshop
University of Malaya
P.O. Box 1127, Jalan Pantai Baru
59700 Kuala Lumpur
Malaysia Tel. 756.5000/756.5425
Fax: 756.3246

**MEXICO – MEXIQUE**
OECD Mexico Centre
Edificio INFOTEC
Av. San Fernando no. 37
Col. Toriello Guerra
Tlalpan C.P. 14050
Mexico D.F. Tel. (525) 528.10.38
Fax: (525) 606.13.07
E-mail: ocde@rtn.net.mx

**NETHERLANDS – PAYS-BAS**
SDU Uitgeverij Plantijnstraat
Externe Fondsen
Postbus 20014
2500 EA's-Gravenhage Tel. (070) 37.89.880
Voor bestellingen: Fax: (070) 34.75.778
Subscription Agency/ Agence d'abonnements :
SWETS & ZEITLINGER BV
Heereweg 347B
P.O. Box 830
2160 SZ Lisse Tel. 252.435.111
Fax: 252.415.888

**NEW ZEALAND – NOUVELLE-ZÉLANDE**
GPLegislation Services
P.O. Box 12418
Thorndon, Wellington Tel. (04) 496.5655
Fax: (04) 496.5698

**NORWAY – NORVÈGE**
NIC INFO A/S
Ostensjoveien 18
P.O. Box 6512 Etterstad
0606 Oslo Tel. (22) 97.45.00
Fax: (22) 97.45.45

**PAKISTAN**
Mirza Book Agency
65 Shahrah Quaid-E-Azam
Lahore 54000 Tel. (42) 735.36.01
Fax: (42) 576.37.14

**PHILIPPINE – PHILIPPINES**
International Booksource Center Inc.
Rm 179/920 Cityland 10 Condo Tower 2
HV dela Costa Ext cor Valero St.
Makati Metro Manila Tel. (632) 817 9676
Fax: (632) 817 1741

**POLAND – POLOGNE**
Ars Polona
00-950 Warszawa
Krakowskie Prezdmiescie 7 Tel. (22) 264760
Fax: (22) 265334

**PORTUGAL**
Livraria Portugal
Rua do Carmo 70-74
Apart. 2681
1200 Lisboa Tel. (01) 347.49.82/5
Fax: (01) 347.02.64

**SINGAPORE – SINGAPOUR**
Ashgate Publishing
Asia Pacific Pte. Ltd
Golden Wheel Building, 04-03
41, Kallang Pudding Road
Singapore 349316 Tel. 741.5166
Fax: 742.9356

**SPAIN – ESPAGNE**
Mundi-Prensa Libros S.A.
Castelló 37, Apartado 1223
Madrid 28001 Tel. (91) 431.33.99
Fax: (91) 575.39.98
E-mail: mundiprensa@tsai.es
Internet: http://www.mundiprensa.es

Mundi-Prensa Barcelona
Consell de Cent No. 391
08009 – Barcelona Tel. (93) 488.34.92
Fax: (93) 487.76.59

Libreria de la Generalitat
Palau Moja
Rambla dels Estudis, 118
08002 – Barcelona
(Suscripciones) Tel. (93) 318.80.12
(Publicaciones) Tel. (93) 302.67.23
Fax: (93) 412.18.54

**SRI LANKA**
Centre for Policy Research
c/o Colombo Agencies Ltd.
No. 300-304, Galle Road
Colombo 3 Tel. (1) 574240, 573551-2
Fax: (1) 575394, 510711

**SWEDEN – SUÈDE**
CE Fritzes AB
S–106 47 Stockholm Tel. (08) 690.90.90
Fax: (08) 20.50.21

For electronic publications only/
Publications électroniques seulement
STATISTICS SWEDEN
Informationsservice
S-115 81 Stockholm Tel. 8 783 5066
Fax: 8 783 4045

Subscription Agency/Agence d'abonnements :
Wennergren-Williams Info AB
P.O. Box 1305
171 25 Solna Tel. (08) 705.97.50
Fax: (08) 27.00.71

Liber distribution
Internatinal organizations
Fagerstagatan 21
S-163 52 Spanga

**SWITZERLAND – SUISSE**
Maditec S.A. (Books and Periodicals/Livres et périodiques)
Chemin des Palettes 4
Case postale 266
1020 Renens VD 1 Tel. (021) 635.08.65
Fax: (021) 635.07.80

Librairie Payot S.A.
4, place Pépinet
CP 3212
1002 Lausanne Tel. (021) 320.25.11
Fax: (021) 320.25.14

Librairie Unilivres
6, rue de Candolle
1205 Genève Tel. (022) 320.26.23
Fax: (022) 329.73.18

Subscription Agency/Agence d'abonnements :
Dynapresse Marketing S.A.
38, avenue Vibert
1227 Carouge Tel. (022) 308.08.70
Fax: (022) 308.07.99

See also – Voir aussi :
OECD Bonn Centre
August-Bebel-Allee 6
D-53175 Bonn (Germany) Tel. (0228) 959.120
Fax: (0228) 959.12.17

**THAILAND – THAÏLANDE**
Suksit Siam Co. Ltd.
113, 115 Fuang Nakhon Rd.
Opp. Wat Rajbopith
Bangkok 10200 Tel. (662) 225.9531/2
Fax: (662) 222.5188

**TRINIDAD & TOBAGO, CARIBBEAN TRINITÉ-ET-TOBAGO, CARAÏBES**
Systematics Studies Limited
9 Watts Street
Curepe
Trinadad & Tobago, W.I. Tel. (1809) 645.3475
Fax: (1809) 662.5654
E-mail: tobe@trinidad.net

**TUNISIA – TUNISIE**
Grande Librairie Spécialisée
Fendri Ali
Avenue Haffouz Imm El-Intilaka
Bloc B 1 Sfax 3000 Tel. (216-4) 296 855
Fax: (216-4) 298.270

**TURKEY – TURQUIE**
Kültür Yayinlari Is-Türk Ltd.
Atatürk Bulvari No. 191/Kat 13
06684 Kavaklidere/Ankara
Tel. (312) 428.11.40 Ext. 2458
Fax : (312) 417.24.90

Dolmabahce Cad. No. 29
Besiktas/Istanbul Tel. (212) 260 7188

**UNITED KINGDOM – ROYAUME-UNI**
The Stationery Office Ltd.
Postal orders only:
P.O. Box 276, London SW8 5DT
Gen. enquiries Tel. (171) 873 0011
Fax: (171) 873 8463

The Stationery Office Ltd.
Postal orders only:
49 High Holborn, London WC1V 6HB
Branches at: Belfast, Birmingham, Bristol, Edinburgh, Manchester

**UNITED STATES – ÉTATS-UNIS**
OECD Washington Center
2001 L Street N.W., Suite 650
Washington, D.C. 20036-4922 Tel. (202) 785.6323
Fax: (202) 785.0350
Internet: washcont@oecd.org

Subscriptions to OECD periodicals may also be placed through main subscription agencies.

Les abonnements aux publications périodiques de l'OCDE peuvent être souscrits auprès des principales agences d'abonnement.

Orders and inquiries from countries where Distributors have not yet been appointed should be sent to: OECD Publications, 2, rue André-Pascal, 75775 Paris Cedex 16, France.

Les commandes provenant de pays où l'OCDE n'a pas encore désigné de distributeur peuvent être adressées aux Éditions de l'OCDE, 2, rue André-Pascal, 75775 Paris Cedex 16, France.

12-1996

OECD PUBLICATIONS, 2 rue André-Pascal, 75775 PARIS CEDEX 16
PRINTED IN FRANCE
(61 97 08 1P) ISBN 92-64-15325-X - No. 49092 1997